THE GIFT OF LIFE 2

Surviving The Waiting List and Liver Transplantation

The Inspirational Story of
One Man's Triumph over Terminal Liver Disease

A Guide for Transplant Patients and Their Families

**By Parichehr Yomtoob,
Laura Yomtoob,
and Deborah Weppler, R.N., M.S.N.**

For information, write to:
Rainbow International Press
P.O. Box 175
Deerfield, Illinois 60015

Publisher's Cataloging-in-Publication
   Yomtoob, Parichehr.
      The gift of life 2 : surviving the waiting list and liver
      transplantation / by Parichehr Yomtoob, Laura Yomtoob,
      and Deborah Weppler.
         p. cm.
      Includes indexes.
      "The story of one man's triumph over terminal liver
   disease and a guide for transplant patients and their
   families."
      LCCN 2004098589
      ISBN 0-9753568-0-1

      1. Yomtoob, David--Health. 2. Liver--Transplantation
   --Patients--Michigan--Biography. 3. Transplantation of
   organs, tissues, etc. in children--United States.
   I. Yomtoob, Laura. II. Weppler, Deborah. III. Title.
   IV. Title: Gift of life two

      RD546.Y66 2005   *362.1'975562'0092*
                                    QBI05-800254

Designed by Erica Erf, Glenview, Illinois
Insert pictures by Michael Kalling, Kalling Graphics
Drawings on pages 40, 160 by Evangelos Misiakos, M.D.

Pictures on the front cover:

First row:

left   *David Yomtoob while on the waiting list, September 1981.*

middle *David Yomtoob with Dr. Thomas E. Starzl two years after the first transplant, June 1983.*

right *David's wedding portrait, July 1994. Photo by Austin Professional Portraiture of Battle Creek, MI.*

Second row:

left   *David Yomtoob while on the waiting list for the second time, October 1999.*

middle *David Yomtoob with Dr. Andreas G. Tzakis two years after the third transplant, August 2002.*

right *David Yomtoob, fall 2004. Photo by Images of Vision Studio of Lowell, MI.*

DEDICATION

In memory of all organ donors, especially the three wonderful angels who gave the gift of life to David. These three wonderful people and their families receive praise and thanks everyday from our family.

In memory of all the people who died of liver diseases and on the waiting list.

In memory of Joe's mother, Monavar, and my mother, Roohieh, who cared for us and gave us their support during David's first transplant in 1981. Joe's mother passed away in 1984 and was not around to see David back on the waiting list. My mother, Rouhieh, was alive while David was on the waiting list; she sent David her prayers, but passed away a month before David received his second liver transplant.

■   ■   ■

To Joshua, Jacob, Rachael, Nathan, Caleb and any additional grandchildren that we may have and their future generation.

ACKNOWLEDGEMENTS

My deepest and sincerest appreciation goes to Laura, my daughter-in-law, for being my first editor and becoming my coauthor. She spent many hours editing and organizing this book, and though it became longer and longer, she never gave up. Her wisdom, support and encouragement made it possible to create this book.

Not enough words are available to show my gratitude to Debbie Weppler, R.N., for providing, writing and editing all of the medical information and for reviewing the entire book for medical accuracy. She made it possible for this book to be published with confidence that everything would be medically accurate and as up-to-date as possible.

Parichehr Yomtoob

We are truly grateful to Dr. Thomas E. Starzl who honored us by sharing his newly written epilogue for his book, *The Puzzle People*, through which we were able to include the latest information on transplantation. Dr. Starzl, the skillful surgeon who pioneered liver transplantation and trained so many of the current transplant surgeons, operated on David in 1981 when he was in a coma. Dr. Starzl and others like him are doing God's work on this earth. We will be eternally grateful to all of them.

Our thanks also go to:
The American Liver Foundation, the American Society of Transplant Surgeons, the National Kidney Foundation, the United Network for Organ Sharing, and the Wilson's Disease Association for allowing us to use valuable information from their publications and web sites for our readers.

Dr. Evengelos Misiakos, a talented artist, who hand drew all the pictures of the liver at different stages for inclusion in this book.

Benjamin and David Yomtoob, who offered us their wisdom and technical expertise, which helped us turn our words into a book. They, along with Rebecca Dahn, David Dahn, and Sara Yomtoob offered us input whenever needed and we deeply appreciate their efforts to bring this book to fruition. My grandsons, Joshua and Jacob Yomtoob, deserve thanks for their help with proofreading. Joe Yomtoob, husband and father-in-law to Parichehr and Laura respectively, was a source of strength and support that provided assistance and vigor throughout the process of writing and publishing.

Thanks are due to Rabbi Richard Address of the Union of Reform Judaism (formerly the Union of American Hebrew Congregations). Rabbi Address provided us with materials on the views of most religions about organ donation as well as the Reform Jewish Study/Program Guide #9, from which the programs and ceremonies for the occasions of donating or receiving an organ included in this book were taken. Additional thanks to Naida Cohn for researching the citations for Appendix 11, "The Power of Prayers," and editing and adapting these prayers and poems used by family and friends praying for and with David. The effort to obtain correct citations was aided by Rabbi Herbert Bronstein, and Rabbi Steven and Patty Mason.

Four unsung heroes of transplantation: Father Gary Graf, Mary Ellen Langlois, Laura Odom and Sharon Kalling, who were living donors of livers and kidneys and shared their experiences with us to guide others who may follow their path. We appreciate their unselfish efforts and learned a lot from their stories.

Dr. Minou Michlin and Nancy Rosenfeld made editorial comments, and Kathleen McKee did professional editing and proofreading for us. Erica Erf provided us with her artistic talents for the cover and designed the pages. Dr. Maria B. Orlowski, Sigalit Zetouni and Jane Fatoorechi provided care and encouragement. We appreciate all of their efforts

Parichehr Yomtoob, Laura Yomtoob and Debbie Weppler, R.N.

David's second and third transplants were miracles. We reserve special thanks and deepest gratitude for Dr. Andreas G. Tzakis, head of the liver transplant team at the University of Miami School of Medicine in Miami, Florida. He accepted the responsibility of the difficult task of retransplantation on David who had built up 18 years of scar tissue from his first transplant. Dr. Tzakis spent hours operating on David, never giving up on him, and giving him second and third chances on life.

Dr. Andreas G. Tzakis was the head of a fabulous transplant team that included Dr. Antonio Pinna, Dr. Jose Nery, Dr. David Levi, Dr. Tomoaki Kato, Dr. Seigo Nishida, Dr. Roberto Verzaro, Dr. Michael Angelis, Dr. Adrian Cotterell, Dr. Sinji Yamamoto, Dr. Joe Tector, Dr. Akin Tekin, Dr. Jose Ortega, and Dr. Michalino Scarlatta. These surgeons spent long hours on David in the operating room and cared for him in the ICU and on the fifteenth floor at Jackson Memorial Hospital in Miami.

David's recovery did not come easy. It took hard work and team effort from practically every department of the University of Miami School of Medicine and Jackson Memorial Hospital to help him recover. The nurses, assistant nurses and transplant coordinators all did whatever they could to get David back on his feet. We were fortunate to have all of them. Debbie Weppler and Jennie Benson were always present to hear our concerns and keep the lines of communication open. We appreciate their hard work and we always will be grateful to all of them.

There were many on the staff of Jackson Memorial Hospital University of Miami School of Medicine who did all they could to make David's four-month stay in that hospital as comfortable as possible. Among them were Jorge Romero and Marie Nicolas, the patient representatives who assisted David and our family willingly and at all times. They all deserve our thanks and gratitude.

In addition to the University of Miami School of Medicine, we visited three other top transplant centers in the United States to find a replacement liver for David. We are grateful to all the medical center staff members who helped us during our two-year journey from 1998 to 2000 especially:

The University of Pittsburgh Medical Center doctors and staff. Dr. Thomas E. Starzl, for taking time from his retirement to visit David in the hospital and for giving him hope, strength and encouragement to get a second transplant. Dr. John J. Fung, Dr. Carlton Gartner and Dr. Jorge Reyes for giving David advice, special care, and preparation for life on the waiting list.

The University of Nebraska medical center in Omaha. Dr. Byers W. Shaw, Jr., Dr. Tim McCashland and Dr. Mark Purviance, for keeping David physically stable and emotionally hopeful during the nine months he waited for a suitable donor in Omaha.

Northwestern University, (Northwestern Memorial Hospital) in Chicago. Dr. Michael I. Abecassis and Dr. Steven L. Flamm, for advising David on the subject of living donor transplants and for putting him back on his feet after a bad episode of encephalopathy.

Dr. John Sereni at the Grand Rapids (Michigan) hospital. He did whatever he could to keep David alive and stable between trips to the centers.

When faced with adversity one always hopes that friends and family will be at your side. When David needed a second liver transplant 17 years after his first, he was a husband to Sara (Lindhurst) and the father of a one-year-old daughter named Rachael. Sara and Rachael stayed at David's bedside and traveled with him from center to center. Sara was his companion and Rachael provided him with a constant sense of purpose.

David's brother Benjamin, Ben's wife Laura (my coauthor), and their sons Joshua and Jacob, along with David's sister Rebecca and her husband David Dahn, gave us unlimited support. They traveled to visit David, to celebrate the holidays, to keep us company throughout our long waiting period, and after David received his second and third transplants, and while he recovered in the hospital. They made us proud of them.

Our brothers, sisters, nieces and nephews did not allow the distance become between us; they stayed in touch by phone and stopped to visit whenever they could.

David's in-laws, John and Johnie Lindhurst, along with Christy, Sara's sister, and Cora Byrd, Sara's grandmother, traveled to visit David and Sara wherever they were, bringing with them their love and support. In Miami, we also had help and support from Sara's aunt and uncle, Connie and Ray Byrd.

People and prayers have meant a lot to us. We knew we had the prayers of relatives and friends from all over the United States and Israel. Many wonderful relatives kept in touch by phone or letter or visited us in person. We also had the prayers and comforting phone calls of our Rabbis and their congregations. We are especially grateful to: Rabbi Eliot and Nancy Rosenstock, Rabbi Morley Feinstein, Cantor Adina Frydman, Rabbi Harold Loss, Rabbi Herbert Bronstein, Rabbi Steven S. and Patty Mason, Rabbi Lisa S. Green, Cantor Richard Cohn, Rabbi Aryeh Azriel, Rabbi Debbie S. Stiel, Cantor Jennifer G. Blum, Rabbi Jeff Kahn, and the congregations of Temple Beth-El, South Bend, Indiana; North Shore Congregation Israel, Glencoe, IL; Temple Israel, West Bloomfield, Michigan; Temple Israel, Omaha, Nebraska; and Temple Israel of Greater Miami, Florida. Two friends, Naida Cohn and Sharon Kalling, helped to coordinate the dissemination of current information by phone or e-mail to waiting friends and family, thereby helping to lighten our load from time to time. We appreciated every card or letter, every phone call, every e-mail that we received, and all of those prayers worked!

Additional and ongoing support has come to us from our friends and colleagues at the Hawthorne School District #73 in Vernon Hills, Illinois, as well as the friends and members of the Rotary Clubs of Deerfield, Riverwoods, Vernon Hills, Mundelein and Libertyville, Illinois. Thanks also for the support from friends in Niles, Albion, Jackson, Lowell, Ypsilanti, Willow Run, Ann Arbor and Grand Rapids, Michigan.

Last, but not least, we are especially grateful to our son David for his will to live and his fighting spirit; to Sara, David's wife, for her support; and to Rachael, David's daughter, for her joyful and playful spirit that brought joy and hope to the dark days of David's illness and recovery.

Parichehr & Joe Yomtoob

TABLE OF CONTENTS

WHY THE GIFT OF LIFE 2?

Our son, David, received his first liver transplant in 1981 at Children's Hospital of Pittsburgh under the watchful eye, superb mind, and skilled hands of Dr. Thomas E. Starzl. David's illness, the diagnosis, the pioneering surgery, his recovery, and our family's crusade to raise public awareness for organ donation became the subjects of *The Gift of Life*, a book I coauthored with Ted Schwarz that was published by St. Martin's Press in 1986.

Seventeen years later, in 1998, David needed a second liver transplant. This time, we found ourselves looking for a book to guide us through our new journey. The success of transplantation throughout the United States by many teams of talented physicians and surgeons had changed the way the medical community regarded transplantation, and the way it thought of the donors and, especially, recipients.

In 1981, David was cared for in the hospital during the six months prior to his first transplant. In 1998, David's wife Sara had to care for him at home and manage the day-to-day crises of his failing liver.[1] And by 1998, the rules regarding when the patients received an organ had changed drastically. Patients on the waiting list now earned points for the time their names were on the waiting lists, not for the condition of their livers. Even though David was very ill, there were many people ahead of him on the waiting lists. We had to watch him deteriorate while hoping and praying that a liver would become available before he was too critically ill to receive it.

We didn't know when it would be David's turn, but we were aware of the grave shortage of organs for transplantation. The waiting list was, and still is, long and it grows longer every day. We could not forget the reality that, in spite of all the public education about organ donations, many potential donors still take their organs to the grave. In some, cases families are never approached to donate; in other cases, loved ones refuse the request.

---

[1] In 2004 the organ placement process changed. See Appendix 3B

We considered a new procedure which takes part of the liver from a living donor. It is extremely risky for both the donor and the recipient, but every member of our immediate family was willing to take the risk. However, David's doctors told us that he wasn't a candidate for this procedure; he needed a whole liver.

We traveled from center to center hoping to find a suitable donor organ before it was too late. When David finally received his second liver, he experienced every setback that a recipient might experience including the failure of the transplanted liver, life–threatening infection, pneumonia, and more. He required yet another transplant and spent months in ICUs and hospital rooms. His recovery probably would have been much faster and easier had he not spent two years on the waiting list.

Once again we felt the need to write a book, one that would raise public awareness about the grave shortage of donor organs and also provide transplant patients and their family with the type of book we needed, but couldn't find, to guide us through David's transplant journey. This time, in addition to telling David's story, we provide factual information from a variety of sources for readers who are interested in the process, regulation, trauma, and drama of organ transplantation.

The Gift of Life 2 is really three books in one:

First, it is the story of David's first transplant and his quality of life afterward.

Second, it is the story of David's second and third transplants, including the two years of waiting for a suitable donor.

Third, it is a resource for patient and family, with a wealth of information about the transplant process including information about the waiting list and how it works, organizations that provide financial assistance, and tips for staying healthy, choosing a transplant center, and communicating with doctors. Medical tests, symptoms, and crises that a patient with liver disease may experience before and after transplantation are described in detail, and we share how our family coped with all of this and what we learned from our experiences. We've even included a sampling of the various religious beliefs surrounding transplantation, and an appendix on "The Power of Prayer" that shares our favorite prayers. All of the medical information has been researched, reviewed, and documented by experts in the field.

We hope that we have created a book that everyone on a transplant waiting list will find both inspirational and educational. We hope this book will bring some light into the dark days in the lives of patients on the waiting list as well as the families who wait with them. We hope that our story will provide a basis for the courage and determination needed to survive organ transplantation. Importantly, we hope that this book will inspire its readers to donate their organs—to give the gift of life!

If this book helps just one patient on the waiting list to receive the organ he or she desperately needs in time, or convinces just one person to become an organ donor, this book will have served its purpose.

1

DIAGNOSIS

First Transplant Center
University of Pittsburgh Medical Center
June, 1998

Sometime down the road, David, you will need another liver," the doctor was explaining to my 29-year-old son. We were in Presbyterian Hospital of Pittsburgh, a world-famous liver transplant center affiliated with the University of Pittsburgh.

The University of Pittsburgh began to build its reputation as a top organ transplant center around the time Dr. Thomas E. Starzl, a pioneer in liver transplant surgery, arrived from Denver, CO in January of 1980. In 1981, at the age of 12, David was only the seventh child to receive a liver transplant at the hands of Dr. Starzl in Pittsburgh.

David lived a good, healthy, normal life in the 17 years after his transplant. We celebrated his Bar Mitzvah like he was a normal 13-year-old. He graduated with honors from high school, went to college, earned a degree in aerospace engineering, and learned to fly an airplane, earning his private pilot's license. After college, he found a job, married his wife Sara, and they had a daughter Rachael, who was now a year old.

Now, 17 years later, we were in Pittsburgh to find out what was wrong with David and the doctor was letting him know that he would need another transplant.

I started thinking about the events that led to this point.

1988 - 1997

Seven years after David's first transplant, Dr. Jeffrey Malatack, the pediatrician who provided David's pre- and posttransplant care in Pittsburgh, discovered that David's bile duct had narrowed, apparently due to scar tissue. Dr. Starzl and his assistant, Dr. Shunzaburo Iwatsuki, became very concerned and suggested surgery to open the bile duct. Nineteen-year-old David was against the surgery. He felt fine, so he saw no reason for surgery. Given the possibility of infection in the bile duct, the doctors insisted on the operation and Dr. Iwatsuki performed the surgery in Pittsburgh.

The Pittsburgh Press

)L. 98, No. 95 ..   SUNDAY, SEPTEMBER 27, 1981   75c In Pittsburgh and the Penr Fayette, Greene, Indiar

Boy In Coma Waits Desperately For Liver

By EDWINA RANKIN

David Yomtoob may be running out of time.

Doctors at Children's Hospital don't know how long the 12-year-old Niles, Mich., youth can remain in a coma before it is too late for a desperately needed liver transplant to do any good.

They are actively seeking a donor for him.

"Unfortunately, some child has to die," said Dr. Carl Gartner, head of the diagnostic referral service at Children's. "We don't want anyone to become ill, but if the situation arises, we know patients we could help if we could find a donor."

David has been at Children's Hospital since August, hoping a suitable liver would become available. Wilson's Disease has caused his own to malfunction to the point where he (Continued on Page A-23, Column 1)

DAVID YOMTOOB
Running out of time?

Boy In Coma Waits For Liver

(Continued from Page A-1)

slipped into a coma Tuesday.

The disease occurs when copper can not be properly eliminated from the body, Gartner explained. Excessive amounts of the mineral build up in the liver, brain and other organs.

Before he went into the coma, David already had started to become weak and his kidneys failed. He has been placed on a dialysis machine.

"But the doctors said all this can be reversible if they put the new liver in," said the boy's mother, Parichehr Yomtoob.

Ordinarily, Wilson's Disease can be treated with medicine, Gartner said. But David's case was diagnosed too late for the medication to do any good.

At first, doctors believed David had hepatitis, Mrs. Yomtoob said. The medication they gave him cured the jaundice and a complete recovery followed. David, an A student, resumed his newspaper route and athletic activities as a baseball, basketball, soccer and swim team member.

But a month later, he became jaundiced again. This time he was admitted to Chicago Children's Memorial Hospital. The diagnosis was Wilson's Disease, Mrs. Yomtoob said.

David's spirits remained high during treatments there and at the Mayo Clinic. Doctors continued to tell him it takes time for the medicine to work, Mrs. Yomtoob said.

But in August, the physicians at Children's Hospital in Chicago gave the Yomtoobs the bad news — only a liver transplant could save her son.

"He was so excited," Mrs. Yomtoob recalled. "I told him we would have to discuss it with his father. He said, 'No. This is what I want. We will do it.'"

They arrived at Children's Hospital here in the middle of August.

Since then, there have been two potential donors.

The first was found Sept. 19 and David was wheeled into the operating room to await his life-giving organ. But then, the bad news. Physicians discovered that the liver was too small, Mrs. Yomtoob said.

"They had told us there would be that possibility," she said. "But they have to prepare the patient several hours in advance."

She said David has remained optimistic, even as he slipped into the coma.

Two days after losing consciousness, another chance arose.

Again, the bad news.

This time the liver appeared to be infected.

It's anyone's guess just how long David can remain in his comatose state before irreparable damage is done. Gartner said there have been cases where adults have been in a coma three years, only to gain full recovery after being given a liver transplant.

Mrs. Yomtoob has been living in David's hospital room, sleeping on a cot by his bed. Occasionally, his optimism would wane and he'd crawl into the bed with her.

Youseef Yomtoob, the boy's father, has been staying at the nearby Ronald McDonald house, a home for families of hospital-bound patients. He was expected to be joined last night by another son, Benjamin, 17; a daughter Rebecca, 10, and his mother-in-law, Rebecca Yomtov.

Inquiries about finding a donor for David may be made by calling D-O-N-O-R-S 7.

David's story whle he was waiting for his first liver transplant.

Pittsburgh Post-Gazette

1983 by PG Publishing Co.   MONDAY, JUNE 20, 1983

Rejoicing: Parents, 20 young people saved by liver transplants say 'thanks'

By Susan Mannella
Post-Gazette Staff Writer

"Your child will not grow up."

The roomful of parents had heard those devastating words and shared the horror of waiting, hoping, praying and waiting some more.

They had spent hours at bedsides, watching as the lives of their children deteriorated and nearly slipped away.

But yesterday they shared a day of banners and balloons, cotton candy and popcorn, clowns, bubbling laughter and splashes in a swimming pool.

The scene, as colorful and joyful as any carnival, was a perfect picture of the way 20 young lives were changed by liver transplant surgery.

Once so sick that their parents thought they would die, the young people, ages 2 to 20, spent the day swimming, running around, playing with balloons and devouring large helpings of popcorn, candy, ice cream, hamburgers, salads and soda.

Their families traveled to Pittsburgh from as far away as Texas, California, Connecticut and Michigan to say "thank you" to Dr. Thomas Starzl and his team of surgeons, pediatricians, counselors and assistants.

They came to share their joy, to publicize a need for donors and push for a change in government regulations that could make it easier for parents to afford the $100,000 surgery.

And they came in the hope that parents who lost their own children and donated their organs for transplants might see the results.

The reunion of successful liver transplant patients at the Green Tree Marriott Hotel was organized by Parichehr Yomtoob of Niles, Mich., whose son David received a new liver in 1981 when he was 12 years old.

Her husband, Youssef, detailed David's battle with liver disease in a speech during lunch.

"In hope of a miracle cure, we went from hospital to hospital, from doctor to doctor. Each time we were told the same thing. 'Your child will not grow up,'" he said.

David, now 14 and an active soccer player and swimmer, became ill in the spring of 1981. No medicine would help him, and his weight dropped to 57 pounds.

A liver that David was supposed to receive was too small and he lapsed into a coma while his parents called friends all over the country, as well as newspapers and television stations, in an attempt to find a suitable donor.

"David was dying as we watched helplessly," Yomtoob said. He and his wife stayed at

(Continued on Page 4, Column 2)

The coverage of the first reunion of the children who have had liver transplants. The event took place in Pittsburgh on Sunday, June 19, 1983. the reunion was organized by Parichehr and Joe Yomtoob.

Just one year later, tests showed that the bile duct had narrowed again. This time they tried to open it with a nonsurgical procedure known as a cholangiogram. This procedure used a balloon-tipped catheter to open the narrowed duct. Shortly thereafter, we received a telephone call from a new Pittsburgh surgeon, Dr. Andreas Tzakis. He explained that David's blood work indicated that the bile duct was, once again, too narrow. Apparently, the balloon procedure had only been a temporary solution to the problem. It was the first time that a surgeon had called us himself!

By that time, Dr. Malatack had left the University of Pittsburgh, so David would send his blood to the Pittsburgh transplant coordinator monthly, and the transplant coordinator would call and give us the test results. We all were able to understand the liver function test results. During David's ongoing problems with the bile duct, all the numbers were normal, except the SGPT and SGOT[1] numbers were high.

Since Dr. Starzl had retired from surgery, and Dr. Malatack gone to Philadelphia, we decided to go to The University of Nebraska in Omaha for another opinion.

As a young surgeon, Dr. Byers W. Shaw had assisted Dr. Starzl with David's surgery and later started his own transplant center at the University of Nebraska. He was happy to see David. He recommended putting a stent in the bile duct to hold it open. Dr. Shaw explained that, similar to a cholangiogram, this procedure used x-rays to guide the tiny instruments that placed the stent in the bile duct and did not require an operation. Although it was still considered to be an experimental procedure, Dr. Shaw felt that it was worth a try. And it did work, for a while. But once again, after a year, the SGPT and SGOT[1] numbers were up again. We returned to Omaha where tests discovered that the stent was gone. It had most likely dislodged and been passed out of the bile duct and into the intestine.

By this time, Dr. Shaw knew that other patients had experienced complications with the stent when it became entangled in surrounding scar tissue, requiring surgical removal. He recommended once again trying the cholangiogram and balloon procedure, which was generally successful in keeping the bile duct open for about a year after the procedure.

After that, David made a yearly trip to Omaha for a checkup, liver biopsy, and the cholangiogram/balloon procedure to open his bile duct. Then he went back to his otherwise normal life.

David began using the University of Nebraska for his transplant-related medical care, but he couldn't let go of his ties to the surgeon who had saved his life. At David's request, Dr. Starzl in Pittsburgh continued to monitor his antirejection medication (cyclosporine) and review the results of the tests and biopsies performed in Omaha. It was unusual for two transplant centers to collaborate on the follow-up

---

[1] Today these tests are more commonly called ALT and SLT.

care for a patient, but David wanted continuity and felt that this was the best way to achieve it. Since this was what David wanted, the two transplant centers accommodated him.

In June of 1997, David's daughter Rachael was born, causing David to postpone his yearly checkup until December. This time, David asked that my husband Joe and I join him in Omaha after the cholangiogram and liver biopsy. The biopsy looked good. In fact, the doctor who performed the biopsy walked into the room afterwards and said, "David, your liver is beautiful." What great news! That was exactly what we wanted to hear.

■   ■   ■

June, 1998

Now, just six months after a biopsy that indicated David's liver was healthy, another doctor was telling us that, sometime down the road, David would need another liver. The shock and trauma for me was exactly like the day we learned that David had Wilson's Disease, the disease that destroyed his first liver. For me, 17 years disappeared and here we were again with a damaged liver that needed to be replaced. "I wonder when he will need the transplant…maybe in five or ten years?" I thought to myself, trying to be positive. David was quiet and didn't show any emotion, so I asked, "What went wrong with the liver?"

"We don't know," the doctor answered.

"What about Wilson's Disease? Could it have returned?" I wanted to know.

The young doctor said, "No, *our experience* shows that Wilson's Disease is in the liver. It doesn't return after a transplant, because the new healthy liver processes copper normally."

Then David spoke up. "*I* am the experience!" he said. The young doctor didn't understand what David meant and went on to insist that the Wilson's Disease was cured when the diseased liver was removed and replaced with a healthy one. What David was trying to explain to this young doctor was that *he* was the longest living liver transplant survivor who had had Wilson's Disease. I wish I had been in the mood to laugh. Of course, since all the doctors were new and young, they didn't know David or his story.

Although they didn't know David's story, they *did* know that David had been off immunosuppressant medication since he had volunteered almost five years ago to participate in a research program proposed by the Pittsburgh team. It was a fairly radical idea. Many doctors did not agree with this type of research, believing that the eventual end result would be organ rejection, but David had embraced the program, citing Tammy Crabtree as living proof of the possibility of success. We first met 20-year-old Tammy Crabtree in Pittsburgh in 1983, at the first reunion of children who had had liver transplants.

■   ■   ■

1983

My husband Joe and I organized the reunion with Dr. Starzl's help, thinking that it would be nice to meet the other children who had had liver transplants and their families. In addition to reuniting the liver transplant patients, our other goal was to promote organ donation. The press was interested in our reunion, and we wanted the public to see these wonderful children so they would understand that transplantation had offered very sick children a chance to return to completely normal lives.

The date of the reunion was set for Saturday, June 12, 1983, which was Fathers' Day. The Perlow family, owners of the Marriott Greentree in Pittsburgh, offered complementary rooms and meals to all of the families. Sandoz, the company that developed the antirejection medication cyclosporine, contributed to the airfare for families that had to travel long distances to get to Pittsburgh. Children's Hospital of Pittsburgh, in cooperation with the Marriott, planned a pool party and brought in a small petting zoo for the children. We made a big poster with pictures of the children both before and after the liver transplant and set it up in the lobby. What an impact that made!

Twenty-two children and their families attended the Saturday reunion. The children were all liver transplant survivors, and Dr. Starzl had performed each of their surgeries, either in Denver or Pittsburgh. The transplant surgeons and pediatricians joined us with their families. In the morning, the children swam in the pool. For lunch, since it had started raining, we went to the ballroom. To my surprise, the petting zoo had been moved to the ballroom!

After lunch, Joe gave a short speech, focusing on the success of the liver transplant program and the difference it had made in our lives. To show our appreciation, we gave "Super Surgeon" and "Super Doctor" plaques to the surgeons and doctors, we gave a basket of flowers to each of their wives, and we thanked them all!

All of children at the reunion looked great. Some of them were now teenagers and some were adults. You couldn't tell that they had ever been critically ill and dying of liver disease. But when you saw their pictures before the transplant, you had to admit that liver transplant was a miracle!

At the reunion, we met Kim Hudson, the longest living liver transplant survivor. She had had her liver transplant in Denver, Colorado, 13 years before David had had his transplant. It was easy to tell the liver transplants that had been performed in Denver from those that had been performed in Pittsburgh. The Denver children took Imuran and prednisone to prevent rejection, so all of them had "moon face," the puffy features and chubby cheeks that come from long-term use of systemic corticosteroids. The Pittsburgh children all had thick hair and bushy eyebrows, their hairiness being a side effect of cyclosporine A. Yet here was Tammy Crabtree, a 20-year-old liver transplant survivor who didn't look like either the Denver or the Pittsburgh children. When we asked what medication she was taking, she answered, "Nothing." She said she felt good and that everything was going well so she didn't feel the medication was necessary. She had stopped several years earlier and was still feeling fine. I don't know what the surgeons' reactions were to Tammy stopping her medication, but she sure made an impression on us.

The press couldn't get enough of the reunion. It made the CBS Evening News and was also reported on all the local television stations and in newspapers across the country. That week, three children's livers became available. The publicity had worked; our message was reaching people.

■   ■   ■

1990

In 1990, seven years after the reunion, David stopped taking his medication. At that time, David was going to college and living away from home. He gave me the news a month later when we were driving to Pittsburgh for his yearly checkup. In Pittsburgh, his blood work showed that his liver enzymes were up.

When David told Dr. Starzl and Dr. Tzakis that he had stopped taking his medication, the two surgeons were upset and lectured David about the dangers of not taking his medication. Dr. Tzakis explained that this was a big problem, especially among teenagers who often decided that since they felt well, they no longer needed their medication. In many cases, by the time these patients returned to the doctor because they weren't feeling well, it was too late and the organ had already been rejected. Due to the shortage of donor organs, some of these patients died on the waiting list for a second transplant. Dr. Tzakis said that some surgeons thought twice before giving new organs to teenagers for fear the organs would go to waste. David got the message and began taking his medication again, but when a new idea to wean transplant patients off immunosuppressants was proposed, David was interested.

The philosophy of the program was that rejection could be treated as if the body had an allergy to the transplanted organ. With allergies, allergy shots gradually *introduce increasing amounts of the allergenic substance into the body. Over many weeks of shots they slowly desensitize the body to the offending substance. Using that same philosophy, the Pittsburgh doctors proposed to gradually reduce the amount of immunosuppressant medication while constantly checking for rejection to see if the body would "get used to" the new organ.*

Since the antirejection medications had many side effects and no one knew much about the long-term effects of taking all these drugs, David preferred not to take them. When David told us he wanted to participate in this program, Joe and I did-n't like the idea and Drs. Malatack and Shaw didn't support this course of action either. However, David—always a risk taker—was over 18 years of age and he was in charge of his own life. We discussed the matter as we always did when making an important decision, but, ultimately, the decision was David's.

David felt that he had a responsibility to help future transplant patients. He reminded us that others before him had volunteered to have a liver transplant before it became a successful operation. Those people went to the operating room knowing that if the operation was not successful, they would be sacrificing the last few days, weeks, or months of their lives. Time that they might have spent visiting with family and saying their good-byes, they would spend in pain and agony attached to a respirator, with IV's in their blood vessels, a feeding tube in the nose, and catheters and bags for their bladder and intestines. Many individuals, before liver transplantation was perfected, made this sacrifice and died. David felt that now it was his turn to give something back. By participating in this research program, he would be contributing to the science of organ transplantation. He hoped fervently that it would work.

■   ■   ■

June, 1998

David hadn't experienced any problems while off immunosuppressants. In the previous five years he had graduated from college, married his college sweetheart, and fathered a child. During that time, his blood work was normal, bilirubin level just 0 or 1, and biopsies showed no signs of rejection.

David wasn't the only one to be weaned off immunosuppressants. Cory Lavigne and Todd McNeely (the first child to receive a liver transplant in Pittsburgh) had received liver transplants a few months before David. They were each two years old at the time of the transplant and had participated in the same program as David. Weaned off immunosuppressants while still in their teens, they had both grown taller and put on weight and we knew from their parents' holiday correspondences that they were both doing great. David had not grown taller since he was already past his growing years. In David's case, the end of the antirejection medication meant the return of his appetite and he went from being underweight to a healthy weight for his 5'4" frame.

On this day, the young Pittsburgh doctor explained confidently to David that the biopsy hadn't shown any signs of rejection. The doctors were excited. I didn't know if they were surgeons, gastroenterologists, or a combination of both. What I did know was that they didn't look like a group who was about to deliver bad news to an intelligent young man who was almost as knowledgeable about liver disease and transplantation as they were. They were excited that David's liver failure was not due to rejection. The doctor explained that the CT scan, ultrasound, and MRI showed fibrosis and cirrhosis of the liver. "That is why the liver is failing, and that is why he will need a new liver sometime down the road," the doctor concluded. I was glad the doctors addressed the issue of rejection right away because it was also on my mind. With David having been off antirejection medication for five years now, I thought that   David might be experiencing a rejection problem. The idea that his liver was dying had never crossed my mind.

Now I understood why Dr. Iwatsuki was so upset earlier. I had seen him in the hallway and, as always, invited him to come in and visit David. He came, but I could tell he was uncomfortable looking at David's yellow eyes and face. He had been thinking about what lay ahead for David and knew he was helpless to stop it. But these young doctors didn't know David and they probably didn't know that much about what he would have to go through to get well. For them, this was not about a person with a dying liver who would spend the next few years fighting just to survive. For these young doctors, this was a victory of science! That David could be off anti-rejection medication for five years with absolutely no signs of rejection offered hope that future transplant patients might not have to endure the side effects of antirejection drugs. That David's liver was dying for other reasons was incidental.

In my mind, the fact that David's new liver had functioned perfectly with no antirejection medication meant that the transplanted liver had become a part of David's own body. As old liver cells had died they had regenerated, replaced by David's own body cells over the last 17 years. Now they were telling David that liver cells had died without being replaced.

I remembered an article that I had read 17 years ago about the liver and its function. It said only a third of the liver is needed to keep the body functioning normally. With a third of the liver working, blood work looks normal and a person feels healthy. The other two-thirds of the liver is reserve. I don't know how accurate the article was, but given our circumstances, it made sense to me. David's liver function tests were normal in December and the biopsy taken in Omaha showed that David's liver was "beautiful." That biopsy had probably been taken from the healthy part of David's liver. But just days before that "beautiful" biopsy, a previous biopsy taken by two young surgeons had proved inconclusive. When the biopsy was repeated two days later by an experienced gastroenterologist, the results were better.

The doctors were leaving David's room to go on to other patients, and go on with the rest of their lives, while David and I knew that our lives were forever changed by those few moments. Although David didn't show any emotion, we both knew that our lives would be in turmoil until David received a new transplant. I knew David, because he was my son. We had been through all of this before, but none of this made sense. "If Dr. Malatack was here, he would explain everything," I said to myself. David's wife Sara didn't show any emotion either, but I didn't know her as well as I knew David and could only guess what she might be thinking. All three of us were devastated. We were numb. In shock and disbelief, we tried to rationalize! After all, except for some jaundice, David looked normal and healthy. He was the one who had driven the seven hours from Michigan to Pittsburgh. Could a sick person do that? But deep down, I knew that the verdict was in and David's sentence was to suffer until he received a new liver. One phrase that the doctor had uttered was echoing in my mind: "sometime down the road . . ."

"We have to keep going," I said to myself. "Everything will be OK soon, but now we have to endure." None of us dared to ask any more questions. I had heard as much as I could handle during those few moments.

The telephone ringing brought me back to reality. It was our daughter Rebecca. She reported that she had gotten a new teaching job and filled me in on some of the details of her wedding plans. I was happy for her, and I was happy that most of the planning for her wedding—just a month away— was already done. Part of me wished we could wait until David was healthy to celebrate Rebecca's wedding. Joe and I had our hearts set on a memorable ceremony in which the whole family would participate. With Rebecca and her fiancé Dave, we had planned a beautiful reception with music and dancing, surrounded by our children and grandchildren. Brothers, sisters, and friends would be arriving from all over the world. Now, knowing that David was ill, celebrating would be difficult. The knowledge that David needed a liver transplant would be a dark undercurrent running beneath our outward joy at Rebecca and Dave's wedding celebration.

I remembered the first time David got sick in 1981. We were planning his Bar Mitzvah, the celebration of his "coming of age" as a Jewish male. The date was set for October 23, 1981. We continued to plan that celebration until he received his liver transplant on September 26, 1981. When it was clear that David would not recover enough to celebrate his Bar Mitzvah in October, we moved the date to March 19, 1982. How wonderful it was when the day finally came! Completely recovered, David looked like any other 13-year-old at his Bar Mitzvah. It was a wonderful evening. A standing-room-only crowd of least 500 people came to wish David well and we celebrated the event with a happy heart.

What wishful thinking! We had no idea when David would be completely healthy again, but we knew we had to go on with the wedding. "This is Rebecca's time," I said to myself. "Just for one night, we can pretend that everything is OK." If David wore some makeup, he wouldn't be so yellow. But, what if the makeup didn't help? What if I couldn't set aside my disappointment and concern about David's health for just one afternoon? My imagination was running away with me, and with good reason. If we had known what would take place at Rebecca and Dave's wedding and what all of us would go through over the next two years, I don't think we would have been able to carry on with the wedding and our lives as optimistically and resolutely as we did.

It was hard to think past that one sentence uttered earlier by the doctor: "Sometime down the road, David, you will need another liver." Our lives would soon be turned upside down, but we still had to think about the present, if only for Rachael, who understood little except that her daddy was sick.

At 4:00 p.m., Sara and I were making plans to take Rachael to the cafeteria for dinner and then back to the Family House, the nearby lodgings that we shared with the families of other patients. When I told David about our plans, he insisted that we stay at the hospital. I didn't think this was fair to Rachael. I reminded David that Rachael had been in the hospital waiting room with us all day. She had taken her afternoon nap in her stroller; now she needed a diaper change and we were out of fresh diapers. David still insisted that we stay. We were arguing, as usual!

I tried again. "David," I said, "Rachael is just a baby and she's tired after spending the whole day in the hospital. You should be thinking about what's best for her." David's answer shocked me and made me realize that he was no longer that 12-year-old that went through everything joking and laughing. He was a father who was worried about his daughter.

David said, "I *am* thinking of Rachael. I don't know how much longer I will be strong enough to play with her." The shock of that answer was my second shock of the day. For 17 years, David had lived without worrying about his liver and without worrying about death, at least not in front of us. No matter what happened with the biopsies and cholangiograms and tests, he never talked about being sick or running out of time. Now, all of a sudden, he was talking about running out of time.

"He must not be feeling good," I thought to myself. "Physically, he knows what is happening with his liver and he senses that this time will not be like the last time. It will be much more difficult to experience as an adult."

It isn't hard to make a child happy, even under the direst circumstances. We had done it before. To ease the pain of needle sticks, we would promise David a milkshake for each time the nurses drew blood and a movie and popcorn for each IV they inserted, and it had worked. But what were we going to do now that David was an adult?

I agreed to go buy the diapers while Sara and Rachael stayed with David. I don't know how I found my way out of the hospital. The expansion of the hospital over the years, adding new wings here and there, made getting anywhere in the hospital a challenge. I thought to myself, "Once again, I find myself in a nightmare in Oakland." (the area around the Presbyterian Hospital of Pittsburgh). I remembered how we had come to be in this place 17 years ago.

■   ■   ■

1981

The road to liver failure was a short one for David. In March 1981, he was a normal sixth grader who had his own paper route and participated in nearly every sport available to sixth-grade boys in Niles, Michigan. He played baseball, basketball, soccer, flag football, and was a member of the YMCA swim team. He was the picture of health and vitality. Then, all of a sudden, he began to fever. A week later, he was jaundiced. In April 1981, we took David to a teaching hospital in Chicago to find out what was wrong. The initial diagnosis was chronic hepatitis. Then a young resident suggested checking David's eyes for Kayser-Fleischer rings, a common symptom of Wilson's Disease. To my surprise, David did have the copper deposits in his eyes. This showed his liver was not able to process copper normally and the copper had been building up in his liver since infancy, causing liver damage.

The doctors were confident that David would recover fully taking the drug D-penicillamin and following a low-copper diet. They told us that the drug would cleanse his body of the copper deposits and his liver would regenerate. This was possible because David did not show any signs of the neurological problems that often accompanied advanced cases of Wilson's Disease. Neurological problems resulted from the brain damage caused by copper deposits in the brain, damage that could not be reversed by drug therapy. David's brain was unharmed and this was something for which to be thankful. With drug therapy and a special diet, he would be able to live a normal life.

The doctors were so optimistic about his condition that they didn't start him on the drug therapy right away. Unrelated to the Wilson's Disease, David also had a Glucose 6 Phosphate Dehydrogenase (G6PD) deficiency that caused red blood cells to break down when exposed to certain foods and drugs. Some things David had to avoid were fava beans, aspirin, and sulfa-based drugs. The doctors drew some blood and sent it to a specialist in California to make sure that David did not have the rare form of G6PD deficiency that was sometimes fatal. They were concerned that the D-penicillamin might cause his hemoglobin to break down, resulting in severe anemia. It took them two months to decide to begin the medication.

Finally, David was hospitalized in Chicago on June 11, 1981, for a liver biopsy and a trial of the Wilson's Disease medication, D-penicillamin. Although a liver biopsy is generally done under local anesthetic, it is not an easy test. A small needle is inserted into the liver and a tiny piece of the liver is extracted for examination. The pathologist makes a diagnosis from that tiny piece. Most liver problems can be diagnosed this way; what makes this test difficult is that the slightest movement by the patient can cause the needle to stray, possibly hitting a blood vessel and causing internal bleeding.

The pediatric gastroenterologist who performed the biopsy used "angel dust" to put David to sleep before performing the biopsy. He claimed that liver patients couldn't tolerate a lot of anesthetic due to their liver disease. The biopsy was done in the morning, but by late afternoon David was still in the Recovery Room. He was having a hard time coming out of the anesthetic. He had become violent and was having what was called a "bad trip." Finally, at 11:30 p.m., he woke up and was normal. The first dose of D-penicillamin was administered.

The next day, David's hemoglobin broke down and David became weaker and more jaundiced than ever. The doctors stopped the D-penicillamin, not knowing why David's red blood cells were breaking down. Was it the angel dust or the D-penicillamin? A few units of blood brought David's hemoglobin count back to normal and the doctors decided to wait a day to make sure David was stabile. The next day there was another breakdown of hemoglobin and another round of transfusions.

For a few weeks, the pattern remained unchanged. There would be a drop in hemoglobin, then more blood transfusions. When 75 percent of David's blood was *coming from transfusions, the doctors decided to try him on the D-penicillamin again. One week later, David stabilized. There was no hemoglobin breakdown, but now there was a buildup of ascitic fluid in David's belly. With his skinny limbs and swollen belly, David was beginning to look like one of those malnourished children that you see in the ads for charities that are trying to end world hunger. To the doctors, this was a sign that David's liver condition was worsening. However, they were happy that David could tolerate the D-penicillamin. They were hoping that the medication would eventually clear David's liver of the excess copper that had built up over his 12 years of life and then his liver would regenerate.*

David was released and asked to return for a checkup in a month. We had stayed three weeks instead of three days! David was sent home with D-penicillamin for the Wilson's Disease, Lasix and Aldactone to reduce fluid retention, and instructions to follow a low-copper and low-salt diet.

We spent the Fourth of July at home and, after the holiday, took David to the Mayo Clinic for another opinion. David was admitted for tests that included a CAT-scan, a review of his record, and an examination of his biopsy slides. They, too, found that David had Wilson's Disease along with hemolytic anemia. David's hemoglobin was breaking down due to the excess of copper in his blood. Ninety percent of David's liver was damaged. We were told that it would take at least three months for the D-penicillamin to clear the copper from David's liver and then his liver would regenerate. As his liver healed, the fluid in his belly would be reabsorbed. The good news was that the fluid in David's belly was not infected. The doctors at the Mayo Clinic did not recommend any minor surgery for David, believing it would be dangerous for him. Liver transplant was never even mentioned as an option. At the time it was considered an experimental procedure, so there was no liver transplant program at the Mayo Clinic. The doctors approved of David's course of treatment and encouraged us to return to Chicago for further treatment.

Shortly after returning home, we had to take David back to Chicago for further treatment. He was unable to eat and had lost a lot of weight. He was weak and dizzy and we thought he might be hemolyzing again. The real problem turned out to be a lack of sodium in his blood. Because he was unable to eat, the medications that he was taking to reduce the fluid buildup in his belly had thrown off his electrolyte balance. This time, David spent a month in the hospital as we watched him getting weaker and weaker. He lost so much weight that we could see his tailbone sticking out and the intravenous feedings didn't seem to be helping.

Finally, in August, the day of reckoning arrived. Test results showed that not only had David's liver not improved, it had deteriorated further. The doctors said that without a liver transplant, David had only three months to live. We were given the name and phone number of a pediatric gastroenterologist in Pittsburgh by the name of Dr. J. Carlton Gartner.

Joe and I were worried. We knew that kidney transplants were becoming fairly routine, but we didn't know anything about liver transplants. As sick as David was, I was not sure David would survive a complicated surgery. But we headed off to Pittsburgh at the end of August, 1981. Dr. Gartner sent an ambulance to transport David from the airport to Children's Hospital of Pittsburgh. In the hospital, we were received by Dr. Jeffrey Malatack. He explained to us that he was one of Dr. Gartner's associates and he would be responsible for David's care.

■   ■   ■

June, 1998

Two days before, when we had arrived in Pittsburgh with David, Sara, and Rachael, I had relived much of the earlier nightmare. Now, the events of the afternoon reminded me that this time, in addition to our family, Sara, Rachael, and Sara's family would suffer along with us. The thought of Rachael brought tears to my eyes. It wasn't fair to her! She was just starting to say "Mama" and "Daddy." I knew how it would feel to have a gravely ill father at home. My own father was sick with kidney failure for a whole year before he died. That was forty-some years ago in the Middle East, before anyone had ever heard or dreamed of kidney transplantation.

Oakland, the area around the University of Pittsburgh, was not the same as it had been 17 years ago. Most of the stores with which I was familiar had moved away, but the drugstore was still there and I bought the diapers there. On the way back to the hospital, I saw a homeless man faint in the street. As someone called 911, I wiped the tears from my face. I knew I would have to be strong, especially for Rachael.

I thought of my grandmother who lived with us during my twelfth year, the year my 65-year-old father was dying of kidney failure. Her strength was an inspiration. From her, I learned that I shouldn't waste energy worrying about why bad things happen. I learned to accept that life is difficult, and that pain and suffering are a part of life, not just something that happens to other people.

■   ■   ■

1964 - 1981

With the birth of each of my three beautiful, intelligent, healthy children, we were thrilled! But always the fear that they might someday face danger or illness lurked in the back of my mind. When I heard or read in the newspaper about accidents involving children, I worried more. Then, our daughter Rebecca became ill at the age of three with pernicious anemia. It was something that we had never heard of, but the cure was easy. She would need a monthly Vitamin B12 injection for the rest of her life. We were upset, but this was something we would manage.

When David was diagnosed seven years later with Wilson's Disease, we were hopeful that his illness would have a similarly quick resolution. The doctors in Chicago told us that David had been diagnosed early and we could expect that, with medication and dietary changes, he would quickly return to a normal life. When he didn't respond to the medication and his health deteriorated more and more, I tried to learn more about Wilson's Disease. I read everything I could get my hands on, even the books in the doctors' library at the hospital. To my dismay, all of the patients I read about in these books who had symptoms like David's had died. I was worried that without a miracle, David would also die.

When we were sent to Dr. Gartner in Pittsburgh, David was put on the waiting list for a liver transplant. While David was on the waiting list, I stayed by his side. During the day, I sat by his hospital bed. At night, I slept on a rented cot in his room. I believed that by being with him all the time, I could pass some of my energy on to him. I felt that my love for him would give him the energy to fight the angel of death, and that he wouldn't give up.

Our home in Niles, Michigan was about eight hours away from Pittsburgh. On weekends, my husband Joe, my mother, and our other children, Ben and Rebecca, would come to visit. When Joe came, he wanted care for David. He encouraged me to get out of the hospital to get some fresh air and enjoy what life had to offer away from the pain and suffering of the hospital. So while Joe was with David, I would go into Oakland to look for a food that David might be enticed to eat or a toy that would amuse him for awhile. I was never able to forget, even for a moment, the gravity of our devastating situation. Whenever I was out of his room, I was terrified that he might die and that it would be my absence that made it possible for him to slip away from us.

■   ▓   ■

June, 1998

Now 17 years after David's first transplant, we knew we would be revisiting those hard days and hoping for another miracle. We knew it wouldn't be easy and there would be no shortcuts. We knew we had to be strong, persevere, and try to be a source of strength for David and his family.

I got the diapers and returned to the hospital. After the four of us had dinner together in the cafeteria, we went back to David's hospital room. While David was in the hospital, he wanted Sara, Rachael, and me to stay in the Family House. When we first inquired, the Family House was full, but then a suite in the basement became available. As we were getting ready to go to the Family House for the night, David asked Sara to come back to the hospital after putting Rachael to bed.

The Family House is a beautifully decorated old mansion. Like the Ronald McDonald house that we stayed in during David's first transplant, the Family House provides a homelike atmosphere for the critically ill and their families while they are away from home. In the Family House, each family has their own bedroom. There are washers and dryers, a large family room, and a kitchen complete with pots and pans, dishes, and utensils. The laundry facilities, family room, and kitchen are shared by all. Each family is responsible for cleaning up after themselves in the kitchen, cleaning their own room, and cleaning the bathroom after use. But the best part is having the opportunity to live in a safe, homey place, and befriend families in similar situations. The Family House is a home away from home.

When we arrived at our room, we noticed that the two air conditioning units had been removed for repair and the floor was wet. That meant Rachael would have to stay in the playpen. We decided to move back to the hotel. Rachael cried as we packed up to return to the hotel; I wondered if she was feeling our pain and disappointment. By the time Rachael was in bed that night, Sara and I were exhausted, but I was unable to sleep.

I went back to the hospital. It was past visiting hours, but I convinced the security guard at the hospital entrance that I wouldn't stay long. When I got to David's room, I found him asleep. The agony in his jaundiced face reminded me of the way he looked while he was in a coma waiting for his first transplant in 1981. I thought I would never see that color and expression on his face again. I was back in the nightmare again.

I decided not to wake him up. He needed the sleep. I had returned just in case he, too, was unable to sleep and wanted to talk. I knew he really wanted Sara, not me, but I told the nurse to let David know that I had come by if he awakened.

On my way back to the hotel, I remembered how we used to stay and sleep in David's hospital room. That was 17 years ago, when he was twelve. Now he was 29, an independent grown man, a husband, and a father. He didn't need a mother to take care of him. Physically, he wasn't very sick, but the idea of a second liver transplant wasn't something he could run from, especially when he wasn't feeling well, so I was glad he was able to sleep.

That night was the first of many sleepless nights for me. I wondered what my role would be now that he wasn't a child anymore. Should I just provide emotional support and wait to see if he would tell me what he expected of me? It would be easy to retreat to the past and resume my old role as mother, caretaker, and medical advocate of my sick child. I had to keep reminding myself that not only was he no longer a child; he was a husband and a father.

Last time, liver transplantation was a relatively uncommon surgery. There were very few medical centers performing liver transplants and not much information to be found on the subject. Now, 17 years later, liver transplants were fairly commonplace, but we were facing a retransplant. We found that a retransplant after ten or more years was a relatively uncommon procedure. There just wasn't a lot of information out there about second transplants after more than ten years.

We remembered one young girl that returned for a second transplant in 1981, while David was recovering from his first transplant. Her first liver had lasted three or four years. Her mother told me that there was some question about whether they would give her another liver at all, since the doctors were concerned about whether her initial disease would return and damage the new liver. The surgeons chose not to give up on her and performed a second liver transplant. Sadly, she died a few days later of uncontrollable internal bleeding.

We also remembered another young man named Ken who received a liver transplant in Denver several years before David. He didn't come to the liver transplant reunion, but his mother wrote to us and we began a correspondence. More than ten years after his first transplant, Ken was a successful young man when his liver began to fail and he was put on the waiting list for a second one. He died waiting for a second transplant. That was all I knew about long-term transplant patients who needed another transplant. David's life was in God's hands; I started praying that God would help David and give all of us the strength we would need to see him through this.

The next day, Sara, Rachael, and I went to visit David. During a quiet moment while Rachael was asleep in her stroller and Sara was on the telephone, we got a big surprise. A very special visitor dropped in to see David: Dr. Thomas E. Starzl! I was speechless. Sara hung up the phone and we greeted him warmly. I could see that he had not changed much from the photo he had taken with David and Sara in 1995. David had introduced Sara to Dr. Starzl at a symposium on liver transplantation that they attended in Japan in 1995. The photo commemorating that event had been framed and proudly displayed in their home ever since.

■   ■   ■

1981

Unexpected visits from Dr. Starzl were not unusual. He came in with the transplant team each afternoon for daily rounds, but many other times he came alone. Late at night or very early in the morning, after he was done in the operating room, he would stop in to check on David before going home. It reminded me of a father checking on his children before going to bed. One time, he even brought a monkey puppet to try to get David to laugh! For me, his most memorable visit happened just a couple days after David's transplant. Dr. Starzl had just gotten out of surgery and dropped in to check on David. Even though David's new liver was functioning properly, he was still in a coma. His urine bag was filled with normal yellow urine, not the dark brown urine that his body had produced while his liver was failing. He was connected to an IV for fluid and a tube in his nose was feeding a special formula into his stomach. The measuring tape around his waist showed that his waist size was normal and that there was no fluid buildup in his belly. Even though I had no experience with what to expect after a transplant, there was no doubt in my mind that the new liver was working. His skin was still a little yellow, but I knew it would take a little longer for his skin color to return to normal.

Under these joyful circumstances (my child was returning to himself!), Dr. Starzl arrived at David's bedside. He looked at David whose eyes were still closed from the coma and said, "David, open your eyes. Move your shoulder. Come on! Give some encouragement to the surgeon!" David just lay there with his eyes closed, not even a muscle twitched. But with that visit, we felt Dr. Starzl's basic goodness and humanity. He wanted to see David getting better. He wanted to see the fastest recovery that David's strengthening body could muster.

As David's mother, I knew he was getting better. I had eyed that empty urine bag hanging on the side of his bed and sat by him during the dialysis sessions as his kidneys began to fail in the two weeks before his transplant. Just the sight of that urine bag filled with normal color urine was enough to convince me that he was getting better. His kidneys were working again! Dr. Malatack had been right when he explained to us that there was nothing wrong with David's kidneys. He had said they had stopped working because his liver wasn't functioning, but after the trans-

plant, his kidneys would start working again. It was difficult to believe at the time, but here was the proof right in front of my eyes.

I did a little mental arithmetic. It had taken six months of liver failure for David to get into this weakened and comatose condition. I figured it would take six months of proper nutrition and rest with his new healthy liver for David to recover fully. I wished I had some encouraging words for Dr. Starzl, but what could I say to this man who was doing God's work on earth? I knew we would just have to wait.

Miraculously, it didn't take anywhere near six months for David to recover. Several days later he emerged from the coma and just one week after the transplant, his liver function returned to normal. Dr. Starzl began calling David his "Superstar." Every time Dr. Starzl saw David, his face would light up. Although David was still paralyzed and it was hard for us to believe he would ever walk or talk again, Dr. Starzl never gave up. He was the one who gave us faith. He said over and over that David would play soccer again and he was right. Three months later, we were home and David was back in school. From what I know about Dr. Starzl, he never gave up on any of his patients.

■ ■ ■

June, 1998

Here he was again, the man who had saved David's life in 1981, our hero. Dr. Starzl sat down on the chair and began talking. He told us that after his heart bypass surgery, his doctor advised him not to visit with patients in the hospital anymore. Obviously, he wasn't following doctor's orders. Speaking directly to David, he said, "I hope you decide to go for a full life once again. You know we can expect long-term survival after a liver transplant nowadays."

The air in the room was heavy, and filled with sadness and despair. No one had the heart to make small talk. We were all heartbroken over David's liver failure. Was it possible that David thought he had failed Dr. Starzl by returning with a damaged liver? Was it possible that Dr. Starzl felt helpless because he was no longer able to take David to the operating room and replace his damaged liver with a healthy one? Dr. Starzl had been retired for several years and was now ill himself. Perhaps he was feeling despair that his time was past and there was nothing he could do for David, except to encourage him to fight for a full, healthy life once again.

All of these thoughts were running through my head, and I wondered why Dr. Starzl would feel the need to encourage David not to give up. He knew David well enough to know about his fighting spirit. David wouldn't give up. What we didn't know about was the grave shortage of livers and the length of the waiting list. In addition, things had changed drastically in the last 17 years. There were strict rules and guidelines that determined which patients would receive the donor organs when they became available. These things that we had yet to learn about were enough to discourage anyone. When I reflected upon this later, I realized that Dr. Starzl was probably aware that our experience would be different this time due to these major administrative changes. He knew we had a long, hard road ahead of us and he came to offer us his support, encouragement, and blessing!

David and Sara said nothing and I felt like I had to fill the silence. I asked, "How is Kim Hudson doing? Is she all right?" At 27 years post-transplant, Kim was the longest living liver transplant survivor. Dr. Starzl said Kim was doing fine. On his way out of the room, he stopped to look at Rachael. He turned to David and Sara and said, "You should have more children." Then, he left as quietly as he had arrived.

I remembered the day David and I first met Dr. Starzl in 1981.

■ ■ ■

1981

Dr. Starzl had a somber, sad look in his eyes. He couldn't believe how deteriorated David's physical condition was. He said, "If a liver comes tonight and it's a good one for David, we will operate tonight. I can't wait for the approval of the Transplant Committee. We don't have much time." Unfortunately, a liver did not come that night, or the next night, or the next, despite our prayers. David was the sickest patient on the waiting list, so he was moved to the top of the waiting list in the country.

■ ■ ■

June, 1998

Today, I saw the same sad look in Dr. Starzl's eyes that I had seen when we had first met. His words and his expression left no doubt that David needed a new liver soon, and his comment about David and Sara having more children gave us faith in a normal life after a second transplant. My heart ached for Dr. Starzl, too. It was a sad situation. None of us knew what the road would be like on the journey ahead, but Dr. Starzl's visit and the knowledge that he was still concerned about David and looking out for him gave us comfort. It was a ray of light in the darkness that I had been living in for the last 24 hours.

Over the years, we had kept in touch with Dr. Starzl. We exchanged cards and letters and I sent invitations to important family events. Dr. Starzl's fighting spirit had changed our world by saving David's life, and his fighting spirit had changed medicine by making liver transplant a successful surgery. I wondered if Dr. Starzl knew that, not only had he operated on David and given him a new chance at life, he had also passed on to David some of his fighting spirit. I would venture to say that anyone who was operated on by Dr. Starzl would attest to a special bond between Dr. Starzl, themselves, and their family.

■   ■   ■

1983

While we were planning the reunion of liver transplant patients, many of the letters and phone calls from the parents of the children expressed the same sentiment: "We must come to the reunion because my child is one of Dr. Starzl's most important patients." My husband Joe and I heard that so often that we decided to include it in the program. At the reunion, Joe told the story of the letters and phone calls and added, "OK, we finally found out who was the most important patient and we are going to announce it today. Would the most important patient please stand up?" Of course, all of the children stood up since we had shared the story with them. To everyone's amazement, Dr. Starzl remembered every patient's name and the details of their disease, surgery, and recovery.

That night, after the reunion, the news ran some video of David at a physical therapy session seven weeks after the transplant. By that time, there were no IV's, bags, or tubes attached to his body. The video just showed a skeleton of a boy being held up by a physical therapist who was trying to get him to stand. Only David's toes were touching the ground, but it was no use anyway. He was too weak and had no muscles to support him. Then, they ran the video from the reunion earlier that day. David was standing next to the pool, a handsome, happy young man in his swimsuit. The reporter asked David what he thought of Dr. Starzl. David said, "I think of him like I think of God. He gave me a new life." That answer from 15-year-old David was broadcast on Sunday, June 12, 1983 all over the country.

■   ■   ■

June, 1998

We wondered if we would find another surgeon like Dr. Starzl, someone who would find a liver for David, champion his cause, and not give up on him. Only time would tell.

The diagnosis had been made and it was time to go home. There wouldn't be any immediate cure to make David feel better, or to give him the energy that his nonfunctioning liver was failing to provide. We would have to wait for another liver transplant. Someone would have to die and the grieving family would have to agree to donate the loved one's liver. Someone perfectly healthy would have their life cut short as a result of a freak accident, massive stroke, or brain abnormality that would cause them to be declared brain dead while their heart was still beating and a respirator was breathing for them. All of these things would have to happen before David would be able to have a lifesaving liver transplant. There would be much heartache and pain. Our hearts still ached every time we thought of David's first donor.

■   ■   ■

1981

On September 18th, a liver became available somewhere in the U.S., and the surgeons thought it would be a good one for David. Dr. Malatack brought us the joyous news and the nurses prepared David for surgery. He was vomiting blood and was almost in a hepatic coma. Dr. Starzl flew to the hospital where the donor was located to help harvest the liver. Our Pittsburgh rabbi arrived and we prayed for the success of the operation.

Many friends and relatives were praying for David and waiting for a sign of hope. My mother and Joe's mother were staying at our home in Niles to provide us with emotional support and to help care for 17-year-old Ben and ten-year-old Rebecca. We called all of them and told them that a liver had been located for David and that the donor was four years old. That was all we knew. Both of our mothers said that the liver of a four-year-old would be too small for David. We didn't argue with them. We just thought that the surgeons would know best. We forgot that our mothers had been housewives in the Middle East where the meat for family meals didn't come from the grocery store. Our mothers had taken live animals to the butcher to be killed and performed the necessary tasks to prepare kosher meat themselves. They had removed the blood vessels and organs from countless animals and were well aware of the relationship between the age of the animal and its organs. However, the surgeons thought that based on weight, this liver might work for David. David had deteriorated so much that he weighed just 57 pounds and looked extremely small for a 12-year-old. The four-year-old donor's weight was 50 pounds. After three weeks of searching, this was the only child's liver that had become available.

At 1:30 a.m., Dr. Malatack arrived with some disappointing news. The liver had arrived safely, but it was indeed too small for David. Putting this liver into David's body would be like executing him on the operating table. This liver couldn't go to waste, Dr. Malatack reminded us, so it would be given to a smaller child. But he reminded us that if a suitable liver for David came tonight, they would operate on David tonight. He reminded us that Dr. Starzl had boundless energy and he would not give up on David.

The child who received that small liver was Benjamin Hollingsworth. Benjamin, born with Alpha-1 Antitrypsin Deficiency, had suffered from liver failure throughout his four short years of life. Benjamin survived the grueling operation and the surgery was a success! A few days later, Benjamin's parents came to visit David. They apologized for Benjamin receiving the liver that we had hoped would go to David. I explained that I felt God wanted this liver for Benjamin, not David. I then went with Benjamin's mother Arlene to visit Benjamin in the ICU. I was amazed that such a sick little boy was able to survive such a long and difficult surgery! He looked great, seemingly unaware that he had just survived an incredible operation. Benjamin's resilience was a thought that would later give me faith and comfort when it was David's turn on the operating table.

In the bed next to Benjamin was a girl who reminded me of Sleeping Beauty, except that she was connected to a respirator. Arlene quietly explained to me that she was brain dead, and the respirator was keeping her alive. Arlene had talked to her parents and felt that they were in no condition to consider the idea of organ donation. I understood well. David was in a coma because of liver failure. Without a new liver, he would die. But at least we had hope. The miracle of a liver transplant might offer David his life back. These parents had no hope for a cure for their daughter. I understood well what her parents were going through and all I could do was to pray for her, for her family, and for David.

Several days later, her family came to understand and accept her condition. In their time of grief, they made her an organ donor. Her liver was put into David and she became the angel who gave David 17 healthy years.

The University of Pittsburgh's policy was that there should not be any contact between the family of the donor and the family of the recipient. They didn't even tell us the girl's first name. We never had the chance to thank the family, but when the local TV news station later interviewed us, we expressed our gratitude to this unknown family and hoped that they would see the program and understand how deeply grateful we were.

As years passed, her spirit was always with us, especially on special days like David's high school and college graduations, and on his wedding day. With the birth of David's daughter Rachael, I thanked her quietly in my prayers and wished that we could share these wonderful moments with her family, too. Throughout the years, I also wrote letters to the Organ Procurement Office in Pittsburgh in the hope that they might call and ask about their daughter's organ recipients, as some families did. If this ever happened, I wanted them to know how their daughter gave new life to David. We never forgot that we were enjoying those special moments with our son because of their daughter's gift and the miracle of liver transplantation.

■   ■   ■

June, 1998

Nancy, the Pittsburgh transplant coordinator, was our link to the transplant surgeons. The coordinator is a nurse who serves as a liaison between the patients and the doctors whenever the patient is out of the hospital. The position was created to facilitate communication between doctors and their patients because the surgeons are very busy and oftentimes unavailable to take a telephone call. The coordinators had all worked at one time as a nurse on the transplant floor of the hospital and were very knowledgeable in their field, capable of doing almost anything for a patient except surgery. A patient who needs help can call the coordinator with their problem. After discussing it with the doctors, the coordinator then helps the patient by educating them, answering questions, and arranging for necessary treatment. Nancy knew David well. She had been his transplant coordinator for many years.

Nancy explained to us that David had a drainage bag connected to his bile duct. David would go home with the bag taped to his abdomen to drain the bile out of his liver so it wouldn't build up and further damage his liver. She showed David how to empty the drainage bag and keep the area clean. We were to return to Pittsburgh in one week so that David could be reevaluated and put on the waiting list.

The idea of going home with the bag made David even unhappier. It was inconvenient and painful and, worst of all, a constant reminder to him that his liver was dying. But as always, he trusted his doctors and accepted their recommendation.

David was released from the hospital and we spent another night in the hotel. That night an unusual thing happened. In the wee hours of the morning, the hotel fire alarm sounded. We gathered up a sleepy Rachael, descended four flights using the stairs, and traipsed outside bleary-eyed, only to find out it was a false alarm! I wished David's liver problem would turn out to be a false alarm, but I knew that was just wishful thinking. The alarm was a warning signal to me that our safe world was crumbling and this was the beginning of a long, painful chapter in our lives. There would be no escaping it, and no shortcuts. I wondered how long it would last. Weeks? Months? Years? I had no idea.

I tried to think about the positive things coming up in our lives. First, we would celebrate Rachael's first birthday. Her birthday party had been cancelled because of the trip to Pittsburgh and now that we were returning home, we could reschedule it. Then, there would be wedding showers and a wedding celebration for Rebecca and Dave. After that, we could look forward to helping David and Sara move into their first house, a brand new home that they were building in Lowell, a suburb of Grand Rapids, Michigan. I hoped and prayed for strength for all of us. I knew that somehow we would manage, but I also knew that these joyful occasions would be bittersweet. I did not imagine that the stronger we got, the harder things would become, but I was sure that David's emotional energy and indomitable spirit would see us through it all. Also, this time there was something else to consider. This time, there was a new life. When things seemed hopeless, little Rachael's joy for life would distract us from our despair and renew David's determination to survive.

On the way home, David and Sara took turns driving and I enjoyed Rachael's company in the back seat. We arrived at David and Sara's apartment in the late afternoon and after dinner, I made the three-and-a-half hour drive to my home on the north side of Chicago.

Reprinted from The Puzzle People: Memoirs of a Transplant Surgeon, *by Dr. Thomas E. Starzl, M.D., University of Pittsburgh Press, with permission from Dr. Thomas E. Starzl and the University of Pittsburgh Press.*

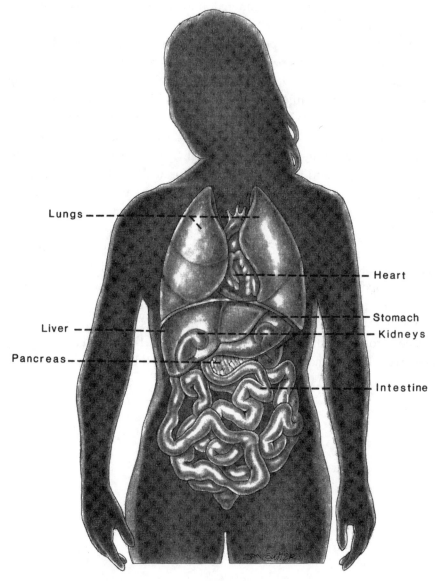

Figure 1. Location in the body of the commonly transplanted organs. Note that every normal person has two lungs and two kidneys. The kidneys are behind the liver on the right and behind the stomach on the left.

Appendix 1

LIVER DISEASE: CAUSE AND PREVENTION

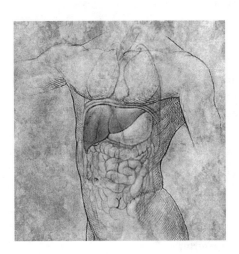

Your Liver... A Vital Organ
(Reprinted with permission from the American Liver Foundation)

Your liver, the largest organ in your body, plays a vital role in regulating life processes. This complex organ performs many functions essential to life. You simply cannot live without it.

The Location of the Liver

The liver, located behind the lower ribs on the right side of your abdomen, weighs about three pounds and is roughly the size of a football.

Functions of Your Liver

This vital organ performs many complex functions. Some of these are:

1. To convert food into chemicals necessary for life and growth;
2. To manufacture and export important substances used by the rest of the body;
3. To process drugs absorbed from the digestive tract into forms that are easier for the body to use; and
4. To detoxify and excrete substances that otherwise would be poisonous.

Your liver plays a key role in converting food into essential chemicals of life. All of the blood that leaves the stomach and intestines must pass through the liver before reaching the rest of the body. The liver is thus strategically placed to process nutrients and drugs absorbed from the digestive tract into forms that are easier for the rest of the body to use. In essence, the liver can be thought of as the body's refinery.

Furthermore, your liver plays a principal role in removing ingested and internally produced toxic substances from the blood. The liver converts them to substances that can be easily eliminated from the body. It also makes bile, a greenish- brown fluid which is essential for digestion. Bile is stored in the gallbladder. The gallbladder contracts and discharges bile into the intestine, where it aids digestion.

Many drugs taken to treat diseases are also chemically modified by the liver. These changes govern the drug's activity in the body.

Your Liver Helps You by:

1. Producing quick energy when it is needed;
2. Manufacturing new body proteins;
3. Preventing shortages in body fuel by storing certain vitamins, minerals, and sugars;
4. Regulating transport of fat stores;
5. Regulating blood clotting;
6. Aiding in the digestive process by producing bile;
7. Controlling the production and excretion of cholesterol;
8. Neutralizing and destroying poisonous substances;
9. Metabolizing alcohol;
10. Monitoring and maintaining the proper level of many chemicals and drugs in the blood;

11. Cleansing the blood and discharging waste products into the bile;
12. Maintaining hormone balance;
13. Serving as the main organ of blood formation before birth;
14. Helping the body resist infection by producing immune factors and by removing bacteria from the bloodstream;
15. Regenerating its own damaged tissue; and
16. Storing iron.

Liver Diseases

There are many types of liver diseases, but among the most important are:

1. Viral hepatitis;
2. Cirrhosis;
3. Liver disorders in children;
4. Gallstones;
5. Alcohol-related liver disorders; and
6. Cancer of the liver.

Symptoms and Signs of Liver Disease

1. Abnormally yellow discoloration of the skin and eyes. This is called jaundice, which is often the first and sometimes the only sign of liver disease.
2. Dark urine.
3. Gray, yellow, or light-colored stools.
4. Nausea, vomiting and/or loss of appetite.
5. Vomiting of blood, bloody or black stools. Intestinal bleeding can occur when liver diseases obstruct blood flow through the liver. The bleeding may result in vomiting of blood or bloody stools.
6. Abdominal swelling. Liver disease may cause ascites, an accumulation of fluid in the abdominal cavity.
7. Prolonged, generalized itching.
8. Unusual change of weight. An increase or decrease of more than 5% within two months.
9. Abdominal pain.
10. Sleep disturbances, mental confusion, and coma are present

in severe liver disease. These result from an accumulation of toxic substances in the body which impairs brain function.

11. Fatigue or loss of stamina.
12. Loss of sexual drive or performance.

If any of these signs or symptoms appear, consult your physician immediately.

Prevention

1. Don't drink more than two alcoholic drinks a day.
2. Be cautious about mixing several drugs; in particular, alcohol and many over-the-counter and prescription medicines do not mix well.
3. Avoid taking medicines unnecessarily. Also avoid exposure to industrial chemicals whenever possible.
4. Maintain a healthful, balanced diet.
5. Consult your physician if you observe any signs or symptoms of liver disease.

Gallstones

Gallstones are formed when the cholesterol and/or pigment in bile crystallize in the gallbladder, forming stones that vary from pebble to golf ball-sized. Sometimes gallstones get stuck in the bile ducts leading from the gallbladder to the duodenum (the first part of the small intestine). The gallbladder and bile ducts then try to push the stones out by muscular contractions. This can cause attacks of excruciating abdominal pain. Blockage of the ducts by stones also prevents flow of bile into the intestines. Bile then backs up into the bloodstream, causing jaundice.

Gallstones are more common in people over 40, especially in women and the obese. Each year, more than 500,000 Americans undergo surgery to remove the gallbladder because of gallstones. An oral medication, ursodiol, is a safe and effective alternative to gallbladder surgery for many patients.

Viral Hepatitis

Hepatitis (meaning an inflammation of the liver) is caused by several different viruses. Hepatitis A is spread through contaminated water and food and is excreted in the stools. Hepatitis B is acquired from exposure to infected blood or body fluids. It can also be transmitted from a pregnant woman to her baby. Hepatitis C is primarily spread through infected blood. Depending on the virus, it may be present in the bloodstream, intestines, feces, saliva and in other body secretions.

Some people with viral hepatitis have no symptoms. In others, the liver may become tender and enlarged. The patient may exhibit symptoms including fever, weakness, nausea, vomiting, jaundice and aversion to food.

In the United States, there are more than **four million carriers of hepatitis**, people who are not ill themselves, but may pass hepatitis on to others.

A vaccine for hepatitis has been shown to be safe and effective in the prevention of infection if given before exposure. It is recommended for all infants, those who come into contact with blood in their work, and for anyone with more than one sex partner. A vaccine for hepatitis A has also been shown to be effective for at least 10 years or longer.

Many people recover from hepatitis without treatment, but others may develop chronic illnesses. Hepatitis B and C are associated with an increased risk of development of cirrhosis and liver cancer. Treatments with interferon are effective in some cases of hepatitis B and C.

Alcohol Related Liver Disorders

There are three separate liver disorders related to alcohol: fatty liver, alcoholic hepatitis, and alcoholic cirrhosis.

Fatty liver, the most common alcohol-related liver disorder, causes enlargement of the liver and right upper abdominal discomfort. The swollen liver is often tender or painful. Severe fatty liver may cause temporary jaundice and abnormalities of liver function. Abstinence from alcohol can effect complete reversal and cure without leaving residual cirrhosis.

Alcoholic hepatitis is an acute illness often characterized by nausea, vomiting, right upper and middle abdominal pain, fever, jaundice, enlarged and tender liver, and an elevation of the white blood cell count. Sometimes alcoholic hepatitis may be present without symptoms. As with fatty liver, treatment is primarily supportive and preventive.

Any disease which is brought on by alcohol abuse cannot be reversed until alcohol intake is stopped. Once alcoholic hepatitis develops, progression to cirrhosis will occur if alcohol consumption continues.

Alcoholic cirrhosis occurs in 10 to 15 percent of people who consume large amounts of alcohol over a prolonged period of time. However, there is considerable variation in the degree of susceptibility of people to given amounts of alcohol, and further research is needed to determine why some individuals are more vulnerable to alcohol than others.

Cirrhosis

Each year over 25,000 Americans die from cirrhosis, the seventh leading cause of death in the United States. In fact, between the ages of 25 and 44, it is the fourth leading disease-related cause of death.

Cirrhosis of the liver is a degenerative disease where liver cells are damaged and replaced by scar formation. As scar tissue progressively accumulates, blood flow through the liver is diminished, causing even more liver cells to die. Loss of liver function results in gastrointestinal disturbances, emaciation, enlargement of the liver and spleen, jaundice, accumulation of fluid in the abdomen and other tissues of the body. Obstruction of the venous circulation often causes massive vomiting of blood.

Anything which results in severe liver injury can cause cirrhosis. Over half of the deaths from cirrhosis of the liver are caused by alcohol abuse, hepatitis and other viruses. Some chemicals, many poisons, too much iron or copper, severe reaction to drugs, and obstruction of the bile duct can also cause cirrhosis.

Some types of cirrhosis can be treated, but often there is no cure. At this point, treatment is mostly supportive and may include a strict diet, diuretics, vitamins, and abstinence from alcohol. However, there has been much progress in managing the major complications of cirrhosis such as fluid retention in the abdomen, bleeding, and changes in mental function.

Liver Disorders in Children

Tens of thousands of American children—from newborn infants to adolescents—are born with or acquire liver diseases, and hundreds die from them every year. The incidence of liver disease is estimated to be as high as 1 in 2,500 live births. There are more than one hundred different types of liver diseases that have been identified in infants and children. The more common of these diseases are:

- **Biliary Atresia** is the absence or inadequate size of bile ducts from the liver to the intestine. More children come to liver transplantation for biliary atresia than for any other single liver disease.

- **Chronic Active Hepatitis** gradually destroys and replaces the normal liver cells with scar tissue through an unknown process which resembles an allergy to the child's own liver tissue.

- **Galactosemia** is an inherited disease in which an enzyme needed to digest milk sugar is missing, causing the milk sugar to build up in the liver and other organs, leading to cirrhosis of the liver, cataracts of the eyes, and brain damage. Unless the baby is taken off milk and given an artificial formula that has no milk sugar, the child will die.

- **Wilson's Disease** causes large amounts of copper to build up in the liver due to an inherited abnormality, causing cirrhosis of the liver and brain damage.

- **Reye's Syndrome** is an acute, rare fatal disorder in which fat accumulates in the liver and the child goes into a deep coma.

- **Cirrhosis** can be caused by any extensive injury to the liver including most of the disorders described above.

Cancer of the Liver

The most common form of cancer of the liver is the spread of cancer from other organ systems to the liver.

Not much is known about cancer which originates in the liver except that it is associated with viral hepatitis and certain parasites, drugs, and environmental toxins. Each year, 1,000 Americans die of primary liver cancer. Chronic carriers of the hepatitis B or C viruses are at increased risk to develop liver cancer.

Hope for Tomorrow Through Research

The liver, the detoxifying factory in the body, has become an increasingly overworked organ. Liver diseases appear to be on the increase. Part of this increase may be due to the increased use of chemicals and a rise in environmental pollutants.

Liver diseases are poorly understood. An adequate investment in effective liver research has the potential of saving billions of dollars and preventing untold human suffering.

The present investment in liver research is scant in relation to the magnitude, destructiveness, and severity of these diseases. Experts estimate that more than half of all liver diseases could be prevented if people acted upon the knowledge we already have.

Each year more than 25 million Americans are afflicted with liver and gallbladder diseases and more than 51,532 die of liver diseases. There are few effective treatments for most life-threatening liver diseases, except for liver transplants.

Research has recently opened up exciting new paths for investigation, but much more remains to be done to find cures.

The American Liver Foundation

The information in "Your Liver" is reprinted with permission from the American Liver Foundation (ALF). ALF is a national voluntary health organization dedicated to preventing, treating, and curing hepatitis and other liver diseases through research and education. The contents of "Your Liver" are for information purposes only. It does not constitute medical advice, and should not be relied upon as such, as ALF does not engage in the practice of medicine. ALF, under no circumstances, recommends particular treatments for specific individuals and in all cases recommends that you consult your physician before pursuing any course of treatment.

American Liver Foundation, Illinois Chapter

27 East Monroe Street, Suite 700A
Chicago, IL 60603
Tel: (312) 377-9030
Fax: (312) 377-9035
Website: www.illinois-liver.org

American Liver Foundation

75 Maiden Lane, Suite 603
New York, NY 10038-4817
Tel: (800) GO-LIVER (465-4837)
(888) 4-HEP-ABC (443-7222)
Website: www.liverfoundation.org
Email: info@liverfoundation.org

50 WAYS TO LOVE YOUR LIVER

(Reprinted with permission from the Thomas E. Starzl
Transplantation Institute website, www.sti.upmc.edu.)

1. Avoid taking unnecessary medications.
2. Don't mix medicines without the advice of a doctor. Certain combinations can cause severe liver damage.
3. Street drugs can cause serious damage and permanently scar your liver.
4. If you drink alcohol, have two or fewer drinks per day.
5. Never mix alcohol with other drugs and medications.
6. Be careful when using aerosol cleaners. Your liver has to detoxify what you breathe in, so when you go on a cleaning binge, make sure that the room is well ventilated, or wear a mask.
7. Bug sprays, paint sprays, and other chemical sprays can be harmful. Be careful what you breathe.
8. Watch what gets on your skin! For instance, insecticides you use on trees and shrubs to kill bugs can be absorbed through your skin, causing liver cell damage.

FACT: Hepatitis B & C are contagious viral infections that cause chronic liver disease.

9. Use caution and common sense regarding intimate contact. Hepatitis viruses live in body fluids, including blood and seminal fluid.
10. The hepatitis B virus also lives in saliva and, unlike the AIDS virus, can be transmitted through this fluid with relative ease.

FACT: If you were stuck with a needle used by a person with AIDS, you'd have a one in 2,000 chance of picking up the AIDS virus. But if that person had hepatitis B, your chances of picking up the virus increase to one in four!

11. Hepatitis C, spread primarily through direct blood contact, can be transmitted through contaminated needles used in tattooing, body piercing, or IV drug injection.
12. Untreated, chronic hepatitis B and C can cause cirrhosis and liver cancer and is the most frequent reason for liver transplants.

13. Many infected people do not have symptoms until liver damage occurs, sometimes many years later.
14. Teach your children what a syringe looks like and tell them to leave it alone.
15. Never, ever, touch a discarded syringe or needle.

FACT: Over 5 million Americans have hepatitis B or C, resulting in an estimated 13,000 to 15,000 deaths annually. Yet many people do not know they are infected until serious liver damage occurs because they have few, if any, symptoms. Who's at greater risk of contracting hepatitis B or C? How do you find out if you're a carrier? Here are some answers.

16. If you or your family has immigrated from Africa, Southeast Asia, Mediterranean countries, or the Caribbean, where hepatitis B affects up to 15 percent of the population, you should have a blood test to determine if you are a carrier. Your doctor can arrange this for you.
17. If you received a blood transfusion prior to July 1992, you may have hepatitis C. As many as 300,000 people may have been infected in this way before the test for hepatitis C was developed.

Who Else Should Be Tested For Hepatitis B and C?

18. Users of intravenous drugs, particularly those who share their needles.
19. Men or women who have multiple sexual partners.
20. Health care (including ambulance) workers.
21. Staff of institutions for people with developmental disabilities.
22. Firefighters, police officers, mortuary attendants or daycare workers.

If anyone in your family or a sexual partner tests positive for the hepatitis B virus, ask your doctor to test you for the virus. If the test is negative, your doctor will vaccinate you against the virus. A simple series of three vaccinations over six months will protect you against the virus for many years.

If You Test Positive For Hepatitis B or C...

23. Consult your doctor. He or she will determine whether you have liver disease and if you need referral to a specialist.
24. If you have hepatitis B, have your family tested.

FACT: Those who have never contracted hepatitis B should be vaccinated.

25. Ask your doctor to screen for liver cancer in order to detect tumors while they are still small and treatable.
26. If you are a pregnant, hepatitis B-infected mother, you can pass the infection to your infants around the time of birth. More than 90 percent of this form of transmission can be prevented by vaccination of the baby.

FACT: Since everything we eat must pass through the liver, special attention to nutrition and diet can help keep you healthy. Here are some tips on eating for a healthy liver/healthy you!

27. Eat a well balanced, nutritionally adequate diet. If you enjoy foods from each of the four food groups, you will probably obtain the nutrients you need.
28. Cut down on the amount of deep-fried and fatty foods you and your family consume. Doctors believe that the risk of gallbladder disorders (including gallstones, a liver-related disease) can be reduced by avoiding high fat and high cholesterol foods.
29. Minimize your consumption of smoked, cured and salted foods. Taste your food before adding salt! Or try alternative seasonings in your cooking such as lemon juice, onion, vinegar, garlic, pepper, mustard, cloves, sage or thyme.
30. Increase your intake of high-fiber foods such as fresh fruits and vegetables, whole grain breads, rice and cereals. A high-fiber diet is especially helpful in keeping your live healthy.
31. Rich desserts, snacks and drinks are high in calories because of the amount of sweetening (and often fat) they contain. Why not munch on some fruit instead?
32. Keep your weight close to ideal. Medical researchers have established a direct correlation between obesity and the development of gallbladder disorders.
33. If you are dieting to lose weight, make sure that you are still getting all the vitamins and minerals your body needs to function properly
34. A regular exercise routine, two or three days a week, will help keep you healthy, too

Here are some signs of liver trouble. If you experience any of these symptoms, please contact your doctor:

35. Yellow discoloration of the skin or eyes.
36. Abdominal swelling or severe abdominal pain.
37. Prolonged itching of the skin.
38. Very dark urine or pale stools, or the passage of bloody or tar-like stools.
39. Chronic fatigue, nausea or loss of appetite.

What to Do If You Have Liver Disease...

40. Follow your doctor's advice on food, exercise, and other lifestyle guidelines. Learn about liver disease and understand how your diet helps you. Learn what and how much you can eat and drink.
41. Contact the American Liver Foundation for a listing of chapters near you. Join the chapter—talking to other people who are also affected by liver disease will help.
42. Invite family and close friends to attend chapter meetings or any learning sessions your local chapter may hold.

FACT: While transplants are not the answer for eliminating liver disease, they are the only hope for survival many liver disease patients have. But there just are not enough organ donors to meet the demand.

43. Consider donating your organs in the event of your death. You can sign the organ donor card on your driver's license if your state has such a program or obtain an organ donor card from the University of Pittsburgh Medical Center or the American Liver Foundation. Be sure to discuss your wishes with your family and your family doctor.

Some Ways You Can Make a Difference!

45. Educate yourself.
46. Educate others!
47. Volunteer some time at a hospital or clinic.
48. Donate to nonprofit organizations like the American Liver Foundation.

And Finally...

49. See your doctor for a checkup on a regular basis.
     Remember, prevention is always the best medicine.
50. Take care of yourself in everything you do. Be a healthy
     "live-er"—keep a healthy liver.

Thomas E. Starzl Transplantation Institute
Website: www.sti.upmc.edu

Adapted from "50 Ways to Love Your Liver" by
The American Liver Foundation
75 Maiden Lane, Suite 603
New York, NY 10038
Tel: (800) GO-LIVER
E-mail: info@liverfoundation.org
Website: www.liverfoundation.org

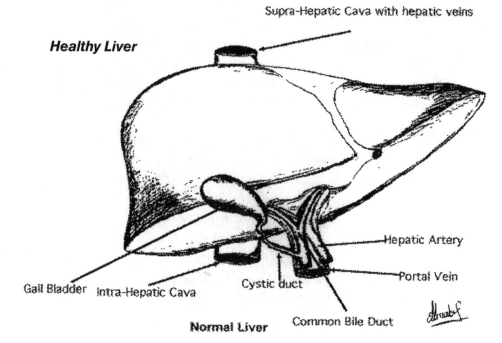

Healthy Liver

Supra-Hepatic Cava with hepatic veins

Hepatic Artery

Portal Vein

Gall Bladder   Intra-Hepatic Cava

Cystic duct

Common Bile Duct

Normal Liver

Figure 1: Normal Liver, *drawing by Evangelos Misiakos, M.D., 2003*

Diseased Liver

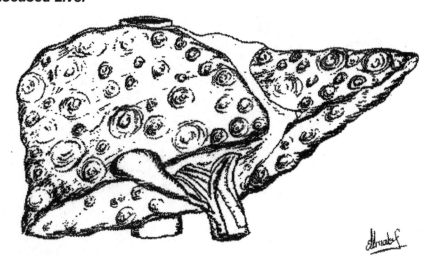

Figure 1: Cirrhotic Liver, *drawing by Evangelos Misiakos, M.D., 2003*

WHAT YOU SHOULD KNOW ABOUT
WILSON'S DISEASE
(Reprinted with permission from the Wilson's Disease Association)

Wilson's Disease is a genetic disorder that is fatal unless detected and treated before serious illness develops from copper poisoning. Wilson's Disease affects one in 30 thousand people worldwide. The genetic defect causes excessive copper accumulation. Small amounts of copper are essential for proper nutrition. Copper is present in most foods, and most people get much more than they need. Healthy people excrete copper they don't need, but Wilson's Disease patients cannot.

Copper begins to accumulate immediately after birth. Excess copper attacks the liver and brain resulting in cirrhosis, hepatitis, psychiatric, or neurologic symptoms. The symptoms usually appear in late adolescence. Patients may have jaundice, abdominal swelling, vomiting of blood, and abdominal pain. They may have tremors, and difficulty walking, talking, and swallowing. They may develop all degrees of mental illness including homicidal or suicidal behavior, depression, and aggression. Women may have menstrual irregularities, absent periods, infertility, or multiple miscarriages. No matter how the disease begins, it is always fatal if is not diagnosed and treated.

The first part of the body that copper affects is the liver. In about half of Wilson's Disease patients, the liver is the only affected organ. The physical changes in the liver are only visible under the microscope. When hepatitis develops, patients are often thought to have infectious hepatitis or infectious mononucleosis when they actually have Wilson's Disease hepatitis. Any unexplained abnormal liver test should trigger thoughts about Wilson's Disease.

How is Wilson's Disease Diagnosed?

The diagnosis of Wilson's Disease is made by relatively simple tests which almost always make the diagnosis. The tests can diagnose the disease in both symptomatic patients and people who show no signs of the disease. It is important to diagnose Wilson's Disease as early as possible, since severe liver damage can occur before there are any signs of the disease. Individuals with Wilson's Disease may falsely appear in excellent health.

Blood, ceruloplasmin, urine copper, eye test for Kayser-Fleischer rings, and liver biopsies are used to make the diagnosis.

Is Wilson's Disease an Inherited Disorder?

Wilson's Disease is transmitted as an autosomal recessive disease, which means it is not sex-linked (it occurs equally in men and women). To inherit it, both parents must carry the gene and pass it to the affected child. Two abnormal genes are required to have the disease. The responsible gene is located at a precisely known site on chromosome 13. The gene is called ATP7B.

Many cases of Wilson's Disease occur due to spontaneous mutations in the gene. A significant number of others are simply transmitted from generation to generation. Most patients have no family history of Wilson's Disease.

People with only one abnormal gene are called carriers. They do not become ill and should not be treated.

More than 200 different gene mutations have been identified thus far. Therefore, it has been difficult to devise a simple genetic screening test for the disease. However, in a particular family, after a mutation (halotype) has been determined in a diagnosed patient, the DNA in first-degree relatives can be tested to determine whether they are unaffected, carriers, or patients. This may help in finding symptom-free, affected relatives so that they may be treated before they become ill or handicapped. Someday a genetic test may help in prenatal diagnosis.

How is Wilson's Disease Treated?

Wilson's Disease is a very treatable condition. With proper therapy, disease progress can be halted and often symptoms can be improved. The treatment goal is to first remove the excess accumulated copper in the body and then prevent its reaccumulation. Therapy must be life-long.

Patients should consult with their physician to see which drug is the most appropriate for them.

Wilson's Disease Association
Kimberly F. Symonds, Executive director
Tel: (888) 264-1450 or (330) 264-1450
E-mail: wda@sssnet.com
Website: www.wilsonsdisease.org

left:
David Yomtoob
on his paper route, 1980.

Below left:
David, Summer 1979.

Below right:
David, Fall 1979.

David, April 1981.

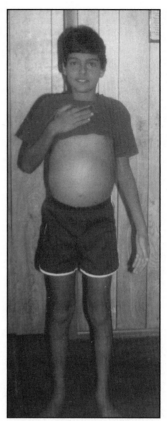

David, July 1981.

David, September 1981.

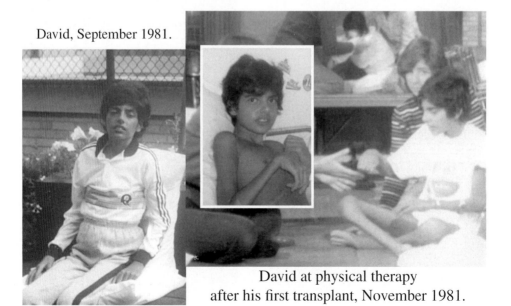

David at physical therapy
after his first transplant, November 1981.

Above:
David with Parichehr,
November 1981.

Inset:
Dr. Carlton Gartner
with David at C.H.P.,
November 1981.

Left:
Dr. Jeffrey Malatack
with David at David's
Bar Mitzvah,
March 1982.

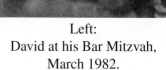

Left:
David at his Bar Mitzvah,
March 1982.

Above:
David carrying the Torah to
the Ark, with Joe looking on.

Below:
David with his grandmothers,
Monavar (L) and Rouhieh (R).

Above:
David at the meeting of the American Association for the Study of Liver Disease, November 1982.

Left:
David, spring 1983.

Below:
David with Surgeon General C. Everett Koop, 1983.

At the march in Washington D.C., spring 1983.
David, wearing the poster, with Todd McNeely (L) and Daniel Butter (R).
In front, Kathy Shannan and Jeanie Andrzejazak.

The first reunion of the children who have had liver transplants, with their doctors, Dr.
Byers W. Shaw (standing, left), Dr. Shunzaburo Iwatsuki (seated in front),
Dr. Thomas E. Starzl(center), and Dr. Basil J. Zetteli (far right), June 1983.

The Yomtoob family at
David's Bar Mitzvah.
Parichehr, Ben, David, Joe, and Rebecca.
(From left)

David taking
flying lessons, 1989.

Parichehr, Rebecca, and Joe with Dr. Starzl
at the Consensus Development Conference in Bethesda, MD, June 20, 1983.

David with Joe at David's high
school graduation, June 1987

David with Dr. Andreas G. Tzakis
and Dr. Thomas E. Starzl
in Pittsburgh, summer 1990.

David's 18th birthday at the publication of *The Gift of Life*.
Photo by the *Jackson Citizen Patriot* newspaper of Jackson, MI

2

EVALUATION

July, 1998

We returned to Pittsburgh one week later, as scheduled. This time, my husband Joe came with us and Rachael stayed with Sara's parents. David's blood work, ultrasound, CT scan, liver biopsy, and other tests had been completed on our last visit. Now we were back to meet with a transplant surgeon and gastroenterologist from the transplant team. They would explain the results, examine David, and fill out the forms that were needed to get David on the waiting list.

We called on Dr. J. Carlton Gartner in his newly decorated office. Dr. Gartner was the head of Pediatric Gastroenterology at the Diagnostic Center of Children's Hospital in Pittsburgh. It was always nice to see Dr. Gartner! Rachael and I had stopped by to see him the week before when David was admitted for tests. He was the doctor who had admitted David to Children's Hospital in August 1981. As an adult, David was no longer under the care of a pediatrician, but we had kept in touch with Dr. Gartner for the last 17 years. He was completely aware of David's situation and was concerned and worried.

In the clinic, we met Dr. Jorge Reyes. Dr. Reyes examined David thoroughly, and recommended that David continue to use the bag for bile drainage. He taught David how to protect the bag with a waterproof covering in case he wanted to go swimming. Dr. Reyes told us that he was working with Nancy, our transplant coordinator, to prepare the necessary papers to get David on the waiting list for a liver transplant. Although we desperately wanted to know, none of us asked how long the waiting list was or what number David would be on that list. We assumed that, as in 1981, the sickest patient would receive the first available liver. We were just happy that we had a doctor in Pittsburgh working to get David a liver.

That weekend, Sara's parents arrived with Rachael. Joe took us all to his favorite restaurant in Oakland called Original, famous for its sub sandwiches and french fries. At the end of the weekend, we all returned home.

At home, David took time off from his position at Smith Industries to rest and recuperate. However, the building of David and Sara's house could not be stopped and, when he could get out of bed, David supervised the construction. Even though he was quiet on the surface, it didn't take much for David to explode. I could only guess that David's dismay at becoming ill, his lack of energy, the pain of the drainage bag, and the disappointment of having to put all of his hopes and dreams for the future on hold were all contributing to his short temper.

Soon we received a call from Nancy in Pittsburgh. All of the paperwork was done and they were placing David on the waiting list, but it would be a while before his turn came. We knew it might be a long wait, but somehow in the back of our minds, we were hoping for special treatment for David. David had willingly participated in experimental medical research, had good medical insurance, and was well-known in the medical community. As Dr. Starzl wrote in his book, *The Puzzle People*, "David Yomtoob played a special role in the acceptance of transplantation by the medical community."

■   ■   ■

1982 - 1983

In October of 1982, we received a conference telephone call from Dr. Starzl and Dr. Malatack. They asked us if we would bring David to Chicago for the meeting of the American Association for the Study of Liver Disease. The meeting would be in the Marriott Hotel in downtown Chicago.

On the day we arrived, David and I found Dr. Starzl in the hall next to the ballroom. He told us that many gastroenterologists didn't believe in the success of liver transplantation. They felt that patients with liver disease were doomed to a slow and painful death after years of suffering from the symptoms of liver failure like nausea, vomiting, diarrhea, itching, fatigue, jaundice, bloated belly, infections, and internal bleeding. These were the same symptoms David had suffered in the spring and summer of 1981, in the six months before his successful liver transplant. The current treatment for liver disease was to treat the symptoms, not to replace the liver. Although some surgeons did try to operate on the liver, these operations usually did more harm than good. Dr. Starzl explained that this meeting was a yearly occurrence, organized for the purpose of sharing ideas, discoveries, and advancements in the treatment of liver disease. To date, not much progress had been made in advancing the idea of liver transplantation.

On that day in November 1982, Dr. Starzl addressed several thousand doctors in the Marriott ballroom. He showed liver transplant slides, graphs, and survival curves, and he spoke of cyclosporine A, the medication that controlled rejection without debilitating side effects. This time, he also had living proof. Dr. Starzl dimmed the lights. A super-large screen at the front of the room was illuminated with video of David in physical therapy during the six weeks after his transplant. Images of a skeletal David without enough muscle to stand or walk filled the screen then faded to three months later, when David was walking. Scenes from one year later showed a happy, energetic child that looked like any other. When the lights went back on, David ran up the aisle to the stage, a smiling, athletic 13-year-old boy. The audience, shocked by the difference between this perfectly healthy boy and the boy they had seen in the early images on the video, rose to their feet clapping. They gave Dr. Starzl and David a standing ovation. Dr. Starzl had very eloquently made his point that there was a cure for terminal liver disease: take the old liver out and put a healthy liver in. With prednisone and cyclosporine A, the antirejection medication, rejection could be controlled. It was time to start referring patients to Pittsburgh and other centers for liver transplantation!

Another effort by David was the march on Capitol Hill in Washington D.C. in the spring of 1983. Throughout our lives in the U.S., we had seen many people march on Washington D.C. for different reasons, but we never thought that someday our family would find a cause so important that we would travel to our country's capitol to demonstrate. The Children's Liver Foundation planned the march on behalf of children who needed liver transplants, especially those children who did not have insurance, as well as the children who had spent many months on the waiting list. Many who needed a liver transplant were there with their families to participate in the march. Also there were the board members of the Children's Liver Foundation and five liver recipients: Daniel Butter, Jeanie Andrzejazak, Todd McNeely, Kathy Shannan, and David. All five of them were Dr. Starzl's patients.

That morning, we gathered on the steps of the Capitol with balloons and banners. Some of the children carried posters. David wore two big signs, one on the front and one on the back. In large letters, David had printed, "Without a liver transplant, I wouldn't be here." David had also pasted photos on the boards that showed how ill he had been before his transplant. From the Capitol, we walked to the White House. That day we also met with a young congressman from Tennessee named Albert Gore. He promised us that he would do what he could to promote our cause.

Through the tireless efforts of Dr. Starzl and other transplant surgeons, the government heard our plea; in August of 1983, congressional hearings on transplantation wrestled with issues related to organ transplantation. The hearings led to a bill, which was named for Al Gore, the congressman most instrumental in its passage.

The Gore Bill allowed children with no insurance to receive funding from Medicaid for their liver transplants. Later, Medicare also began funding liver transplants.

We also participated in the Consensus Development Conference, sponsored by the National Institutes of Health (NIH). The Consensus Development Conference took place in Bethesda, MD from June 20 – 23, 1983. A panel of top doctors and surgeons from around the world were gathering to consider the classification of liver transplantation within the medical community. Liver transplantation was considered to be an experimental procedure because the general feeling was that results were too poor for it to be classified as a service. At Dr. Starzl's urging, Dr. C. Everett Koop, acting Surgeon General, agreed to organize a Consensus Development Review, essentially a trial by jury, to hear the arguments of Dr. Starzl and other proponents of liver transplantation. The verdict produced by the review panel would define national policy for the United States and determine whether medical insurance would cover the cost of a liver transplant for desperately ill patients.

Eager to help Dr. Starzl with his mission, a group of us traveled to Bethesda with our children after the Fathers' Day 1983 reunion of children who had liver transplants. Now our children were healthy, but we vividly remembered the pain and suffering they had experienced with liver failure. We wanted the same health and happiness that our children were now enjoying for everyone who was suffering from liver disease. We knew that the outcome of these hearings would be important for all of the others who came after us.

We brought a big poster showing pictures of the children both before and after their liver transplants. We set this poster up where it would be seen by all. When it was time for the conference, we registered and got settled in the big auditorium. As the day wore on, we could not believe our ears! Except for Dr. Starzl's positive report, we heard nothing but reports of the pain and suffering caused by liver transplant surgery. The quality of life after liver transplantation was questioned over and over. When we raised our hands to speak, we were ignored. No one was willing to hear our side of the story.

On the second day, once again the quality of posttransplant life was questioned. We quietly lined the children up in the aisle and encouraged them to walk with us to the front of the room where the panel was sitting. When the children reached the front, my husband Joe picked up Jennifer Fissel, a 12-year-old who had received a liver transplant ten years before. Joe didn't ask permission to speak. He just said, "Here is Jennifer, living a normal life ten years after her transplant."

The panel was shocked! Here was living proof, standing right in front of them, and disturbing their meeting. We quietly returned to our chairs as Dame Sherlock, a world famous gastroenterologist from London, England spoke up. She said, "The children should be playing outside in the sun instead of attending this meeting." Dr.

Congress Considers Transplant Legislation

Congress is considering a number of bills intended to assist in the procurement of donor organs and advance the art of transplant surgery.

In the House, legislation introduced by Representative Albert Gore, Jr. (D.-Tenn.) would authorize U.S. financial aid to organ procurement organizations and buttress the nation's ability to provide liver and other life-saving organ transplants.

The Gore bill—H.R. 4080, the National Organ Transplant Act—has been approved by the House Energy and Commerce Committee, a subcommittee of which has jurisdiction over health measures. H.R. 4080 is pending in the House Ways and Means Committee.

Specifically, the Gore bill would:

• Authorize one-time grants to "strengthen and expand local organ procurement organizations" in the U.S.

• Support a national organ donor-recipient computer matching system.

• Establish an agency in the U.S. Public Health Service to coordinate federal organ transplant policies and programs.

• Provide for a scientific registry of organ transplant patients.

• Permit Medicare and Medicaid to specify certain medical centers for transplant surgery and "other complex medical procedures."

• Require the Public Health Service to report annually on the "scientific status" of transplant procedures. The report would be made available to Blue Cross-Blue Shield and other commercial health insurers.

• Provide for Medicare payment for "immunosuppressive drugs" for 36 months after a transplant paid for by Medicare.

• Prohibit the buying and selling of human organs.

S. 2018, the Senate companion to H.R. 4080, was introduced by Senator Edward M. Kennedy (D.-Mass.). It is pending in the Senate Labor and Human Resources Committee.

Sen. Kennedy is also the sponsor of a measure to establish a National Task Force on Organ Procurement and Transplant Reimbursement.

That bill, S. 1728, would:

• Assess current organ procurement programs.

• Develop a nationwide plan to educate the public and improve organ donor networks and organ procurement systems.

• Establish a 12-member panel to make recommendations to the U.S. government and private health insurers on transplant reimbursement procedures.

Rep. Don Ritter (R.-Pa.) has introduced H.R. 3977, the House companion to S. 1728.

A similar bill has been authored by Sen. Orrin Hatch (R.-Utah) and Rep. Edward Madigan (R.-Ill.). It combines features of H.R. 4080, S. 2018, and S. 1728.

Other lawmakers interested in organ procurement are: Senators Daniel Akaka (D.-Hawaii) and Mark Andrews (R.-N.D.) and Representatives Dan Marriott (R.-Utah), Steven Gunderson (R.-Wisconsin), and Charles Stenholm (D.-Texas).

Children's Liver Foundation families from coast-to-coast converged on Washington, D.C. one Spring weekend to dramatize the need for research into pediatric liver disease and to make their case for a U.S. ruling that liver transplant surgery is no longer experimental. They were joined by Reps. Guy Molinari (R.-N.Y.), Jim Courter (R.-N.J.) and Al Gore (D.-Tenn.) at a press conference in the House of Representatives.

Rep. Albert Gore, Jr.

The man we know today as former Vice-President Al Gore was an early and spirited supporter of liver disease research, and and liver transplantation.

Starzl rose and apologized for our intrusion, adding that the time had come for all of us to enjoy the sun. I wondered if those doctors realized that without liver transplantation, these children wouldn't have been alive to play in the sun. The only sun they would have had was the sun warming the earth over their small graves!

We understood that the doctors had a mission and were feeling the weight of their responsibility. But we also had a mission and a responsibility. We left the room feeling that we had helped to further our cause. At the same time, we were hoping and praying that our actions wouldn't bring about a negative outcome for Dr. Starzl, who was so tirelessly promoting the cause of liver transplantation. After an all-night session, the panel concluded that liver transplant should be classified as a viable medical service, not an experimental operation.

The next time we saw Dr. Starzl, my husband Joe apologized for our impulsive behavior at the Consensus Development Conference. Dr. Starzl told us that we couldn't have done a better job of giving our message to the panel if we had planned it!

■   ■   ■

July, 1998

I was only a mother who wanted the best for her son, but the reality was that there were strict rules and regulations governing organ distribution. Although David's case had been well known across the country as one of the early liver transplant success stories, the rules would not allow Nancy or anyone else to favor one patient over another. As the transplant coordinator, Nancy was trained to treat all patients by the same set of rules and guidelines regardless of their circumstances. Patients were arriving in Pittsburgh from all over the world. Almost everyone who needed a liver transplant wanted to get it in Pittsburgh because of the reputation for success that Dr. Starzl had built over the years. No other center could compete with Pittsburgh's reputation. More transplants had been done in Pittsburgh than in any other center in the world!

During the third week of July 1998, David contacted Lori, his coordinator at the University of Nebraska in Omaha. Lori suggested that David come to Omaha to be evaluated for the Omaha waiting list, and David agreed. This time, Rachael stayed with us in Chicago. David and Sara made the trip to Omaha, taking the results of all the tests done in Pittsburgh to meet with Dr. Shaw and other members of the transplant team. David and Sara returned pleased with the way they had been received. David was instructed to follow a low-fat diet to ease the diarrhea that he had been suffering from for weeks.

A low-fat diet for David basically meant a no-fat (or no-food) diet, since all of his favorite foods—like pizza and grilled cheese—were high in fat. He didn't have much appetite anyway, so this didn't bother him. He just didn't eat much, and his condition worsened. On one occasion, he passed out causing Sara to become frightened and call 911. David was taken to the hospital by ambulance and tests clearly showed that his liver was failing. He was released after treatment for his symptoms. We were beginning to feel desperate; David's liver was failing and we didn't know how much longer he would be able to hang on.

Appendix 2A

EVALUATION FOR THE WAITING LIST

Understanding the Blood Chemistry Profile of the Liver Transplant Candidate

(Parts reprinted with permission from the Patient and Family Guide to Liver Transplantation, developed by the pretransplant and posttransplant coordinators at the University of Miami Department of Surgery, Division of Transplantation.)

Early stages of liver disease normally can be seen in the blood test called a "chemistry profile" ordered by doctors during a routine checkup. Some early stages of liver damage, if diagnosed early and on time, can be treated and the liver will regenerate and will function normally. For example, early diagnosis is very important in the case of the patient with Wilson's Disease whose liver has been damaged by a buildup of copper over the years. With proper medications and a low copper diet, the Wilson's Disease patient may live a normal life and never need a liver transplant.

Blood levels of these substances are measured by the blood chemistry profile:

- *Albumin: (normal 3.4-5.2 g/dl)*

  Albumin is a protein produced by the liver. It is necessary for normal growth and development and to maintain muscle mass. This protein also helps keep natural fluids in the bloodstream. When the liver is not functioning properly, it cannot convert the digested nutrients (which have been absorbed into the bloodstream from the small bowel and pass through the liver) into albumin. Therefore, the body steals protein from the muscle mass, resulting in weight loss. A low albumin level also contributes to the formation of ascites (fluid collection in the abdomen) and lower leg edema or swelling.

- *Ammonia: (normal 32-45 g/dl, depending on the method used)*

Ammonia is a byproduct of protein metabolism. Ammonia is converted to urea by the liver and excreted by the kidneys. If the liver is not able to perform this function, the elevated ammonia level will result in decreased mental activity, progressing from lethargy to somnolence (sleepiness) to coma. This condition is called "encephalopathy." Patients with severe liver dysfunction are instructed to decrease their total protein intake, thus helping to control this encephalopathy.

- *Alpha Feto Protein (AFP): (normal <20 ng/ml)*

AFP is the tumor marker, specific for liver tumors. Although it is not always indicative of a tumor, it is an indication that is taken into consideration.

- *Alkaline Phosphates (ALP): (normal 29-93 IU/L)*

This enzyme level will rise when the excretion is impaired because of blockage in the bile ducts.

- *Bilirubin (TBILI): (normal 0.2-1.2 mg/dl)*

Bilirubin is the bile pigment in the blood. It is a waste product of the breakdown of hemoglobin. An increase may reflect the breakdown of red blood cells or liver disease. When the liver is not functioning normally, bilirubin levels can increase, often resulting in jaundiced (yellowed) skin and eyes.

- *Blood Urea Nitrogen (BUN): (normal 7.0-23.0 mg/dl)*

This is a blood test that reflects the kidneys' ability to handle nitrogen, a breakdown product of protein in the liver. It is carried in the blood to the kidneys. The body gets rid of BUN in the urine. Low levels of BUN are common in liver disease when the kidneys are working properly. An increased BUN may be due to various kidney disorders. At times, an elevated BUN after liver transplant is due to steroids, dehydration, or a side effect of Prograf (the antirejection medication).

- *Calcium: (normal 8.8-10.7 mg/dl)*

  Calcium is a mineral that comes from the bone. A constant blood calcium level is necessary for good bone strength, a strong heartbeat, and normal function of the nerves and muscles.

- *Creatinine: (normal 0.6-1.4 mg/dl)*

  Creatinine is a waste product found in muscle and blood that is removed by the kidneys. It is produced at a constant rate. A disorder of kidney function lowers excretion of creatinine, resulting in an increase in the blood level of creatinine. An elevated creatinine level may reflect kidney disorder. After liver transplant, it can indicate toxicity of antirejection medications.

- *Glucose: (normal fasting value 66-110 mg/dl)*

  A glucose test is a measure of blood sugar level. Increased glucose levels are seen in diabetics and in patients with impaired pancreatic function. Increased glucose levels are also common in individuals on steroids.

- *GGT: (normal 7-50u/l)*

  GGT is an enzyme that is made in the bile duct or bile tracts. An increase may mean a blockage in the bile duct, damage to the bile duct because of blocked blood flow, or rejection after transplantation.

- *Hematocrit (HCT): (normal 37.7-53.70%)*

  HCT measures the hematocrit, which is the percentage of red blood cells in the blood. Red blood cells carry oxygen to all parts of the body. Fatigue is one of the primary symptoms of a low HCT.

- *Platelets (PLT): (normal 142.0-424.0 k/ul)*

  PLT is a measure of the number platelets in the blood. Platelet cells form blood clots when the body is injured. A low platelet count may cause the person to bruise easily and to bleed longer when injured.

■ *Potassium (K+): (normal 3.5-5.1 mmol/1)*

Potassium is a body salt primarily found inside body cells.
Diuretics or "water pills" can lower the potassium level. Anti
rejection medication also can raise the potassium level.
Potassium is needed for normal heart and muscle
functioning.

■ *SGOT/ AST: (normal 10-34 u/l)*

AST is an enzyme released when high-energy cells are injured.
The liver, heart, kidneys, and blood have many high-energy
cells. AST is primarily found in the liver. An increase in AST may
reflect damage to the liver, such as cirrhosis, hepatitis, viral infection, and posttransplant liver rejection.

■ *SGPT/ALT: (normal 6-40 u/l)*

SGPT is an enzyme that is primarily found in the liver. An
increase in SGPT may reflect damage to the liver, such as cirrhosis, hepatitis, viral infection, and posttransplant liver rejection.

■ *Total Protein: (normal 6.3 – 8.2 g/dl)*

The total protein level reflects the combination of blood proteins.
Abnormalities are seen in individuals with poor nutrition and
liver disease.

■ *White Blood Cell (WBC): (normal 4.8 – 10.8/mm3)*

White blood cells help fight infection. If the WBC is high or low,
it may indicate infection or transplant rejection. WBCs also
defend the body against invasion by foreign organisms, such as
bacteria, virus, or fungus.

Diagnostic Tests Used to Evaluate the Condition of the Patient's Organs

(Information taken with permission from the Patient and Family Guide to Liver Transplantation, developed by the pretransplant and posttransplant coordinators at the University of Miami Department of Surgery, Division of Transplantation, Miami, FL.)

When the blood chemistry profile shows abnormality in the liver function, the doctors order diagnostic tests to learn about the condition of the liver, the amount of damage, and the type of liver disease. If test results indicate that the liver is severely damaged and doctors find little possibility that the liver will regenerate or heal itself, liver transplant may be recommended. When transplant is necessary, the diagnostic test results are also used to help the doctors decide where the patients will be placed on the waiting list.

Most tests completed at one center will be accepted at other centers if actual copies of the x-rays, CAT scans, ultrasounds, MRIs, and other results are provided along with the diagnostic reports. If any biopsies were performed, other centers will require the actual slides for review.

Doppler Ultrasound of the Liver

This is a noninvasive procedure that provides the transplant surgeon with information necessary for the surgical procedure, such as the portal vein size, direction of flow, liver vessel patency (whether they are open and unblocked), and liver size. Cysts or masses may also be recognized.

Computerized Tomography (CT) Scan of the Abdomen with Contrast

The CT scan provides series of cross-sectional images in sequence that combine to build a three-dimensional picture. This scan will identify abnormal structures or masses, and may also give information regarding the size of the liver, which will be useful in determining a suitable donor. A contrast media (dye) may be used to enhance the images either by drinking the contrast media or by intravenous injection.

MRI (Magnetic Resonance Imaging)

This technique provides images through a combination of computers, radio waves, and a powerful magnet. Serial images are obtained to identify masses and give information about the size and structure of the patient's liver. This test may be requested if the patient is unable to tolerate the dye required for the CT scan.

Esophagogastroduodenoscopy/Upper Endoscopy

A flexible tube is passed through the mouth into stomach, and the physician visually inspects the esophagus, the stomach, and the first portion of the small bowel (the duodenum). The physician is looking for varices (distended blood vessels), inflammation, and/or ulcers.

Flexible Sigmoidoscopy

Patients over 40 years old will be required to have this test for cancer screening. A long tube is passed into the rectum to visually inspect the lining (mucosa) of the rectum and sigmoid colon. If polyps are identified, a biopsy will be performed.

Colonoscopy

If the sigmoidoscopy identifies polyps, the physician will require a full colonoscopy to visualize more of the colon.In this test, however, the scope is passed further into the colon.

Liver Biopsy

Physicians remove a small sample of liver tissue and inspect the tissue to determine the cause of liver failure. The liver biopsy may be obtained in one of four ways:

- Percutaneous biopsy: by inserting a needle through the skin into the liver.
- Laparoscopic biopsy: through a small tube introduced into the abdomen to visualize the liver.
- Transjugular biopsy: through a catheter inserted into the jugular vein.
- Directly: by excising a small sample of the liver during an abdominal surgical procedure.

Cardiology Evaluation

Based on the age of the patient and the history of the illness, the patient will be asked to have several examinations which will provide the physicians with information to establish the relevant cardiac risk for patients who undergo transplantation. All patients will at least have an EKG, echocardiogram, and chest x-rays; however, additional tests from the following list may also be required:

- *Electrocardiogram (EKG):*

  This is a graphic picture of the heart's electrical activity obtained by placing 12 leads or electrodes on the chest, arms, and legs. The rhythm of the heart is traced onto paper for the physicians to inspect. Abnormal rhythms and/or abnormal heart rate are detected in this manner.

- *Two-dimensional Echocardiogram:*

  An echocardiogram can determine the size, shape, and position of the heart, and the movement of the heart valves and chambers. The physician providing this evaluation must measure the pulmonary artery pressure.

- *Thallium Stress Test:*

  A stress test is used to detect coronary artery disease. Exercise will enhance any potential abnormalities and better evaluate the heart's potential ability to tolerate the anesthesia and the stress placed on the heart during the transplant procedure.

- *Dobutamine Stress Echocardiogram:*

  This is the preferable method to study the heart. It combines the Echocardiogram and the Stress Echocardiogram into one exam to provide information on both the electrical activity and the functional ability of the heart. During this test, pulmonary artery pressure is also accurately measured.

- *Right Heart Catheterization:*

  This test allows the physicians to measure the pressure in the right side of the heart directly to check for pulmonary hypertension. Pulmonary hypertension is extremely dangerous for someone undergoing liver transplantation. If there are indications of this condition by echocardiogram, direct and accurate pressures must be measured.

■ *Cardiac Catheterization:*

Cardiac catheterization provides visualization of the vessels to determine patency of the coronary arteries, heart size, structure of the valves, and pulmonary pressures.

■ *Cardiac Consultation:*

The patient may be asked to see a specialist in the field of cardiology to give the transplant team his/her opinion as to the risk of liver transplantation. The cardiologist will utilize the above data to reach a conclusion.

Pulmonary Evaluation

Again, based on individual health status, the patient may be asked to undergo pulmonary function tests and arterial blood gases. If he/she smokes, it is very important that he/she does not smoke from this time forward. Smoke paralyzes the cilia, very fine hair-like structures that help clear secretions from the patient's lungs. This is critical in avoiding pneumonia, especially when undergoing a long surgical procedure, such as a transplant.

■ *Pulmonary Function Test:*

This test measures the ability of the patient's lungs to expand and the capacity for gas exchange. The patient will be asked to sit in a special booth and breathe through a mouthpiece. A clip will be placed on the patient's nose to prevent air exchange other than through the mouth.

■ *Arterial Blood Gases:*

Arterial Blood Gas analysis will provide information as to how well the patient is oxygenated. This is a simple blood test, but the blood is drawn from an artery instead of a vein.

Renal (Kidney) Evaluation

Evaluation of the kidney function is important to determine if there is any chronic kidney failure. Diabetes and hypertension can predispose kidney failure. The medications the patient will be on after the transplant can decrease the effectiveness of the kidneys as well. The patient's doctors must identify those issues before the transplant. A small number of candidates have required both a liver and a kidney transplant.

■ *Creatinine Clearance:*

All patients are required to complete a 24-hour urine collection for creatinine clearance. This will help the physician identify chronic renal failure, which could necessitate a kidney transplant along with the liver transplant.

- *Glofil:*

  If the creatinine clearance is abnormal, the patient will be asked to have a Glofil done. This test will further evaluate kidney function for final determination.

- *Nephrologist Evaluation:*

  A transplant nephrologist (kidney specialist) will evaluate all patients with an abnormal creatinine clearance, Glofil, and/or history of renal disease.

Psychological-Sociological Evaluation

All patients being evaluated for transplantation must be seen by a social worker or interdisciplinary team. The focus of this evaluation is on long term compliance and support systems for the patient/family. If it is identified that there is a substance abuse history, a team of substance abuse specialists will evaluate the candidate in an effort to make the transplant a successful one.

Dental Evaluation

The patient will be asked to see a dentist who can provide a letter stating that the patient is in good oral health and free of infection. This may require fillings, tooth extraction, or gum surgery.

Gynecological Evaluation

For the female transplant candidates, it is necessary to complete certain cancer screening procedures in an effort to assure that the patient is in good general health. The patient is asked to see a gynecologist for a Pap smear and have a mammogram performed.

Blood Work

- *Tissue Typing:*

  Blood will be taken to establish your blood type. The patient's blood type is a key component in identifying an appropriate donor.

- *PRA:*

  This blood test measures how well the patient should match with any potential donor.

- *Virology:*

  The patient's blood will be tested for many different viruses, including hepatitis, cytomegalovirus (CMV), and HIV.

- *Chemistries:*

  Liver function tests and kidney function tests will give important information in determining when transplant is indicated for the patient.

- *Hematology and Coagulation Studies:*

  Blood count, platelet count, and clotting studies are also important in determining the status of the patient's liver condition and general condition.

Other Preparation

The patient will be tested to determine resistance to common posttransplant infections. If necessary, the patient will be vaccinated to protect against these posttransplant health risks.

- *Tuberculosis (TB)/Mumps Skin Test:*

  The patient will be asked to have both a TB skin test and a mumps skin test. Skin testing is useful in determining present or past exposure to an infectious organism. Most of us have had the mumps when we were young. Sometimes patients with end-stage liver disease do not react to the antigens used in the TB test; therefore, the mumps skin test is used as a control. If the patient has a negative reaction to the mumps and a negative reaction to the TB, indicates that the patient is not reacting to the test rather than the TB test results actually being negative. (The doctors hope for a positive mumps and negative TB skin test).

- *Hepatitis A and B Vaccine:*

  Based on the virology results, all liver and intestinal transplant candidates who are not protected either through previous exposure or previous vaccinations are required to be immunized against the Hepatitis A and B viruses. This will help prevent the acquisition of these viruses after the transplant while immunosuppressed.

- *Pneumovax:*

  This vaccination protects the patient against the pneumococcal virus which is the most common virus causing pneumonia. If the patient has not had this vaccine, it is recommended that the patient be vaccinated.

Appendix 2B

CARE AND COVERAGE CONSIDERATIONS

Paying for Liver Transplant Surgery

Medical bills for a liver transplant generally top $250,000, depending on the condition of the patient at the time of transplant and the severity of post-operative complications, if any. It is important to contact your insurance company (if you have one) early in the process, and make sure you understand what is covered and what is not. Medicare and Medicaid patients should also talk to the transplant team social worker to learn how their Medicare/Medicaid status will affect the course of their treatment.

In the case of liver disease and liver transplant, most insurance plans, including Medicare and Medicaid, will pay for the cost of the surgery. Sadly, there are still patients who do not have medical insurance and are ineligible for Medicare or Medicaid. These are the patients who may need to turn to fundraising efforts to be able to afford this life-saving surgery. Fortunately, most of the fundraising efforts we came to know about were successful and received generous response from the community and general public. Additionally, there are many organizations that can assist patients in obtaining financial support for medical treatment listed in the Financial Resources Directory at the end of this appendix.

How Insurance Coverage Influences Care

Skyrocketing hospital costs have had insurance companies trying to influence medical practices with their coverage policies. Many insurance companies limit what their policies will pay for certain procedures and dictate how many days of hospitalization will be covered based on the reason for admittance and/or procedure performed.

When my children were born, a new mother stayed in the hospital with her baby for four days. If the baby was born by Caesarian section, they stayed in the hospital for two weeks. Now, new mothers are discharged one day after vaginal births, and two days after Caesarian section, largely due to insurance coverage limitations.

It is very important for patients to work closely with their doctors and insurance companies to coordinate their medical care. Patients need to understand whether there are differences between what their doctor thinks would be best for them and what their insurance company is willing to cover. Some hospitals base their medical practices on what the insurance company will cover without informing the patient. Unless the patient makes a concerted effort to keep these lines of communication open, they may be denied the opportunity to make their own decisions about what is in their best interests. For example, some hospitals release patients before they feel well enough to go home, telling the patient that they no longer require hospitalization, instead of telling them that their insurance will no longer pay for their stay. Some doctors may forego necessary tests, telling patients that they don't need the test rather than that the test is not covered by their insurance.

Advocacy

To receive the best possible medical care, every patient needs to be their own advocate. This means:

- educating oneself about the illness and treatment options;

- understanding the details of insurance coverage;

- researching your health facility and others to make sure you are in the best facility for your needs;

- understanding the difference between what is in your best interest and what your insurance company will pay for;

- taking responsibility for participating in and completely understanding treatment decisions;

- keeping lines of communication with doctors and staff open, and alerting them when symptoms change or worsen;

- questioning the doctors and medical staff about things you don't understand; and

- inquiring about alternatives and seeking second opinions if you don't agree with your diagnosis or treatment plan.

As the patient's disease progresses and symptoms become more severe, it is helpful if a friend or relative is available to assume the role of advocate for the patient. Hospital staff, especially nurses, are increasingly overworked and overscheduled. The concerned advocate will be able to monitor the patient closely and alert medical personnel to the patient's needs when the patient is unable to do so. An advocate may help hospital nurses by attending to some of the patient's basic needs and may also act as a go-between to facilitate communication between doctor and patient, as the patient becomes increasingly debilitated. Patients who are cared for and supported by friends and relatives have better outcomes than similarly ill patients who do not have this support network. More about Advocacy is discussed in Appendix 8B – The Roles and Reactions of Family and Friends.

Financial Resources Directory

(Reprinted with permission from UNOS' patient Web site, www.transplantliving.org.)

The following organizations may provide assistance to transplant candidates or recipients and their families. This is a sample listing and should not be interpreted as a comprehensive list or an endorsement. Ask your transplant financial team for the latest information or help.

The types of assistance that may be provided are:

- Financial
- Patient Education and Advocacy
- Prescription Drug Assistance Programs

Financial Assistance

Air Care Alliance
4620 Haygood Rd.
Virginia Beach, VA 23455
(800) 296-1217
www.aircareall.org

American Kidney Fund
6110 Executive Blvd., Ste. 1010
Rockville, MD 20852
(800) 638-8299
www.akfinc.org

American Liver Foundation
75 Maiden Lane, Suite 603
New York, NY 10038-4810
(800) 465-4837, (800) GOLIVER
webmail@liverfoundation.org
www.liverfoundation.org

American Organ Transplant Association
3335 Cartwright Road
Missouri City, TX 77459
Contact: Ellen Gordon Woodall, Executive Director
(281) 261-2682
(281) 499-2315
www.a-o-t-a.org

Angel Flight
American Medical Support Flight Team
3237 Donald Douglas Loop South
Santa Monica, CA 90405
(888) 426-2643
www.angel-flight.org

Provides free air transportation on private aircraft for needy people with healthcare problems and for healthcare agencies, organ procurement organizations, blood banks, and tissue banks. No fees of any kind. Volunteers serving the public since 1983.

Burkhead Foundation
P.O. Box 105723
Jefferson City, MO 65110
www.burkheadfoundation.org

Children's Organ Transplant Association
2501 COTA Dr.
Bloomington, IN 47403
(800) 366-2682

Fujisawa Patient Assistance Program
P.O. Box 221644
Chantilly, VA 20153-1644
(800) 477-6472

Provides help on a one-time-only basis, if the medication is available. For several of the drugs, the program replaces what has already been given to the patient.

Medicare Hotline
(800) 638-6833

National Insurance Consumer Hotline
(800) 942-4242

National Organization of Social Security Claimants' Representatives
(888) 431-2804
www.nosscr.org

National Transplant Assistance Fund
3475 West Chester Pike, Suite 230
Newton Square, PA 19073
(610) 353-9684, (800) 642-8399
(610) 353-1616
NTAF@transplantfund.org
www.transplantfund.org

Nielsen Organ Transplant Foundation
580 W. 8th St.
Jacksonville, FL 32209
(904) 798-899

National Foundation for Transplants
1102 Brookfield, Ste. 200
Memphis, TN 38119
Contact: Janice Hill
(800) 489-3863, (901) 684-1697
(901) 684-1128
jhill@transplants.org
www.transplants.org

Patient Education and Advocacy

These organizations may be able to provide patient education and patient advocacy services. This is a partial listing and should not be interpreted as a comprehensive list or an endorsement.

American Association for the Study of Liver Diseases
6900 Grove Rd.
Thorofare, NJ 08086-9447
Contact: Susan Nelson, Account Executive
(609) 848-1000
(609) 848-5274
aasld@slackinc.com

American Association of Kidney Patients
100 S. Ashley Dr., Ste. 280
Tampa, FL 33602
Contact: Kris Robinson, Executive Director
(813) 223-7099, (800) 749-2257
(813) 223-0001
AAKPnat@aol.com
www.aakp.org

American Center for Transplant Resources
1512 Arboretum Dr.
Chapel Hill, NC 27514
Contact: Chuck Hutson, Executive Director
(919) 932-7845
(919) 932-7847

American Diabetes Association
1701 North Beauregard St.
Alexandria, VA 22311
800-DIABETES or 800-342-2383
www.diabetes.org

American Heart Association
7272 Greenville Ave.
Dallas, TX 75231-4596
(800) 242-8721   www.americanheart.org

American Liver Foundation
1425 Pompton Ave.
Cedar Grove, NJ 07009
Contact: Alan P. Brownstein, President & CEO
(973) 256-2550, (800) 465-4837
(973) 256-3214
info@liverfoundation.org, abrownstein@liverfoundation.org
www.liverfoundation.org

American Medical Association
515 N. State St.
Chicago, IL 60610
Contact: Reed V. Tuckson, M.D., Group Vice President
(312) 464-5000
(312) 464-4184

American Organ Transplant Association
3335 Cartwright Road
Missouri City, TX 77459
Contact: Ellen Gordon Woodall, Executive Director
(281) 261-2682
(281) 499-2315

American Share Foundation
6464 Dempsey Ave.
Van Nuys, CA 91406-6015
Contact: John S. Abbott, President
(818) 781-1006
(818) 781-4113
jsabbott@ix.netcom.com

American Society for Histocompatibility & Immunogenetics
P.O. Box 15804
Lenexa, KS 66285-5804
Contact: Debbie J. Elder, Executive Director
(913) 541-0009
(913) 541-0156
ashiamp@aol.com

American Society of Minority Health and Transplant Professionals
P.O. Box 8324
St. Louis, MO 63132-0324
Contact: Tereasa D. Parks-Thomas, President
(314) 991-1661
(314) 991-2805

American Society of Nephrology
1200 19th Street, N.W., Ste. 300
Washington, DC 20036-2422
Contact: Sherri A. Mara, Executive Director
(202) 857-1190
(202) 223-4579
Sherri_Mara@dc.sba.com

American Society of Transplantation
National Office
236 Route 38 W., Suite 100
Moorestown, NJ 08057
Contact: Susan J. Nelson, Executive Director
(856) 231-8500
(856) 231-4664
ast@ahint.com
www.a-s-t.org

American Society of Transplant Surgeons
2000 L Street, NW, Ste. 200
Washington, DC 20036
Contact: Katrina Crist, Executive Director
(202) 416-1858
(202) 416-1744
www.asts.org

American Thoracic Society
1740 Broadway
New York, NY 10019
Contact: Marilyn Hansen, Executive Director
(212) 315-8700
(212) 315-6498
www.thoracic.org

American Urological Association
1120 N. Charles St.
Baltimore, MD 21201
Contact: G. James Gallagher, Executive Director
(410) 727-1100
(410) 223-4370
AUA@Interserv.com

Association of Organ Procurement Organizations
One Cambridge Ct.
8110 GateHouse Rd., Ste. 101 West
Falls Church, VA 22042
Contact: Daniel Whiteside, DDS, Executive Director
(703) 573-2676
(703) 573-0578

Center for Liver Diseases
1500 NW 12th Ave., Ste. 1101
Miami, FL 33136
Contact: Eugene Schiff, M.D., Director
(305) 547-5787

Children's Liver Alliance
3835 Richmond Ave., Ste. 190
Staten Island, NY 10312-3828
Contact: Lisa Carroccio, Chairwoman & Founder
(718) 987-6200
(718) 987-6200
Livers4Kids@earthlink.net
www.liverkids.tk

Coalition on Donation
Post Office Box 2484
Richmond, VA 23218
Contact: David Fleming, Executive Director
(804) 782-4920
flemingd@unos.org
www.donatelife.net

Children's Organ Transplant Association, Inc. (COTA)
2501 COTA Dr.
Bloomington, IN 47403
Contact: David Speicher, Executive Director
(812) 336-8872
(812) 336-8885

Forum of ESRD Networks
1527 Huguenot Rd.
Midlothian, VA 23113
Contact: Denise Daly, Administrator
(804) 794-2586
(804) 378-7351
forum@richmond.infi.net

Hepatitis Foundation International
30 Sunrise Terrace
Cedar Grove, NJ 07009
Contact: Thelma King Thiel, Chairman and CEO
(201) 239-1065
(201) 857-5044

Insulin-Free World Foundation
750 S. Hanley Road, Ste. 360
St. Louis, MO 63105-2682
Contact: Deborah Butterfield, Executive Director
(314) 727-4247, (888) 746-4439
(314) 867-3713
insulin-free@insulin-free.org,
dbutterfield@insulin-free.org
www.insulin-free.org

International Society for Heart and Lung Transplantation (ISHLT)
Suite 200
Addison, TX 75001
Contact: Amanda Rowe, Executive Director,
(972) 490-9495
(972) 490-9499
ISHLT@ishlt.org
www.ishlt.org

International Transplant Nurses Society
Foster Plaza 5, Ste. 300
651 Holiday Dr.
Pittsburgh, PA 15220
Contact: Nancy Stitt, Executive Director
(412) 928-3667
(412) 928-4951

Joint Commission on the Accreditation of Healthcare Organizations
1 Renaissance Blvd.
Oak Brook Terrace, IL 60181
Contact: Dennis O'Leary, MD, President
(708) 916-5600
(708) 916-5644

Juvenile Diabetes Foundation International
120 Wall Street, 19th Floor
New York, NY 10005
Contact: James E. Mulvihill, D.M.D., CEO and President
(212) 785-9500, (800) 533-2873
(212) 785-9595

The Kidney Transplant Patient Partnering Program
An educational service of Roche Laboratories, Inc.
(800) 893-1995

The Living Bank
P.O. Box 6725
Houston, TX 77265-6725
Contact: Bruce Conway, President/CEO
(800) 528-2971
(713) 961-0979
info@livingbank.org, bconway@livingbank.org
www.livingbank.org

National Kidney Foundation
30 E. 33rd St.
New York, NY 10016
Contact: John Davis, Executive Director
(212) 889-2210
(212) 779-0068
johnd@kidney.org
www.kidney.org

National Minority Organ and Tissue Transplant Education Program (MOTTEP)
Ambulatory Care Center
2041 Georgia Ave., NW, Ste. 3100
Washington, DC 20060
Contact: Katherine Woods Erwin, MD, Executive Director
(202) 865-4888
(202) 865-4880

National Organization for Rare Disorders
P.O. Box 8923
New Fairfield, CT 06812-8923
Contact: Abbey S. Meyers, President
(203) 746-6518, (800) 999-6673
(203) 746-6481
nord@ix.netcom.com

National Transplant Assistance Fund
6 Bryn Mawr Avenue
P.O. Box 258
Bryn Mawr, PA 19010
(800) 642-8399
(610) 527-5210
NTAF@transplantfund.org
www.transplantfund.org

North American Society for Dialysis and Transplantation
c/o Wadi Suki, M.D.
550 Fannin St., Ste. 1273
Houston, TX 77030
Contact: Wadi Suki, M.D., Treasurer
(713) 790-3275
(713) 790-5053

North American Transplant Coordinators Organization (NATCO)
P.O. Box 15384
Lenexa, KS 66285-5384
Contact: Deidre Panjada, Executive Director
(913) 492-3600
(913) 541-0156
natco-info@goAMP.com
www.natco1.org

The Partnership for Organ Donation
2 Oliver St.
Boston, MA 02109-4901
(617) 482-5746
(617) 482-5748
info@organ-donation.org
www.transweb.org/partnership

Second Wind Lung Transplant Association, Inc.
9030 W Lakeview Ct.
Crystal River, FL 34428
(888) 222-2690
(352) 563-0728
www.2ndwind.org

Transplant Foundation
1801 NW 9th Avenue, Suite 150-B
Miami, FL 33136
(800) 533-3172
(305) 243-7591
www.transplantfoundation.org

Transplant Recipients International Organization, Incorporated (TRIO)
1000 16th St., NW, Ste. 602
Washington, DC 20036-5705
(202) 293-0980, (800) 874-6386
(202) 293-0973
triointl@aol.com
www.trioweb.org

Prescription Drug Assistance Programs

Patient assistance programs for the three most prescribed immunosuppressive medications are available by contacting:

Roche Patient Assistance Program (Cellcept)
(800) 772-5790

Novartis Patient Assistance Program (Cyclosporine)
(888) 455-6655

Prograf/Fujisawa Patient Assistance Program (Prograf)
(800) 477-6472

Abbott Patient Assistance Program (Gengraf)
(800) 633-9110

3

COPING

July, 1998

Meanwhile, life marched on. My dear friends, Sharon, Pat, and Naida hosted a wedding shower for Rebecca in Niles, Michigan. We had lived in Niles for 20 years, raised our children there, and worshiped at Temple Beth-El several miles away in South Bend. During the ordeal of David's first transplant in 1981, these people helped our family, prayed for us, and gave us support and strength. Many people in Niles and South Bend knew us only through the media and had sent us cards and letters. We had kept in close touch with our friends and, through them, the small town of Niles and the membership of Temple Beth-El had followed David's progress after we moved.

Normally, the drive from the Chicago area to Niles would take about 2 1/2 hours. That day, the traffic was very bad and it took us 4 1/2 hours. By the time we finally got to Sharon's house, we were two hours late and a few of the guests had already left. Sara was still there. Sara's mom had stayed with David and Rachael, so that Sara would be able to attend the shower without worrying. Sara had brought her video camera and was recording the occasion. I admired her courage and unselfishness and hoped that she could forget about what was happening with David for a few hours and just enjoy the shower.

Even though everyone tried to be cheerful, their long faces showed their concern for David. Some asked about David's prognosis and his possibilities for receiving a new liver soon. I was grateful for their concern, but I noticed Rebecca's wedding shower becoming overshadowed by concern for David. In spite of everything, it was a lovely shower and Rebecca enjoyed seeing old friends and opening her gifts. My daughter Rebecca was good at making the best of any situation.

After the shower, while we were busy loading the car, Sharon tried to comfort Sara. Sharon's family had had their share of problems when Sharon donated a kidney to her sister, and she assured Sara that she knew what they were going through. Sharon reminded Sara that she had been with our family through David's first transplant and promised Sara that she would help in any way she could, just as she had back in 1981. All of the emotions that Sara was so bravely keeping inside rose to the surface and she burst into tears, leaving Sharon's house with red-rimmed eyes. I felt bad for Sara; I knew it must have upset her to cry in front of Sharon. She was a private person and preferred not to burden others with her worries.

I wondered how we would get through the wedding. Many of the guests we invited to Rebecca's wedding were our dearest friends and relatives, and many of them had been with us through David's first transplant. I hoped they would be able to set aside their concerns for David for one evening so that Rebecca and Dave's wedding would be a true celebration. I decided I would have to come up with a way to minimize the sorrow at the wedding.

My oldest son Ben and his wife Laura were giving another wedding shower for Rebecca and Dave the following weekend. Before the guests arrived, we all gathered at their house for a Family Meeting. I brought up the subject of the long faces and Sara's tears at the last shower and suggested that it might be best not to discuss David's condition at the wedding. Many of the guests who were arriving from out of town didn't know that David needed a second transplant. If we shared this information at the wedding, our guests would naturally express concern, sympathy, and offer comfort. I didn't know if we would be able to maintain our composure and the last thing I wanted was for us to be crying about David at Rebecca's wedding! I asked everyone in the family to pretend that everything was OK, for just that one night, and to save the discussion of David's health for the day after the wedding. It was a difficult decision to make, to consciously decide to hide our feelings. Joe, Ben, Laura, David, Sara, Rebecca, and Dave all remained silent, but no one disagreed; our decision was made and the meeting was over.

My heart went out to David. I didn't know how he was dealing with all of this. Throughout all of his 29 years, every time he got sick, I dropped everything and ran to his side to devote my complete attention to him until he got well again. I hoped and prayed David would understand. If David's illness and uncertain future overshadowed Rebecca's wedding, no one would feel like celebrating. Who would dance and rejoice with Rebecca and Dave if all they could think about was David's declining health? For over a year, we had all worked hard to prepare a beautiful celebration for this day. Ben and David both had beautiful weddings with out-of-town guests, music, dancing, and much rejoicing and celebrating of that happy moment. Now, it was Rebecca's turn.

Laura and Ben had planned a beautiful couples' shower for the bride and groom. Rebecca and Dave's friends were there, and Laura had decorated everything with her special touch. We played party games, ate a wonderful lunch, and enjoyed ourselves. David tried very hard to be cheerful. He spent a lot of time outside with Rachael on the backyard play gym. Rachael was not yet ready to go down the slide by herself, and David helped her patiently, enjoying her delight. With his swollen legs, yellow eyes, and jaundiced face, it was impossible to forget that he was suffering from liver failure.

After the shower, in order to follow through with our plan, I called my friend Sharon in Niles. The ladies at the Niles wedding shower were the only ones who knew that David needed a second liver transplant. I asked Sharon to call each shower guest and ask her not to spread the news about David until after Rebecca's wedding celebration. Sharon didn't agree with our decision to keep quiet about David's condition, but she said she would do as I asked.

We felt like we were on the high wire, doing a balancing act between David's health crisis, and Rebecca's wedding day. We knew we were doing everything we could for David, and now we wanted to be sure that Rebecca's wedding day was everything she had dreamed it would be. We were even formulating a plan for what to do if a liver was found for David on the night of Rebecca's wedding. We were planning how to handle it without causing a major disruption that would detract from the wedding. If Rebecca's wedding were ruined, we would never be able to make it up to her. We wouldn't be able to turn back the clock or rewrite history. That memory would be forever forged in our minds.

In the weeks before the wedding, we received a call from Nancy in Pittsburgh. She gave David and Sara instructions for arranging the emergency trip to Pittsburgh, in the event that a liver was located for David.

By mid-July, I realized that because I had spent two weeks in Pittsburgh, I was behind on the wedding preparations. "Well," I told myself, "if I have to, I'll stay up late every night between now and the wedding. We'll get everything done." There was a lot of sewing to be done. I wanted to sew a special dress for Rachael to wear to the wedding, and make bows to decorate the chairs that would be used by the guests during the ceremony. I also needed to alter the dress that I was going to wear to the wedding, and alter the dress that Rebecca would wear to the Friday night dinner party that we were having in our home for all of the out-of-town guests. Many of our relatives would be there, and we wanted to make and freeze some special dishes that we knew everyone would enjoy. We had made all of these plans before David became ill.

I was fortunate that my older sister Edna had arrived on July 17th, three weeks before the wedding. Edna, an excellent seamstress, realized my desperation and got to work right away. She worked beside me tirelessly, working on the sewing projects I had planned, plus making special tablecloths for the Friday night party. Edna even volunteered to alter Sara's and Laura's bridesmaid dresses. The two of us working side-by-side for a special occasion reminded me of the days that my mother and I spent working together to prepare for David's Bar Mitzvah in 1981.

■   ■   ■

1981

My mom arrived from Israel in March. David's Bar Mitzvah was set for October 23, 1981. Mom came six months early, so we could spend some time together before we got busy with preparations for the ceremony and party that would mark David's coming of age as a Jewish male. Mom had been in Israel, and Joe and I in the United States since 1962. She hadn't traveled much — this was only her third trip to the U.S.— so we wanted to take her sightseeing. We were going to drive to California and back, stopping to see the attractions along the way.

Unfortunately, David experienced the first symptoms of Wilson's Disease and liver failure just two weeks after her arrival. Instead of sightseeing, my mom ended up taking care of Rebecca and Ben while Joe and I dealt with David's health crisis in Chicago and Pittsburgh. It wasn't easy for her. Mom didn't speak much English, but she managed to get along with the help of our Niles friends, Sharon and Nooshi. Joe's mom was there to help her part of the time, too.

When David received his transplant in September, my mom decided to stay until he recovered enough to have his Bar Mitzvah. Joe's mom had heart problems and could not tolerate the cold Midwestern winters, so she left to spend the winter with relatives in Texas and California. As David struggled through his recovery in Pittsburgh with me by his side, my mom continued to care for Rebecca and Ben. During this time, she and Rebecca formed a tight bond.

When David and I came home, my mom and I began working to get ready for his Bar Mitzvah. Joe's mom soon joined us. We had watched as David spent weeks in a coma; we had lost hope because, deep down, we really didn't believe in the miracle of liver transplant. We didn't believe he would ever again be well or experience the joy of life. Joe's mom and my mom had shed a lot of tears over David. Seeing David's return to health gave them a tremendous burst of energy. They were in their early seventies, but they worked for David's Bar Mitzvah as if they were in their twenties. They forgot about their own health problems and the aches and pains that come with old age. They cooked all day and urged food on all of us. They didn't like the fact that I had lost 25 pounds during David's illness and recovery. They would place bowls of cut fruit in strategic places around the house, hoping that I would snack enough to get back to my normal weight, but I was so excited to be back home preparing for David's Bar Mitzvah that I couldn't eat. Their support was wonderful and the fact that they cared so much meant a lot to us.

A home-cooked dinner on Friday night, a party on Saturday night, sewing tablecloths, relatives arriving from all over the country! David's Bar Mitzvah celebration was an important event for our family and it soon became an important event for our small town of Niles and for our congregation, Temple Beth-El in South Bend, where we worshiped. The people of Niles and the members of Temple Beth-El had been praying for David since he had been put on the waiting list for a liver transplant. The local newspaper covered David's story and ran updates whenever there was new information. We invited nearly everyone we knew to David's Bar Mitzvah. My Temple Sisterhood friends who felt helpless while we were in Chicago and Pittsburgh baked and baked for the Bar Mitzvah. Five hundred people came to the temple that Friday night to see David's miraculous recovery with their own eyes. Dr. Malatack and two of our nurses drove from Pittsburgh to South Bend for the event. In spite of their busy schedules, they managed this visit by driving straight through overnight and switching drivers whenever one of them got tired. Our friends in Niles opened their homes to them; our family doctor, Dr. Frederick Lindenfeld, and his wife Marlynn hosted Dr. Malatack. Everyone was happy and excited to be sharing the joy of David's Bar Mitzvah with us. It was a time to dance and celebrate! David's Bar Mitzvah was also a celebration of his return to health; as Joe said in his speech on David's Bar Mitzvah night, "David was born again!"

■   ■   ■

JULY, 1998

I couldn't believe how much energy I had back then for David's Bar Mitzvah, and how tired I was now, preparing for Rebecca's wedding. The joy of David's recovery had given me energy, but now the disappointment of his illness was draining me when I needed energy to prepare for the wedding. Something else was also weighing heavily on my mind. My mom, who had traveled to the United States for David and Sara's wedding, would not be with us to celebrate Rebecca and Dave's wedding because she was fighting a battle of her own. A year before, at the age of 88, she had been diagnosed with colon cancer. At her Israeli doctor's suggestion, she bravely consented to surgery to remove the cancer. I think she consented, in part, because David's liver transplant had helped her become a believer in modern medicine and surgery. She recovered nicely, and six months later flew to California for my niece Iris's wedding. Shortly after the wedding, she suffered a severe asthma attack and spent the rest of her visit in a California hospital, right up until the day she returned to Israel. It was hard for me to admit it, but my mother's health was beginning to fail. She had always been the rock of my existence, the one person I could lean on knowing that, no matter what the problem, the comfort and the wisdom that I needed to sustain me were only as far away as her next airmail letter. And now she said she didn't have the energy for a trip to the United States. That might have been true, but I had the feeling that her fear of getting sick and becoming a burden while here was also playing a part in her decision not to come. She never wanted to be a burden to anyone and for that reason, at the age of 89, she still lived independently in her own home in Israel. We would all miss her terribly, but I felt that her decision not to come might, in a small way, be a blessing for her. I had told her that David would need another liver transplant, but I didn't tell her how seriously ill he was. It would have been extremely painful for her to see how sick David was and not have the energy to help us through this crisis, as she had done 17 years ago.

It wasn't easy to think about these things, but I reminded myself that the happy days would be back again. Meanwhile, we had Rebecca's wedding to celebrate. I prayed for strength for all of us, and asked God to help us find the joy in our hearts in spite of our pain.

Everyone in the family had a special role to play in Rebecca and Dave's wedding. Ben and David were groomsmen, and Laura and Sara were bridesmaids. Edna and I made one-year-old Rachael a special dress and she would walk down the aisle alongside Sara. Ben and Laura's seven-year-old son Josh would be a ring bearer along with Dave's nephew Gavin. And by some miracle, we had convinced Ben and Laura's four-year-old son Jacob to be the "flower boy," despite the teasing of his older brother.

David, Sara, and Rachael arrived on Wednesday, August 5th, coming a day early so they would have a day to settle in and rest up before the Thursday rehearsal dinner. David looked thinner and more jaundiced than the last time we saw him and we hoped that the excitement of the next few days would not prove too much for him.

On Thursday afternoon, we went to the rehearsal at the hotel where the wedding and reception would take place in just two days. Dave's parents, Gay and Donna Dahn, gave the rehearsal dinner that night at a restaurant near Dave's house in Elgin. We all enjoyed meeting Dave's out-of-town family and his close circle of friends. David especially enjoyed himself and, in the spirit of the evening, invited Dave and his friends to go golfing the next day. They all agreed to meet early the next morning for 18 holes. We were not sure that David would be able to get up and get going that early, but he surprised us all. The next morning, the day of our dinner party, they left to go golfing in a cool damp morning mist that promised rain. It began to rain while they were golfing, but they played on, finishing their last holes in the rain. I had considered asking David not to go, to save his strength for the wedding, but I did not. Instead, I rationalized that since he was able to get up early, he must be feeling OK. It made me feel good to see his enthusiasm for golf and friends override his fatigue and illness. I also knew that even if I had tried to stop him, I would not have been able to. David had a mind of his own.

Back at home, everything was ready for the dinner party, just the way we'd planned it. Thanks to Edna's help and hard work, the dresses were ready, the food was prepared, and the house was beautifully decorated with bridal tulle and white silk roses. Sara had used her artistic talent to paint a street sign directing the guests to our house and Laura had made a fancy dessert. Everything was just the way we imagined, except that it was raining—we'd expected a beautiful summer day and had rented tables and chairs for outdoor dining. Early in the day, Edna reminded me that we should start thinking about serving dinner indoors. I agreed with her, but I was still hopeful that the rain might stop. In the Middle East, where it hardly ever rains, a rain shower on a special occasion was a good omen. "God is sending his blessing," is what we used to say whenever it rained on our celebrations.

Joe's sister Angie and her husband Pat came over early to help with the last-minute preparations. It was still raining. In fact, I couldn't remember ever having seen that much rain in August before. Finally, at 4:00 p.m., we decided to bring in the tables and chairs. As the warm summer raindrops hit us, I remembered how I had cried every day in the shower back in 1981 when we had lost all hope for David and feared he might die. Back then, I spent all of my days and nights in his hospital room and the only place that I had the privacy to cry was in the shower. I also remembered another old Middle Eastern saying about the rain, "Our emotional pain is so bad that even the skies and heavens are crying for us." It was true. Our emotional pain was great, but I was not planning to cry. This time it was different. This time we had hope. David had an excellent chance of making a full recovery and living out a wonderful future. It was just a matter of time.

While Joe and the others were setting up the tables and chairs indoors, I slipped upstairs to get ready for the party and I waited for the telephone to ring. Each day since David had been put on the waiting list, I waited for the telephone to ring. No matter where I was or what I was doing, I was waiting for the telephone to ring. And every time the telephone or my cell phone rang, my heart started pounding, hoping that the call meant a liver for David. Each time, I was disappointed.

I noticed that I didn't have much time to get ready so I took a quick shower, applied my makeup, put in my contacts, and dressed carefully. When I went downstairs, I was pleased that none of the guests had arrived yet and that I would be able to greet them at the door. Joe looked up as I walked into the kitchen and I smiled at him, hoping he would show his appreciation with a compliment as he so often did. I was puzzled by the strange expression on his face. He asked me in a grave voice, "Have you seen your face in the mirror?"

I had just put on my makeup and put my contact lenses in. Of course, I had looked in the mirror, I told him.

"Go look at your face in the mirror," he said with that same funny expression.

I went to check my face in the powder room, thinking that maybe I had applied my lipstick sloppily or that my mascara was running, but my makeup was fine. But in spite of my carefully applied makeup, my eyes and the new lines on my face betrayed the pain and agony I was feeling inside. Joe was right—this was not the face of a happy mother-of-the-bride. It was the face of a mother who was spending day and night waiting for the phone to ring, waiting for the news that the waiting was over, waiting for the news that they had found a liver for David. As I looked into the mirror, I realized that I would be unable to follow the rule that I had asked everyone else to follow. I might be able to act like I was having a good time, but I would not be able to forget the agony of David's failing liver, nor would I be able to hide the toll that it was taking. I took a deep breath and smiled at myself in the mirror, but I couldn't change the expression in my eyes. "Whoever said that the eyes are the mirror to the soul was right," I thought to myself. I regretted choosing contact lenses this evening instead of my eyeglasses; the bifocal lenses in my glasses would have hidden the expression in my eyes. I had worn my glasses all day as we worked to get ready for the party and Joe hadn't noticed anything unusual about my eyes until now.

It was too late to go back upstairs for my glasses; the guests were beginning to arrive. I could hear Joshua's and Jacob's voices in the foyer as they greeted their cousin Rachael. I tried to refocus my thoughts to the joy that my three angels, my grandchildren, had brought into my life. Joe started the Persian music. The music was telling me that it was time to celebrate and I remembered Joe's speech at David's Bar Mitzvah: "To everything there is a season, and a time to every purpose under heaven. A time to be born . . . a time to plant . . ." Now it was time to celebrate Rebecca and Dave's wedding. Even though David was thin and jaundiced, he would be okay for the next two days.

With these thoughts, I left the bathroom and went for hugs from Josh and Jacob. "Give me some energy," I said, holding my arms wide, and they flew into my arms. I always told them their hugs gave me energy, and it was true. Hugs from the people I love renew me in both body and spirit. I took Josh and Jacob by the hand and brought them into the living room to introduce them to the friends and relatives they had not yet met. As I visited with everyone, I smiled and smiled until the muscles in my face began to hurt. Our Middle Eastern culture was on my side. I had been brought up feeling free to express myself. In our culture, it is normal to express feelings of sadness and sorrow when a loved one is ill. Since I was smiling and happy on the outside, I knew that all of our Middle Eastern friends and relatives would assume that everything was fine.

A few of the guests did notice that David did not look well, especially those friends and relatives who had last seen him at his own wedding celebration four years before when he was at his healthiest and handsomest. My friend Minou expressed her concern to Joe, who in keeping with my request, replied that it was only a temporary problem that would soon be resolved.

As the evening wore on and I began to tire, I decided that the best way to hide my pain was on the dance floor. We had cleared some space for dancing in the middle of our small living room. As I began to dance, others joined in. Then Rachael found us and began trying to imitate our Persian dance steps. That brought laughter and joy to everyone. Around 10:00 p.m., the guests began to leave. Rebecca and Kelley, a bridesmaid and close friend, left to spend the night in a nearby hotel where we had booked a room for them in case the party went late. Even though it was not too late, I was glad we had made those arrangements. I didn't want my worry to spoil her mood and I knew that Rebecca would have a good time with Kelley.

I was thankful that the party had gone well. "One more night, just one more night to get through, before I can devote myself fully to David," I promised myself. As I lay in bed that night, I thanked God for giving me the strength to get through the party. I asked God to help me live each day in the moment, to find the joy in each moment without worrying about the past or the future. That way, whatever happened, I would have no regrets.

By the next morning, the rain had stopped. We got up early and Kelley and Rebecca came by to dress for the wedding. Joe's sister Angie was a professional stylist and she swept Rebecca's hair up into beautifully arranged curls on top of her head, and fixed them in place with a tiara and lots of tiny pearls. Even without her dress, Rebecca was already a beautiful bride! Kelly, who had gotten married several months before, had plenty of wedding and bridesmaid experience. She saw to all of Rebecca's needs and it was a big relief to have Rebecca so well taken care of by her good friend.

David did not want to get out of bed, but Sara managed to wake him up and get him going, and then pack to stay the night in the hotel where the wedding and reception would take place. With a hotel room, they would be able to enjoy the wedding celebration without worrying about the late-night drive home. On their way to the hotel, they were picking up a babysitter we lined up to help with Rachael. That way Rachael could go back to the hotel room with the babysitter and go to sleep when she got tired, and David and Sara could enjoy the party.

Edna had done a wonderful job of altering my dress. It was a pleasure just to put it on. When I was done getting ready, I made a quick call to my mother in Israel. Joe and I told Mom how much we missed her. We also told her David was here for the wedding, and he was still doing okay.

By 2:30 p.m., we were all ready to go. Even though the ceremony was not until 5:30 p.m., we needed to be to the Embassy Suites early for pictures. Rebecca and Dave had chosen the Embassy Suites in Schaumburg, in part, because it was located halfway between our house in Riverwoods and Dave's house in Elgin. It also appealed to us because the out-of-town relatives could get there from the airport without driving through the traffic of downtown Chicago. Since both the ceremony and reception were in the hotel, no extra driving would be required for guests staying at the hotel.

By 3:30 p.m., the entire wedding party had assembled at the hotel and was ready for pictures. Rebecca was a radiant bride-to-be and everyone else looked stunning—the men in their tuxedos and the women in their long burgundy gowns. Rachael looked like a ceramic doll in her fancy white dress with her pale skin, wide eyes, and curly dark hair, and Joshua and

Jacob looked like little men in their tuxedos. The children drew attention wherever they walked.

But David was thin and jaundiced. More jaundiced than he had been the day before. More jaundiced, in fact, than he had been at any time since this nightmare had started. In July, when I had mentioned the possibility of special makeup to David, he had gotten furious, shouting, "What will you do for my eyes? How am I supposed to cover the yellow in my eyes?" Clearly he had expressed his feelings about the makeup. I explained that I was thinking about the pictures. From a distance, you would not see the whites of his eyes. I just wanted him to look as normal as possible in the pictures, especially in the group pictures that would be distributed to all the relatives. Those pictures would be displayed proudly in our homes for years to come. I could see that he was distressed, so I told David that the decision was his and, from that day on, I never brought up the subject again.

The photographer was tense and irritable. He barked out his orders and we assembled on command. He cajoled and shocked us into nervous laughter for the pictures. I tried to laugh and smile as best I could, but at one point my oldest son Ben took exception to his rude suggestions and asked him to speak more respectfully to me. I wondered why the friend who recommended this photographer hadn't told us about his poor manners. Finally, the pictures were over.

I realized that I had managed to pass the last hour without waiting for the phone to ring. I was grateful that David had brought his cell phone and I wouldn't have to carry one tonight and wait for it to ring.

The marriage ceremony was beautiful. It was set in the middle of an elegant indoor courtyard. The burbling fountain was strewn with rose petals. The children performed as coached, all except Jacob, to the delight of all present. Not having been instructed in this particular matter, he grabbed the rose petals from his top hat and threw them to the ground instead of "sprinkling" them as a flower girl might have done. Rebecca and Dave pledged their love and devotion in front of 200 guests and there was much rejoicing. After the ceremony, everyone gathered for a brief cocktail party at nearby bistro tables then headed into the ballroom for dinner.

On a laminated paper placed at each table, Rebecca and Dave asked guests not to bang their glasses to encourage the bride and groom to kiss. Instead, they requested guests to gather their table and sing a love song to the bride and groom. Joe and I were sharing our table with Ben, Laura, Josh, Jacob, David, Sara, Rachael, and Rachael's babysitter. We got up first, and sang "The Barney Song." "I love you, you love me, we're a happy family…"

we sang. Soon, other tables followed us. Our Persian relatives sang a Persian love song, the Israeli relatives sang a Hebrew love song, and many others followed. Everyone was having a great time and, briefly, I forgot about David's illness.

A short time later, almost as if in punishment for my momentary peace, I noticed that something was terribly wrong. I noticed that David's smile was crooked. He was singing and it looked like he was making funny faces, when I knew he was not. My heart began to pound. What's wrong now, I wondered? David seemed happy. He seemed like he was having a good time. What could possibly be wrong? Did his smile look crooked to me because he had lost 10 pounds in the last month? What else could it be? Stroke? Heart attack? I didn't think so. David was still standing; in fact, he was heading out onto the dance floor. My imagination was running wild and I knew if I didn't stop it, Joe would soon be reminding me about my face. I might have spent the rest of the night worrying about it, but I told myself that this was not the time to worry. Tomorrow we would deal with it. The unfortunate reality was that, for whatever reason, David looked worse tonight than at any time since his transplant 17 years ago. Even if he had agreed to wear the makeup for the pictures, it would have been his crooked smile that gave him away, reminding us how ill he was and how helpless we all were.

Trying to get past my worry, I asked Josh to dance with me, then Jacob, and of course, later on I danced with Ben, David, and Dave. I didn't know when I would ever again have the opportunity to dance with all of these handsome young men in tuxedos. It was like a dream come true. The band was good, playing both American and Israeli dance music, and a tape of Persian dance music played during their breaks. It seemed like everyone was dancing and having a good time except for Ben. He seemed to be having a hard time getting into a celebratory mood and spent some time in the hotel lounge watching sports on TV. I thought that he must not be as good at hiding his feelings as Joe and I were at hiding ours. "He is young," I thought to myself, "but he is still doing better than I would have been able to do at his age." I felt that he was doing the best he could.

By coincidence, Rebecca had chosen my birthday as her wedding date. My children had dropped off gifts for me earlier in the day. Between dances, Joe announced to all the guests that it was my birthday. He surprised me with a short speech and a bouquet of roses, and everyone wished me a happy birthday.

About an hour after midnight, the party ended. As guests left for home or their hotel room, we promised everyone that we would be back for brunch the next day. Then Edna, Joe, and I returned home. I hated to take my dress off. Edna's work on my fancy, ivory mother-of-the-bride dress made it so comfortable and so well-tailored that it reminded me of the dresses Edna made for me in Iran when she was a teenager and I was a little girl. As I took off the dress, I hoped that I would have occasion to wear it again someday. "Perhaps for one of my grandchildren's weddings if I live that long and don't gain any more weight," I thought as I hung it carefully in the closet. By the time I went to bed, it was 3:00 a.m., the end of a beautiful wedding celebration. As I drifted off to sleep, I wondered when we would be able to celebrate like that again with all of our relatives and dear friends. I hoped that next time we would all be celebrating with a happy heart. The end of Rebecca's wedding day marked the end of another year of my life. Where I would be on my next birthday? Would David be healthy by then? When would he receive a new liver? I had no answer for any of these questions; it was in God's hands.

The next morning, we rose early to return to the Embassy Suites to have brunch with the friends and relatives who had spent the night there. David and Sara were coming down to breakfast when we arrived. As soon as we greeted each other, David confessed that when our friend, Bob LaZebnik, had asked how he was feeling, David had told him about his situation. He had also confided in his cousin Monica that he would need another liver soon.

"It's all right," I said. "The wedding is over. Now, we can tell everyone."

David touched the side of his face. "I have no feeling on this side of my face," he said. A light went on in my head. That was the reason for his crooked smile the night before.

I wanted David and Sara to return to our house with us. Some of the relatives whose flights were leaving later in the day were coming back to our house and I thought it would be nice for David to have a chance to visit with them in a quieter setting. But David had other ideas. He said they would be leaving for their apartment in Michigan right after breakfast. He had paperwork to do for the house that they were building, and they were planning to move as soon as it was finished, so they had lots of packing and organizing to do. David asked if I would come next week to help them pack and I agreed to help them out.

That was David's way of coping with physical or emotional pain—ignore it and just keep busy with everyday life. I was more concerned about David's health than about the packing and moving. On our way home, I called David's transplant coordinator from the car and told her about the paralysis in his face. She recommended that he see a doctor as soon as possible, so I called David's apartment and left a message on his answering machine relating my conversation with his transplant coordinator.

When we arrived home later in the day, after dropping off some relatives at the airport, we had a message from David on our answering machine. It said, "I will go to the emergency room. And Mom, please don't call my transplant coordinator without my knowledge." Once again, I had overstepped my boundaries. I had forgotten that he was 29 years old and capable of managing his own health and had done what I would have done when he was just twelve years old. I was worried and I let my concern get in the way of treating David like an adult. Deep down, I was terrified that the paralysis in his face might somehow be related to Wilson's Disease. I had met a few Wilson's patients over the years who had sustained progressive neurological damage as a result of the copper deposits in their brain tissue. Even though they had normal liver function and hadn't needed a liver transplant, these patients' neurological damage was apparent in their faces. Their faces twisted into a grimaces at unexpected times, they had trouble chewing and swallowing their food, and they tended to drool. Now, here was David with no feeling in one side of his face. Was this monstrous disease once more plaguing my son? I tried to comfort myself with the knowledge that Wilson's nerve damage tended to come on gradually, and David's problem seemed to have developed literally overnight. I thought of Dr. Sternlieb, a Wilson's Disease specialist that we met at the meetings of the American Association for the Study of Liver Disease. Even though it was Sunday afternoon, I decided to call him at home. I told him David's story and asked him if he had ever heard of Wilson's Disease recurring with similar symptoms. He said no, in all his experience, Wilson's Disease had never returned after a liver transplant. That was a relief!

Later that night, David called. After waiting hours in the hospital, he had seen a doctor. The diagnosis was Bell's Palsy, a paralysis of the facial nerve that was probably unrelated to his liver disease. Although Bell's Palsy is sometimes caused by trauma to the facial nerve or an unknown infection, the cause cannot always be pinpointed. The doctor had explained to David that even though it had come on overnight, it would not go away that quickly; the symptoms would gradually disappear over a matter of weeks or months. In some cases, David was told, the patient does not completely recover; we would just have to wait and hope that David would regain the use of his muscles on that side of his face. Until then, eating and drinking would be much more difficult. With David struggling to keep from losing weight, that was one problem he didn't need!

On Tuesday, Edna helped me get ready to go to David and Sara's apartment to help them with the packing. Even though Edna's flight for Israel did not leave until Sunday, I knew she would be in good hands. Joe's sister Angie was still in town, and Edna's daughter Ilana and her husband Shmouel would also be in Chicago for a few days. The house was still full of fresh flowers, decorations, and gifts from the wedding, but I would just leave everything behind and go. I understood why David was in such a big hurry to move. He wanted to make sure that Sara and Rachael were settled in the new house before he got too ill to take care of them. Indeed, before he became so ill that he would have to depend on his family to take care of him.

I said goodbye to Joe and Edna and pulled out of the driveway with a heavy heart. The busy days of planning and preparing for Rebecca's wedding were behind us now. I had said goodbye to all of the friends and relatives who had come for the wedding, and told them that I hoped I would see them again soon. Privately I hoped that the next time we were all together, everyone was healthy and happy and there were no dark clouds hanging over anyone's future. As I drove toward Michigan and all the concerns of the wedding fell away, I could clearly feel that a page was turning and a new chapter in our lives was beginning. This chapter would be about the nightmare of watching David slip away from us. It would be full of pain and heartache, and there was no telling how long it would last.

Appendix 3A

COPING MECHANISMS FOR THE PATIENT AND FAMILY

In most cases, liver failure doesn't happen overnight. For months or years before liver disease is diagnosed, the patient may suffer from nonspecific symptoms including fatigue, poor appetite, and diarrhea. It may take a number of tests, such as blood chemistry, x-rays, liver biopsies, and CT scans, before the diagnosis of liver failure is reached. Since the patient has suffered these symptoms off and on for years, experiencing periods of recovery and relapse with no major ill effects, the need for a liver transplant almost always comes as a big shock to patients and their families.

Accepting the Diagnosis

The time after diagnosis is a time for patients and their families to educate themselves, gathering as much information as they can on the subject of their illness. While learning about the disease, it is also advisable to seek a second and, if necessary, third opinion. This will help the patient and his/her family to accept the reality of their diagnosis with proper knowledge and understanding.

In seeking another opinion, there is no need to repeat all of the diagnostic tests. Most doctors will accept the x-rays, liver biopsy slides, and test results from other hospitals and use them to make diagnoses and treatment recommendations. However, if the patient has any doubt about his diagnosis or the accuracy of his test results, a fresh set of tests may be helpful in either confirming or calling into question the previous results.

Managing Guilt

After the tests are done, the diagnoses made, and the patient's name is put on the waiting list, the reality of a liver transplant begins to sink in. With this realization comes a feeling of guilt. We learned this when our 12-year-old son David asked, "How can I pray for me to live, when I know another child must die so I can live?"

These feelings of guilt are not easy to deal with, and some recipients carry this guilt with them long after their transplant. A clergyperson or counselor may help put that feeling to rest, explaining that life and death are not in our hands. Only God decides who will live and who will die. When we were able to accept that David's life was in God's hands, we found a measure of peace. We never prayed for anyone to die, we only prayed that David would stay healthy and strong until a donor liver became available.

Adjusting to Changes in Character and Relationships

As healthy individuals, we wake up in the morning and live our lives as if we will live forever. Only a grave accident or terminal illness in the family brings us to the realization that we or one of our loved ones may die prematurely. Unless we are in total denial and delude ourselves that nothing bad can happen, the realization that we are vulnerable to death at any time brings with it a change in character and a change in our outlook on life.

These changes can cause conflict between family members. For example, when a mother who has always taken care of the other family members experiences liver failure, she may not be able to fulfill her responsibilities to her family as before. Instead of being the caregiver, she will need the help of others to survive. The roles of everyone in the family will change as the caregiver becomes someone who now needs care. A few exceptional families will handle these types of changes seamlessly and without conflict, but most will struggle with the changes in everyday life, roles, and relationships.

Once again, talking things over with an experienced psychologist, family therapist, or clergyperson will help. As an impartial observer and a trained professional, the counselor can help the patient and family members cope with their emotions, accept the situation, and redefine their roles in the family.

Dealing with Financial Hardship

Major illness and transplant surgery will be a drain on family finances. Although money is the last thing anyone wants to worry about when a loved one is ill, this is another issue that, for most families, cannot be ignored. Before financial obligations get out of hand, it is helpful to take a close look at the family finances and make a budget for the necessities. Most families will realize that it is necessary to make changes in everyday spending habits, take on part-time jobs when time allows, or dip into "rainy day" savings. Other resources for working out financial problems are the patient's insurance company, the transplant team social worker, the patient's clergyperson, a financial counselor, and trusted friends and relatives.

Some Words of Wisdom . . .

Here is what we learned from the experience of having to cope with the nightmare of the waiting list and multiple liver transplant surgeries:

1. Understand that everyone copes differently. Give each member of your family the freedom to cope in their own way.
2. Don't dwell on the past or seek to assign blame for the illness. Accept that you cannot change the past and save your energy for the days ahead, when you will really need it.
3. Accept that no person on earth has control over who will live and who will die. Instead, embrace the power you do have—the power to improve the lives of those around you with love and understanding.
4. Learn as much as possible about the illness, treatment options, and recovery path. Use this information to prepare yourself for the days ahead. Most transplant centers have support groups. Join one and use it as a source of strength and information.
5. Be an active participant in treatment decisions. Your opinion is important to your doctors and surgeons.
6. Find a good counselor and see them regularly to help maintain family harmony and keep the lines of communication and understanding open.
7. Forgive and forget past conflicts. Your family needs this more than ever now, and this is another area in which your counselor can help.
8. Accept that this crisis may last for a long time, months or even years. Make the most of each day and don't waste time and energy asking "Why me?" This chapter of your life may be spent coping with illness and suffering, but it will not last forever. Remember that better days are ahead and that the good times will return.
9. Don't let the pain and suffering overwhelm you. You are not alone. Everyone around you is also suffering—the

patient, family members, loved ones, and friends. Acknowledge their suffering, as well as your own, but don't let it consume your life. Continue to celebrate birthdays, holidays, and life events, and try to find a little joy in each day.

10. Be grateful for the love and support you receive from those around you. Love and support are as important as food and medication to patients and their families.

Appendix 3B

THE WAITING LIST AND HOW IT WORKS

The United Network for Organ Sharing (UNOS)

(Taken with permission from the UNOS Web site: www.UNOS.org.)

The United Network for Organ Sharing is a private, nonprofit organization that manages the nation's organ sharing system, seeking to improve transplant outcomes by increasing organ sharing and making the most of every organ that is donated. UNOS also collects and analyzes data submitted by transplant professionals, making this data available to the public, transplant community, government, and others who request it.

The Organ Placement Process

(Reprinted with permission from "UNOS Facts and Figures" on the UNOS Web site: www.UNOS.org.)

Prioritizing Patients for Transplantation

Each organ type has its own individual distribution policy reflecting the unique medical considerations of each type of transplant. However, certain general factors apply to all organ allocation policies:

- Patients who are close biological matches with a particular donor offer (including blood type, body size, and/or tissue typing match) are given priority. Closer matching tends to result in better long-term survival after transplantation.

- For heart, liver and intestinal organs, patients whose medical status is most urgent receive priority over those whose medical status is not as urgent.

- When possible, organs are offered first to patients locally, then to a larger region, then nationally. This is done to minimize organ preservation time, which is associated with better transplant survival. However, there are exceptions to this sequence for particularly well-matched organ offers and for the most urgent category of liver patients.

- The policies strive to ensure equivalent access for patients who might be at a disadvantage because of the progression of their disease or their ability to receive suitable organ offers. For example, most policies afford children special priority because of the medical risks they face while awaiting transplant.

- Waiting time is used to break ties between patients who are similar in other respects. Patients who have waited longer at their current medical status receive priority over those who have waited less time.

The UNOS computer system is programmed to consider each of these issues automatically when matching donor organs to patients awaiting a transplant. Therefore, the patients ranked highest will be those who have both the greatest need and greatest likelihood for a successful transplant.

Matching Organs with Patients in Need: The Organ Offer Process

When a deceased organ donor is identified, a transplant coordinator from an organ procurement organization enters medical information about the donor into the UNOS computer system. The system then matches the donor's medical characteristics with the medical information of candidates awaiting a transplant. The computer generates a ranked list of patients for each organ recovered from the donor. The transplant team of the first person on the match run is offered the organ needed. Often the top-ranked patient may not get the organ for one of several reasons, including the following:

- he or she cannot be located or cannot reach the hospital in time for a transplant;

- he or she is temporarily too sick to receive a transplant;

- the medical team believes the organ would not benefit the candidate due to the donor's age or medical condition;

- medical tests performed after the initial offer show the candidate's immune system would likely reject the organ.

If an offer is turned down for one transplant candidate, the organ is offered to the next candidate on the match run. These offers continue until the organ is placed or until no potential recipient can be located in time for a successful transplant.

UNOS Organ Center

The UNOS Organ Center places many organs and also helps members with running computer matches, arranging transport for organs, updating patient records, and providing information about organ-sharing policies. The Organ Center is staffed 24 hours a day, seven days a week, 365 days a year. If a catastrophe prevents use of the current facilities, operations can be switched in minutes to a fully equipped disaster recovery site.

UNOS Regions for Organ Allocation
(Reprinted with permission from "Who We Are" on the UNOS Web site, www.UNOS.org.)

The national UNOS membership is divided into 11 geographic regions. This regional structure was developed to:

- facilitate organ allocation, and
- provide individuals with the opportunity to identify concerns regarding organ procurement, allocation, and transplantation that are unique to their particular geographic area.

The map below shows how the nation is divided into organ allocation regions:

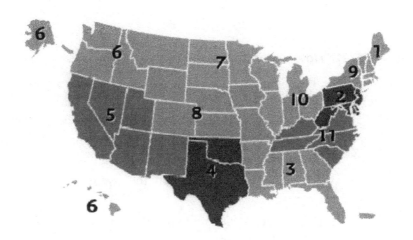

Why are organs allocated by region?

Organs are first offered to patients within the area in which they were donated[1] before being offered to other parts of the country in order to:

- reduce organ preservation time;
- improve organ quality and survival outcomes;
- reduce costs incurred by the transplant patient; and
- increase access to transplantation.

The Patient Prioritizing System: MELD and PELD

(Reprinted with permission from "Questions and Answers for Patients and Families about MELD and PELD," with permission from UNOS)

UNOS operates the Organ Procurement and Transplantation Network (OPTN) under federal contract. On an ongoing basis, the OPTN/UNOS continuously evaluates new advances and research and adapts these into new organ transplant policies to best serve patients waiting for transplants.

As part of this process, the OPTN/UNOS developed a system for prioritizing patients waiting for liver transplants based on statistical formulas that are very accurate for predicting who is most likely to die soon from liver disease. The MELD (Model for End-Stage Liver Disease) is used for adult patients and the PELD (Pediatric End-Stage Liver Disease Model) is used for pediatric patients.

These questions and answers for patients and their families will explain the reasons for adopting this system and how it will affect patients on the waiting list.

What is MELD? How will it be used?

The Model for End-Stage Liver Disease (MELD) is a numerical scale, ranging from 6 (less ill) to 40 (gravely ill), that is used for adult liver transplant candidates. It gives each individual a "score" based on how urgently he or she needs a liver transplant within the next three months. The number is calculated by a formula using three routine lab test results:

- bilirubin, which measures how effectively the liver excretes bile;
- INR (prothrombin time), which measures the liver's ability to make blood clotting factors; and

---

[1] With the exception of perfectly matched donor kidneys.

- creatinine, which measures kidney function (impaired kidney function is often associated with severe liver disease).

The MELD score replaced the previous Status 2A, 2B, and 3 categories. The Status 1 category for patients who have acute liver failure and a life expectancy of less than seven days without a transplant remains in place as the highest priority for receiving an organ and is not affected by the MELD system.

A patient's score may go up or down over time depending on the status of his or her liver disease. Many patients will have their MELD score assessed a number of times while they are on the waiting list. This will help ensure that donated livers go to the patients in greatest need at that moment.

What is PELD? How does it differ from MELD?

Candidates under the age of 18 are placed in categories according to the Pediatric End-stage Liver Disease (PELD) scoring system. PELD replaced the previous Status 2B and 3 for pediatric patients; Status 1 remains in place and is not affected by PELD.

PELD is similar to MELD but uses some different criteria to recognize the specific growth and development needs of children. PELD scores may also range higher or lower than the range of MELD scores. The measures used are as follows:

- bilirubin, which measures how effectively the liver excretes bile;
- INR (prothrombin time), which measures the liver's ability to make blood clotting factors;
- albumin, which measures the liver's ability to maintain nutrition;
- growth failure; and
- whether the child is less than one year old.

How is waiting time counted in the system?

Under the previous system, waiting time was often used to break ties among patients of the same medical status. Various studies, including one done by the Institute of Medicine, reported that waiting time is a poor indicator of how urgently a patient needs a liver transplant. This is because some patients are listed for a transplant very early in their disease, while others are listed only when they become much sicker.

Under the MELD/PELD system with a wider range of scores, waiting time does not have to be used as often to break ties. Waiting time will only determine who comes first when there are two or more patients with the same blood type and the same MELD or PELD score.

If a patient's MELD or PELD score increases over time, only the waiting time at the higher level will count. (For example, someone who has waited 40 days with a score of 12, and 5 days with a score of 15, would only get credit for 5 days of waiting time at the score of 15.) However, if the patient's MELD or PELD score decreases again, he or she would keep the waiting time gained at the higher score. (Using the earlier example, if the patient's score goes from 12 to 15 and back to 12, he or she would have 45 days of waiting time at the score of 12.) Patients initially listed as a Status 1 would also keep their waiting time if their condition improves and they later receive a MELD/PELD score.

Patients with higher MELD/PELD scores will always be considered before those with lower scores, even if some patients with lower scores have waited longer. (For example, a patient waiting for one day with a score of 30 will come ahead of a patient with a score of 29, even if the patient with a 29 has waited longer. This is because the patient with a score of 30 has a higher chance of dying on the list.)

Do MELD and PELD account for all conditions?

MELD/PELD scores reflect the medical need of most liver transplant candidates. However, there may be special exceptions for patients with medical conditions not covered by MELD and PELD. If your transplant team believes your score does not reflect your need for a transplant, they can seek a higher MELD/PELD score than the one determined by lab tests alone.

Is this system likely to change?

As transplant professionals apply and learn from the system, some changes will likely be required to better meet patients' needs. In fact, this system is designed to be flexible and allow improvements. In transplantation, as in all scientific fields, new studies are taking place all the time to learn how to save more lives and help people live longer and better.

How do I get on the waiting list for a liver?

Only the patient's transplant center team can decide if and when it is appropriate for a patient to be placed on the waiting list. While the MELD or PELD score determines a patient's immediate need for a transplant, there are many other factors involved in the decision to list a patient for a liver transplant. The patient's center will still need to make the final decision about putting him/her on the list. Please speak to your doctor about your specific medical circumstances and your MELD or PELD score.

Who sends the MELD/PELD data to UNOS?

There is a MELD/PELD calculator on the UNOS website that can be used to calculate your MELD/PELD score. However, using the MELD/PELD calculator does NOT automatically put you on the list or change your place on the list that is maintained by UNOS.

For patients already on the waiting list, each liver transplant program is responsible for updating the laboratory and clinical values needed to calculate their patients' MELD or PELD scores. These values must be entered on a regular basis, based on the patient's current MELD/PELD score. For example, centers must enter in new laboratory data at least once a week for patients on the list with very high MELD/PELD scores, but only once per year for patients on the list with very low MELD/PELD scores. Thus, patients will have their labs drawn based on this schedule to make sure their MELD/PELD scores are up-to-date. The center can also update a patient's MELD or PELD score if the patient gets sicker.

How high will my MELD or PELD score have to be before I can get a transplant?

Once listed, getting a liver transplant depends on several factors, such as:

- blood type;
- the number of other patients listed within the local area;
- the illness level of the other patients waiting in the local area; and
- the number of organs available in the local area or region.

The important thing to know about the MELD/PELD system is that it will increase your chance of getting a liver as your need for a liver increases. A similar system tested in UNOS Region 1 was shown to decrease the number of deaths for patients waiting for a liver transplant.

What if I have more questions?

If you have any further questions or concerns, you should contact your transplant team for further information. Additional details about the OPTN, UNOS, allocation policy, and patient informational resources are available on the following websites:

- http://www.optn.org
- http://www.unos.org
- http://www.transplantliving.org

4

DESPAIR

Second Transplant Center
University of Nebraska Medical Center
August, 1998

David and Sara's apartment was actually a townhouse in Kalamazoo. It is one of the nicest townhouses that I have ever seen. Located in a quiet wooded area, their balcony and walkout lower level looked out onto a serene, beautifully landscaped pond with a bubbling fountain in the middle. Ducks and geese floated around the pond and butterflies visited the wildflowers at the water's edge. Whenever I was there, I enjoyed sitting on the balcony while playing with Rachael or rocking her to sleep. This beautiful natural setting always reminded me of God's grace, and I often prayed there, thanking Him for all His blessings, especially David's health and the health of our whole family, our three beautiful grandchildren, my children's graduation from college, and their success in their jobs. Now, here I was again on this balcony and I still had something to be thankful for: we had gone 17 years without a major tragedy and now my youngest child Rebecca was happily married. Even though David and Sara would be moving to a home of their own, I knew I would always miss this balcony and the fountain. This time, however, there was no time to sit down and reflect. I was here to help them get ready to move. I went inside and helped pack, played with Rachael to keep her occupied while Sara was busy, and watched David sink into the depths of despair.

Anyone who has ever built a house knows that it is not easy to deal with builders. They give you a completion date, but often this date doesn't mean much. They finish the house according to their own schedule and at their convenience. To say that David was anxious to move was an understatement. When it was time to go for the walkthrough, David took Sara's father John with him. Sara's parents lived just 20 minutes away in Battle Creek, Michigan and were always around whenever David and Sara needed advice or a helping hand. I don't know what happened between David, John, and the builder that day at the house, but I do know that Sara's father was not happy with David's attitude. One evening, not long afterwards, John and his wife Johnie came to talk to David. They were both unhappy with his attitude and told him that if he kept acting as he had been, they would not help David and Sara move. I asked Johnie to go easy on David. "David is very sick." I said, "He is afraid that he may go into a coma or die before they find a liver for him, and he just wants to see Sara and Rachael settled in their new home before that happens."

Johnie replied, "I am dying, too. I have cancer that could come back at any time, but I'm not acting like that." I didn't have an answer for that. She was right. Two years before, in 1996, she had been diagnosed with non-Hodgkin's Lymphoma. She had gone through six months of chemotherapy and now her cancer was in remission. But who knew how long she'd be cancer-free? A cancer like that could recur at any time.

We all sat down in the living room, and Johnie told David about a time when John had been very ill. Sara and her sister Christy were just little and John had been hospitalized for a long time. Even though it was extremely difficult to take care of a sick husband and two little girls, they hung on and worked through it. Eventually John recovered and life got back to normal. When she finished her story, we were all crying for the sad times in the past, the hard times that were ahead, and the uncertainty of the future. Sara's parents were trying to tell David that they had been through tough times too, and had survived. There was no reason to be angry, this would pass. They wanted David to know that even though he was the one that was sick, we were all in this together and we would be right here by his side to help him through.

When there was just one day left until moving day, we were happy to find that we were almost done packing, thanks to the help of Sara's younger sister Christy. But David was not doing so well. He was vomiting and unable to hold down any food, so he called the doctor. The doctor made some suggestions to address his symptoms, but I knew that his problems were all the result of his failing liver. Fortunately, there was no blood in his vomit, so we knew that he wasn't bleeding internally. What were we going to do? Just as in 1981, David's health was going downhill and we were going from crisis to crisis. At least back then, he had been hospitalized and we felt comfortable that he was receiving around-the-clock care. Now, with changes in the insurance industry affecting the way that doctors cared for their patients, they would not hospitalize David. Since David was still conscious and ambulatory, there was no reason to admit him to the hospital.

I was scared. I wondered how we would keep David alive and healthy until a liver became available. One name kept coming back to me, Dr. Jeffrey

Malatack. He was the one that Dr. Gartner had charged with David's care back in 1981. He was the one who made sure that David had received proper care, both physically and emotionally. He was the one who kept David alive the first time, constantly monitoring his nutritional status, keeping his spirits up, and giving all of us hope until a liver became available. David and I had kept in touch with him and I knew he was just a phone call away. From the day David was put on the waiting list, every time I spoke to Dr. Malatack I could tell by his voice that he was just as heartbroken as we were. But this time, when I called him at home and told him about David's vomiting, he reminded me that there was nothing he could do for David medically now and that David needed to work with his transplant coordinator and local doctors to manage his care. But he added that if I needed to talk to someone, he would be there for me. I thanked him and said goodbye.

As I set the phone back on its cradle, I felt a big sense of loss. The reality that I had been unwilling to face was that Dr. Malatack lived in Philadelphia, hundreds of miles away from Michigan. He had a busy pediatric practice and had relinquished responsibility for David's medical care 11 years ago when David became an adult. He had five children of his own and the last thing he needed on a Sunday afternoon in August was a telephone call from me with sad news about David. I knew that Dr. Malatack's inability to do anything for David was as upsetting to him as it was to me. I was embarrassed once again for retreating to the past and bringing pain and disappointment to the doctor who had become like a member of our family. I felt that David's future was as important to Dr. Malatack as the future of his own children. "We'll never find another Dr. Malatack," I thought to myself. "We were so fortunate to have him in 1981, but those days are over and it's time to find a new doctor."

David made an appointment with his doctor in Grand Rapids. Grand Rapids was almost 45 minutes away from Kalamazoo. Since Sara was busy with Rachael and packing, David agreed to let me drive him to the doctor's office. I knew that David must be very sick to let me drive him anywhere. He had never liked my driving and whenever we went anywhere together, he drove. According to David, I used my brake too often.

On our way to Grand Rapids, David started vomiting. He was vomiting so much that I pulled over to the side of the road, called 911, and waited for the ambulance to come. The ambulance took David to the emergency room and I joined him there along with Sara, Rachael, and Sara's sister Christy. David was admitted to the hospital and we met the young resident who would be responsible for his care.

"You know there isn't much we can do," the doctor said. "David needs a new liver and we don't have a transplant program at this hospital." He recommended the University of Michigan transplant center; we told him that David was already on the Pittsburgh and Omaha waiting lists. He admitted David to a private room, gave him IV fluids to prevent dehydration, and ordered several tests for the next day. David felt very weak and I was concerned that he might choke on his vomit, so I stayed with him in the room and eventually dozed off in the recliner. It was just like August 1981. The most comfortable place for me was near David so I could hear his breathing and know that he was alive. As evening came and David felt more settled, he asked me to return to his apartment in Kalamazoo and spend the night there. I knew it would take 45 minutes to get back to his apartment, more if I got lost in the city of Grand Rapids, and at least 45 minutes to get back in the morning during rush hour. Since I wasn't very sleepy and I wanted to be at the hospital early in the morning to meet David's gastroenterologist, I decided I was better off staying with David.

The gastroenterologist arrived the next morning and reviewed the tests that were scheduled for later in the day. One of the tests was an x-ray of David's hip. The gastroenterologist explained that when they examined David, they had seen some abnormality, perhaps some degeneration, in the hipbone.

"Is there anything you can do for it now?" David wanted to know. The doctor said no, there was nothing they could do for his hip right now. "Then please cancel this test," David requested. David had first started limping in April 1998 and having seen an orthopedic doctor for the pain and stiffness, he already knew that the only cure for his ailing hip was hip replacement surgery. But right now he needed a liver more than he needed a new hip.

The gastroenterologist accepted this and went on to address the issue of David's failing liver. He thought that we should go to Omaha. He felt that with all of the problems David was experiencing, he would be moved up on the waiting list. David called his coordinator in Omaha and she agreed with the gastroenterologist. She said she would begin preparing for David's admission to the hospital in Omaha. She added that if David was having problems keeping food down, it was time for him to be fed intravenously.

What David had been most afraid of had happened. Instead of moving into the new house, David and Sara would be moving to Omaha. They would not have the chance to spend even one day and night in the new house they had been working so hard on for the last six months. They would have to leave all their belongings packed in boxes in the apartment that they were supposed to vacate by end of the month and move to Omaha, leaving their new home empty and unoccupied. We had all tried so hard to get them into the new house before David was hospitalized with advanced liver failure, but we had failed. Now the movers would be canceled and David and Sara would drop everything and go to Omaha, even though there was still no liver available for David.

David had explained to me that the first patients to be considered for an available liver were the ones in the ICU. Those are the patients with complete liver failure, bleeding problems, requiring a respirator, or with conditions so serious that they need the around-the-clock care that you can only get in the ICU. After the ICU, the patients who are hospitalized are considered before those that are ambulatory and living outside the hospital. It made sense for us to go to the hospital in Omaha. There, David would have a much better chance of getting a liver than he would 600 miles away in Michigan.

Sara asked me to go with them. She was worried about what might happen to David on the flight from Grand Rapids to Omaha. I agreed, and my husband Joe made the airline reservations. Sara's father John drove us to the airport. Rachael would stay with John and Johnie until we were settled in Omaha. I didn't even have time to pack, but that didn't matter much because all I had was the small suitcase I brought when I came to help David and Sara pack up their apartment.

The flight was uneventful. During our plane change in Chicago, Joe was there to help us transfer from one flight to the other. I felt like I was being transported back in time to 1981. Here it was, a beautiful summer day, and we were taking David to a transplant center. I was hopeful that in Omaha David would receive the care he needed to stay alive and healthy enough to have a transplant when a liver became available. After the transplant, we would then move them to their new house. I figured we would spend a month or two in Omaha.

One of the passengers on the plane asked why we were going to Omaha. After hearing our reason, she proudly told us that the Omaha transplant center was one of the best in the country and that Robert Redford's son had received a liver transplant there.

When the plane landed, we took a cab to the hospital where David was admitted and settled. Sara and I got a room at the University House, an old building that had been renovated into a hotel-style residence specifically for out-of-town patients and their families. It was connected to the hospital so we could walk from University House to the hospital entirely indoors, eliminating the need for a car. On each floor, there was a laundry room and a small kitchen equipped with a microwave and refrigerator. It was convenient and comfortable, and the price was reasonable. We had stayed there in 1990, when David and I came for a second opinion about his bile duct problems. Other times when we were in Omaha, we had rented a car and stayed in a hotel. Until we found out more about David's prognosis, University House would be a safe place for Sara and me.

David was in the Liver Special Care Unit in the hospital and Sara and I took turns staying with him during the day. I was there on the second day when a group of doctors, headed by the gastroenterologist who had done David's "beautiful liver" biopsy in 1997, came into his room. As far as I knew, David hadn't been examined by a doctor or surgeon even though he had been admitted the day before. "It's about time," I said to myself. "Now they will come up with a plan to keep David healthy and strong until his transplant." I imagined they would order IV feeding, some physical therapy to prevent muscle atrophy, and perhaps some psychotherapy for David's emotional health. I also hoped the therapist would help us to cope with David's bouts of encephalopathy. The advanced liver disease had affected David's brain tissue, and he'd had a few episodes of uncharacteristic behavior and disorientation that were scary and upsetting.

The gastroenterologist held a little, old book in his hands and started to speak. I held my breath so I wouldn't miss a word. It only took a few seconds for me to feel as though I had fallen into the middle of one of those bad dreams where there is some terrible problem and you are desperately begging the people around you for help, but no one can hear you or see you. This gastroenterologist wasn't talking about liver disease; he was talking about facial paralysis, teaching his students about Bell's Palsy and using David as the visual aid! There was no mention of David's failing liver or treating David's malnutrition and encephalopathy. It made me feel sick. I didn't know if they had asked David's permission for this little show-and-tell. Even if they had asked him, with his encephalopathy I didn't know if he would have understood what he was agreeing to.

We were no strangers to these dog-and-pony shows. Since Wilson's Disease is such a rare liver disorder, David had endured many of these sessions during his first transplant ordeal. I sat quietly and listened, but what I really wanted to do was get up, show these doctors the door, and say, "Enough is enough! David has already been the subject of more medical school show-and-tells than a medical school cadaver! David's liver is the problem, not his face. You're a gastroenterologist; you should be talking to us about how you're going to keep David alive and healthy until his transplant. You should be teaching these students how to treat a patient with advanced liver failure!" But I said nothing.

The doctor droned on and on. Next he was showed his students the book, explaining that this book describing Bell's Palsy was an antique, and that Bell's Palsy was discovered by a Scottish surgeon named Charles Bell over 200 years ago. I was seized with the irrational desire to jump up, grab the book, throw it out the window, and then ask this doctor what had happened to David's "beautiful liver." Just six months ago, this gastroenterologist had performed a biopsy on David's liver and told us that it was beautiful. If he knew anything at all about liver disease, I wanted him to explain how this could be so, how David's liver could be "beautiful" just six months ago and failed beyond repair now.

Of course, I was just fantasizing. Although I felt we deserved answers to these questions, voicing these private thoughts would have been totally out-of-character for me. I knew that medical schools and teaching hospitals were already aware of this dilemma. Sometimes it wasn't clear what their priority was. Was it teaching or was it healing? Some of the experienced teachers forgot that they were doctors first, and that their patients and their families were human beings who deserved to be treated with compassion, respect, and dignity, not like a medical school cadaver that could not see, hear, or understand what was going on. Unfortunately, this gastroenterologist did not realize that he was teaching his attentive students another lesson besides the one about Bell's Palsy. He was teaching them an attitude. Without even realizing it, they were also absorbing his callous treatment of David, and his lack of concern for David's physical and emotional suffering. I knew that this teaching session could have been done more tastefully. When David was in Children's' Hospital in Pittsburgh in 1981, we never felt as though David was a show-and-tell subject. With Dr. Malatack, we knew David was a person first, not just a case. Whenever possible, he used photos and videotape of David in his teaching to avoid parading strangers through our hospital room.

The Bell's Palsy lecture ended and the gastroenterologist led the students from the room. What was going to happen to David? We still didn't know. All we knew was that the gastroenterology students had seen an actual case of Bell's Palsy and admired a rare medical text that their teacher had located from the who-knows-where—perhaps from his own collection?

I received my next big shock the very next day. When I arrived to sit with David for the day, I discovered that they were getting ready to discharge David from the hospital because they needed the bed. A patient who had recently received a liver transplant was ready to be transferred from the ICU to David's room.

"What will happen to David?" I asked.

"He will see a doctor in the clinic twice a week," the nurse replied.

"What about his food? He is losing weight," I asked desperately.

"We'll schedule an appointment with one of our dieticians," she replied.

"But what about the vomiting?" I protested.

"He hasn't vomited today," was the nurse's reply.

Of course he hadn't vomited today, because he hadn't eaten! I gave up. They had already made up their minds. It was time to go wherever we were going. We really didn't understand their reasoning. We took David back to University House and I asked for another room for myself so David and Sara could have some privacy. They didn't have another room, but they gave me a rollaway bed.

That evening, Joe's nephew Simon Boostanfar called. Simon was a pediatrician in Los Angeles and he knew a transplant surgeon who had just opened a new center there. This surgeon had been trained in Pittsburgh and knew David. He was willing to evaluate David and put him on the waiting list. Since the center was new, the waiting list was short. David refused. He was comfortable in Omaha and with Dr. Shaw. Dr. Shaw had assisted Dr. Starzl during David's first transplant and had helped David through his years of bile duct problems. David believed that he would receive his new liver here in Omaha when he became sick enough to move to the top of waiting list.

I knew Dr. Boostanfar wanted to help David, but I think David was afraid that someone might be "pulling strings" for him. It was not easy for David to live with the fact that someone had to die so that he might live. To go to L.A. and receive a liver transplant when he wasn't the sickest patient in the country might deprive a dying person of a liver. David didn't want to live with that. I was David's mother and I wanted the best possible treatment for my son, but he was 29 years old and the decision was his. I wondered how sick he would have to get before receiving a liver here in Omaha. In my book, he was very sick already.

After David went to bed, Sara and I sat on the sofa. We were numb. "Where do we go from here?" we wondered. The only comfort that we had was that if David had a crisis, we were close to the hospital. But there were lots of loose ends that were bothering me. Who would oversee the completion of their house in Michigan? Why had David been discharged from the hospital so abruptly?

Sara was silent, lost in her own thoughts. I tried to work through what was happening to us. David's discharge had caught us off guard, but I guessed that the reasons were related to insurance coverage. Finally, Sara and I went to bed. But I knew that even if I could get to sleep at all, I would continue to think about this in my dreams.

The next day, the three of us tried to figure out what to do. David and I remembered how, in 1981, Dr. Starzl and Dr. Malatack had taken over David's care unselfishly and with a fierce determination to keep him alive. Against the odds, they had shepherded David through the experimental liver transplant process and brought him back from the verge of death. Neither one of them was available now. Dr. Starzl was retired and Dr. Malatack was a pediatrician in Philadelphia. But we had a ray of hope: Dr. Shaw was here in Omaha. He had assisted Dr. Starzl with David's first transplant and he had been seeing David for checkups throughout the last ten years. Now he was Chief of Surgery here at the University of Nebraska. Perhaps he would be David's advocate and see us through this process.

We wondered what our next step should be. In desperation, David called Lori, his transplant coordinator, and made an appointment with Dr. Shaw. In the afternoon, we met with Dr. Shaw in the liver clinic. David was much thinner and more jaundiced than he had been in July and Dr. Shaw was astonished by what he saw. He said, "David, what's happened to you since we saw you last month? You look horrible! I'm scared." We told Dr. Shaw that we were all scared and didn't feel comfortable trying to manage David's health so far away in Michigan.

"You need a liver soon," Dr. Shaw said. We were glad that he agreed with us and didn't even think to ask about the waiting list.

"Will you operate on me when the time comes?" David asked Dr. Shaw.

"Yes," said Dr. Shaw. "You know you will have to take antirejection medication after the transplant, don't you?"

"Yes, I know," David said.

"If only you hadn't stopped taking your antirejection medicine," Dr. Shaw admonished.

I felt bad for David, and I reminded Dr. Shaw that none of the many biopsies David had here in Omaha over the years had ever shown any signs of rejection, and neither had his most recent biopsy, done last month in Pittsburgh. Dr. Shaw talked a little bit about "chronic rejection." I didn't know much about that, but I still didn't like him blaming David for this. After all, David had been under Dr. Shaw's care for the last ten years. Even though Dr. Shaw didn't agree with David participating in the program to stop his medication, no one knew for sure what was causing David's liver failure. David had participated in that program to eliminate his antirejection medication for all the right reasons. He felt he was helping to further knowledge in the field of transplantation and that there was an excellent chance that the program would be successful. At this point, nothing would be gained by blaming David and holding him responsible except to deepen his fear and despair. Even if Dr. Shaw was right and David was wrong, now David might be paying for it with his life. How much more punishment did he need?

In 1983, Dr. Shaw was considered to be one of Dr. Starzl's top protégés. There was a rumor that he would take Dr. Starzl's place as head of the transplant program when Dr. Starzl retired. That's why we were so surprised when Dr. Shaw moved to Omaha to start his own transplant program. It wasn't that there was anything wrong with Omaha. It was just that with Dr. Shaw's credentials, he could have gone anywhere! He could have chosen a larger university or a well-known hospital that was already in the process of opening a transplant center. Instead, he had chosen the University of Nebraska and turned it into one of the top transplant centers in the country. When a reporter once asked him why he had chosen to come to Omaha, he joked that it was because of the lake. There is no lake in Omaha!

I'm sure Dr. Shaw had good reasons, and whatever they were, they were good enough for David. David followed him to Omaha because he trusted Dr. Shaw's surgical skills and experience. David felt that since Dr. Starzl was retired, Dr. Shaw was the next best thing and if he needed an operation, he wanted Dr. Shaw to perform it. We had heard about other excellent surgeons on the transplant team in Omaha, but David didn't know any of them. He was so thrilled that Dr. Shaw agreed to perform his liver transplant that he was willing to overlook any criticism or negative comments that Dr. Shaw might make.

"We can't change the past," I said to Dr. Shaw. "Where do we go from here?"

"Have any of our gastroenterologists examined you, David?" Dr. Shaw wanted to know.

"Yes," David said, but didn't elaborate.

"Are you happy with him?" Dr. Shaw asked.

I cut in, "Is there another doctor we could see?" Then, David also spoke up and said that he, too, would like to see a different gastroenterologist. I knew that we were thinking about the same thing. That little Bell's Palsy show-and-tell session had left us with a poor impression of the gastroenterologist we had first seen in the hospital. Dr. Shaw advised us to make an appointment at the liver clinic to see another gastroenterologist by the name of Dr. Timothy McCashland.

"What would you do if this was your son?" I asked Dr. Shaw. I always ask doctors that question in the hope that they will put themselves in our place and help us to make the same decision that they would make for their own loved one. Dr. Shaw's answer was honest, but not very helpful.

"I don't know what I would do," he replied. He probably had never given this type of situation much thought or perhaps it was too much of a burden for Dr. Shaw to try to picture of one of his loved ones in David's position. Transplant doctors like Dr. Shaw had to watch some patients die on the waiting list of liver failure or from complications after transplant surgery, while they were able to save the lives of others. These doctors had to live with the knowledge that one small mistake during surgery could cause death or irreversible damage. If Dr. Shaw tried to treat each of his patients the way he would a member of his own family, he wouldn't be able to do his job!

Dr. Shaw then explained to us that there was a shortage of donor organs. Without thinking, I decided to mention an issue that haunted me and was causing a lot of pain and heartache for all of us. "What about a living related donor transplant?" I asked. "Could I give half of my liver to David?"

Dr. Shaw's eyes widened. "Half of your liver is about 500 grams. That's way too small for David. He's a grown man." Maybe Dr. Shaw was thinking that I was too old and just didn't want to say so. I hadn't been thinking about my age! I was 56 years old, but I didn't feel any different than when David was 12 years old and I was 39 and we were waiting for a liver for David. I had offered part of my liver back then, too, but of course they weren't doing partial organ transplants back then.

The next day, we met Dr McCashland in the liver clinic. He remembered David from the Chicago 1982 meeting of the American Association for the Study of Liver Disease. Dr. McCashland had been in the audience that day. When he was done examining David, he paged Dr. Shaw. Dr. Shaw arrived and Dr. McCashland reported the results of David's tests and X-rays. It was no surprise to us when he reported that David needed a liver transplant soon. We already knew that.

"When is Labor Day?" Dr. Shaw asked.

"In two weeks," Dr. McCashland replied.

"Maybe by then we will have a liver for David," Dr. Shaw said.

Dr. McCashland scheduled some more tests. He wanted to make sure that David's Wilson's Disease hadn't returned, so he ordered an eye exam to check for Kayser-Fleischer rings (copper deposits in the eyes that indicate the presence of Wilson's Disease). Dr. McCashland also suggested a visit to the dietician so that we could devise a menu that would agree with David so he could put on some weight and maintain it. We left the meeting with a good feeling. Even though the diagnosis wasn't good, hope was just around the corner—maybe just two weeks away, by Labor Day! At home, I checked the calendar. If everything went well, in two months we would be back home and life would be normal again.

We knew why Dr. Shaw had mentioned Labor Day. That was the sad thing about holidays, if you were waiting for a donor organ. We knew that while others were planning to visit loved ones, take a long-awaited vacation, or make one last trip to the lake, all that travel would lead to accidents and one of those accidents might produce a liver for David. Holiday travel accidents were something that most people only considered briefly, perhaps when they heard a statistic on the evening news. The prospect of all this holiday travel made us hopeful and sad at the same time—hopeful that Labor Day would bring a liver for David, but sad to think that someone looking forward to a happy vacation would have to die for that to happen. How ironic it was that, just as in 1981, we found ourselves at a transplant center, hoping that Labor Day would bring David a liver.

■   ■   ■

1981

Ben was the one who first introduced us to the concept of liver transplantation. In 1981, while David was hospitalized in Chicago, I came home to get a few days rest and Joe went to stay with David in Chicago. In spite of the hospitalization and medication, David was not getting better. Seventeen-year-old Ben had been doing some research and suggested that if things continued to go on as they had been, David might need a liver transplant. I said that there was no such thing as a liver transplant. We had heard of heart and kidney transplants, but not liver. To our surprise, a month later, when it was clear that David wasn't going to get better, a kidney specialist suggested that it might be time to take David to Pittsburgh for a liver transplant. He knew Dr. Starzl through his work with kidney transplant patient, and had recently become aware of his pioneering work in the area of liver transplantation.

We were worried about how to break the news to David who was taking his medication and patiently waiting for his liver to be clear of the copper. He would be terrified by the prospect of surgery and upset that he wouldn't recover in time to start school in the fall. With all he had gone through in the past few months, Joe and I decided not to tell him right away. We would leave the explanation up to the doctors.

They were professionals who worked with young transplant patients all the time; they would know what to say.

On afternoons when David was feeling good, I would take him out of the hospital in his wheelchair. We would go to the grocery store and cruise the aisles, in hopes that David would see some food that he was interested in eating. On this particular afternoon, our outing had been uneventful; I had wheeled David along the quiet tree-lined street to the store where we picked out a couple of cans of spaghetti. But on the way back, David said, "Mom, I'm tired. I need to lie down." I spread a blanket on the ground under a tree and laid down the pillows that I had stashed in the wheelchair. I helped David out of the wheelchair and settled him on the pillows. By those days, David wasn't talking very much; he rarely had the energy to carry on a conversation. But after a few moments of rest, David asked, "Mom, I get tired so easily. How will I go back to school in the fall?"

This felt like the right moment to bring up the subject of liver transplantation. I said to David, "Maybe you don't have to go back to school this fall. The doctors have been talking about an operation for you that will make you feel better. It's called a liver transplant, and the only surgeon who can perform this operation is at Children's Hospital in Pittsburgh."

David didn't even let me finish what I wanted to say. "Pittsburgh!?" he exclaimed as his eyes lit up. I could tell that he wasn't thinking about the surgery.

"What's the big deal with Pittsburgh?" I asked.

"The Steelers!" he said.

I was trying to talk about a life-threatening experimental operation, and he wanted to talk about the Steelers? "Who are the Steelers?" I sighed.

David knew that I knew absolutely nothing about sports, so he tried to explain things on a level that I could understand. "Remember that black and gold jacket that you bought for me last year? I wanted that jacket because it was the colors of my favorite football team, the Pittsburgh Steelers." As I helped David back into the wheelchair, I told him that we hadn't made any decisions yet and that we would have to discuss this whole matter with his dad. We were both silent on the way back to the hospital.

After I got David settled back in his hospital bed, he spoke up. He said, "You and Dad always say you want what's right for me, but I am sick and tired of being sick. If the transplant will make me better, then what is there to think about?"

"This is a risky surgery," I said. "It's not like changing the inner tube on your bike tire."

He understood that I was afraid. "Don't worry, I'll survive it. I promise," he assured me.

At that moment, I knew he had made up his mind. Even though he was not yet

13, he had made an adult decision that would alter the course of his life. In Judaism, parents are required to teach their children right from wrong and impart their morals and values during the first 12 years of the child's life. At the age of 13, he is no longer considered a child and becomes responsible for his own life and decisions. It was August 1981 and David would not be 13 until October. Already he was showing signs of maturity; he had made his first adult decision. He chose life! He was taking a risk, but he had faith that he would survive.

A few days later, we went to Pittsburgh and we learned that Labor Day is a hopeful time for people who are waiting for a donor organ. David was put on the waiting list for a liver transplant and Dr. Starzl gave us more good news: David would be at the top of the waiting list for a donor liver.

Later I could see that David was troubled. When I asked him what was wrong, he replied, "How can I pray for me to live, when I know someone will have to die so that I can live?" Our faith in God helped me to answer him. I explained to him that life and death were issues that were out of our hands. Who would live and who would die, all of that was in God's hands. All we had to do was to pray for his strength, to pray that he would stay healthy and strong until a liver became available.

■   ■   ■

For 17 years, my feelings about organ donation had not changed. In my prayers every night, I thanked God for the generosity of the families who donated their loved ones' organs to save the lives of those desperately ill patients on the waiting list. But at the same time, I questioned God. Why did David's recovery mean that someone had to die first? I would never understand.

Now, in 1998, one thing was different from David's first transplant. This time there was no question about the success of liver transplantation. Even though we all believed in the quality of life over the quantity of life, there was no question in our minds about whether or not David should have a liver transplant. The only question was where. Should it be Pittsburgh or Omaha? We were already in Omaha and needed to remain here for a few more weeks. But in 1981 in Pittsburgh, they had kept David in the hospital until they found a liver for him and they let me stay in his room. Even so, we knew that things were different now. Most treatments were now performed as outpatient procedures and hospitalization was kept to a minimum. Even if we went to Pittsburgh, I didn't think we could expect David to be admitted to the hospital indefinitely while he awaited a liver transplant. Here in Omaha, the University House could offer each patient a room with a hotel-type arrangement. I felt we would be comfortable here until David's time came and, most importantly, David trusted Dr. Shaw.

The papers for closing the deal on David and Sara's house in Michigan arrived by overnight mail at the University House. After carefully following the all of the instructions, David and Sara signed the papers. Now, for the first time in their lives, they owned their own home! For six months, they had endured the frustration of dealing with the builders, eagerly anticipating the day when they would move into the house that they had built. Now their belongings were packed in boxes in their apartment in Kalamazoo and their new house was sitting empty in Lowell. Worst of all, they were 500 miles away living in temporary housing, David was very ill, and their dream of moving to their new home would have to wait until after David received a liver transplant. With two more weeks until Labor Day weekend and a six-week recovery period for David, we figured we would be here for at least two months.

We decided that the one-bedroom unit at University House just wouldn't be large enough. Sara's parents were going to bring Rachael in a couple weeks and the small room, with its hotel-style arrangement, was no place for a one-year-old to spend two months. In the University House office, we inquired about furnished apartments near the hospital. The women there were warm and friendly and gave us a list of places to choose from, including some furnished apartments owned and maintained by University House. The University House apartments were specifically for hospital patients and their families, but there was a waiting list for vacancies. They put our name on the waiting list. Another waiting list! They also told us about the Leid Center, a brand new building going up next to the hospital. This beautiful new transplant center would have suites that would allow liver transplant patients and their families to live together. Patients would have the medical care they needed and live with their families while awaiting transplant and afterwards, during their long recovery. Unfortunately, that center would not open until January 1999. "That won't do you much good," one of the office staff told David. "By that time, you'll have your transplant and be back home in Michigan."

We went to see a furnished apartment that was advertised in the newspaper. The apartment was old, it was on the second floor, and it could only be accessed by the outdoor staircase. There was no elevator, and we would have to cross a busy street to get to the hospital. This just would not do! I had hoped for a newer, more modern apartment on the first floor or with an elevator. We were told that, to find an apartment like this, we would have to look in a different area of the city, 30 to 60 minutes away from the hospital. There we would find a newer apartment, but it would be unfurnished and we would be required to sign a lease.

We went back to our list from the University House. There was a "Potter's House" on the list. The women at University House had told us that it was designed for transplant patients and the setup was similar to a Ronald McDonald House. It was located just five short blocks from the hospital. We called and made an appointment with Marty, the manager.

Potter's House was an old mansion that had been renovated for transplant patients by a nonprofit organization and then turned over to the University of Nebraska. Marty Anthis and her husband Michael managed the place for the University. I had stayed in the Ronald McDonald House and the Family House in Pittsburgh, and found both of them to be comfortable and convenient for patients and family. However, Potter's House is unique and special because of Marty and her family.

Marty's family has its own transplant story. Marty and Michael have pictures of their three beautiful daughters in their office at Potter's House. Unfortunately, two of the girls were born with biliary artresia. This was highly unusual, since biliary artresia is not an inherited disorder. It was also tragic, because the disease is fatal, with death usually occurring in early childhood. When Kim, Marty and Michael's firstborn, was diagnosed with biliary artresia, they traveled all over the country in search of a cure. In Omaha, they found the solution. Kim was two when she received the liver transplant that saved her life. (Kim is now twenty years old, married, and the mother of a healthy baby.) After Kim's liver transplant, Marty and Michael's second daughter Lori was born. Lori was also diagnosed with biliary artresia and battled the side effects of liver failure for 2 years before receiving a liver transplant. Tragically, by the time she received the transplant, she was just too ill and didn't survive the life-saving operation.

After their ordeal, Marty and Michael settled their family in Omaha and accepted the responsibility of managing Potter's House. Potter's House was now their home. They lived in an apartment in the basement and they took every family that walked through the doors not only into their home, but also into their hearts, regardless of race, nationality, or creed.

When we arrived, a young liver recipient and Potter's House volunteer named David led us into the living room. I noticed a small group of children watching television and thought how normal it was to see kids watching cartoons. Marty took us for a tour of the house. She apologized for the carpet, which was still damp after being steam cleaned earlier in the day. I marveled at how clean and organized the place was. Then Marty showed us the cleaning supplies and explained that everyone cleaned up after themselves. Since everyone felt at home, everyone did their share. Marty said she had two rooms available, so I asked about the possibility of having my own room. She explained that each family got only one room, but that I could occupy the extra room until it was needed for a new patient. We decided to give life at Potter's House a try and we moved our things to Potter's House.

Even though we were living there, we didn't get to know all of the residents. Some of the patients spent their days in the hospital, arriving home late at night and leaving early the next morning to return to the hospital. One family that we did get to know well was Charlene's family. Charlene, in her mid-thirties, and her younger sister were both single mothers. Charlene had accompanied her sister and her sister's son Derrick to Potter's House. Four-year-old Derrick had received an intestinal transplant and was in and out of the hospital with problems related to his condition. Charlene's junior-high-age son and her sister's eight-year-old son were also with them in Potter's House; Charlene's high-school-age daughter had stayed at home in Texas with relatives. Since Charlene was the older sister, she took responsibility for the whole clan. While her sister stayed with Derrick in the hospital, Charlene cooked, cleaned, and took care of the children. She had a lot of energy and she was supportive to the other patients as well. Soon the boys warmed up to David, and he spent time talking to them whenever he was awake and out of our room. Just as we were settling in, we realized that this would not be a good place to bring Rachael. There was a wide staircase going from the first floor to the third floor and, with Rachael's interest in stairs, we would probably spend most of our time either following her up and down the stairs, or trying to keep her away from them. It was an accident waiting to happen.

David's condition remained the same: the diarrhea, the nausea, the vomiting, the encephalopathy, and once in a while, the anger. He got very angry with me once when I called his coordinator during one of his crises and asked her for help. After David felt better and was able to talk on the phone, he called the coordinator back and told her to ignore all of my telephone calls, now and in the future. He wanted Sara to make the phone calls for him, not me.

I was worried about David's emotional state, so I asked him to make an appointment with Dr. Purviance, the psychologist on the transplant team. David agreed and made the appointment.

Seeing a psychologist was nothing new for our family. About a year after

David's first transplant, we noticed that our family was growing apart. We could no longer relate to each other in the same way we had before David's transplant, so we made an appointment with a good psychologist. After several sessions, we began to see progress. Rebecca and David began to understand each other better and we put a plan in place, complete with rewards and consequences, to help them communicate with each other. It brought some order to our home—not the way that it was before David's liver transplant, but the way that it needed to be with David and Rebecca both approaching their teenage years.

Now, in Omaha, Sara expressed some reservations about seeing the psychologist. I reasoned with her that it wouldn't hurt to go once. If we didn't think he could help us, we didn't have to go again. Sara agreed to go.

Sitting in Dr. Purviance's office, we all had a chance to express our feelings. He was able to help David understand Sara's feelings and my feelings. As David's mother, I didn't have to be there by his side; he was a grown man. I was there because I wanted to help. Dr. Purviance helped David understand that when I did something like call his coordinator, it was because I cared and wanted to help—not because I wanted to control his life. He told all three of us that these were hard times and that we all needed one another and had to stick together.

That meeting helped, but there were still times that David got angry with me for no apparent reason. If David got tired of having me around, we both knew he could just ask me to go home or have Dr. Purviance ask me to go home, but I hoped he wouldn't. It was Sara who had asked me to come. When Rachael was here, they needed my help because Sara couldn't take care of David and Rachael at the same time. Everyone in our family knows that I don't like to be around angry people, whether or not they are my children. But in this case, I could make an exception for David; I felt he had every reason to be angry.

A mother's instinct is to help her child through crisis and kiss the pain away. I was able to do that for David in 1981, but now that he was an adult, I was helpless. David knew how sick he was and all the motherly love in the world could not alter David's perception of reality. Maybe it was my helplessness that was the cause of David's anger towards me.

■   ■   ■

1981

When David was sick, he was thrilled to have all of my attention. Even before the liver disease, if David and I were driving somewhere without Ben and Rebecca, he would sometimes jokingly say, "Mom, let's run away together somewhere." By the time he was so sick that it was just the two of us in the hospital room, it wasn't fun anymore. We both missed Joe, Ben, and Rebecca. But there was no anger.

As a child, David didn't have much of a temper. He was a happy, easy-going child that looked up to his older brother Ben. When Rebecca was born, there was no jealousy. He adored Rebecca and helped me spoil her. He obeyed the rules and stayed out of trouble; we never had to use harsh discipline. He had never even had a temper tantrum! He was interested in everything and loved playing with other children. David usually knew what he wanted and he went after it; he was a straight-A student. He was only stubborn about his food and clothes. He was a picky eater and he didn't like itchy fabric or tags in the back of his shirts that tickled his neck.

When he became ill, he endured everything without complaining. At first, we tried to keep him occupied with indoor activities that he loved, like building model rockets and playing foosball or pool. As the illness progressed, he smiled less and less and lost interest in playing. But he never got angry.

■   ■   ■

Just before Labor Day, Joe, Ben, and Sara's parents moved David and Sara's packed boxes to their new home in Lowell. As luck would have it, we received a call from University House letting us know that our name had come up on the waiting list and there was a furnished apartment available for us. We could move in immediately.

The University of Nebraska Health System was located on Emily Street. Next to it, under construction, was the Lied Transplant Center. Up the hill, past the hospital, there were three sets of three-story apartment buildings. Each building had between six and nine one-bedroom apartments, a laundry room, and a storage room. All of the apartments were furnished. Perhaps it was the age and condition of the apartments that made me think of student housing the first time we saw one. David and Sara were assigned to a ground floor apartment in the third building. They had one bedroom, one bathroom, a living room with kitchenette, and a view of the parking lot. There was no comparison with the view they had from their townhouse in Michigan. The apartment was old and small, but it was furnished. We felt that for the two months we were going to be there, we could live with it. On the plus side, it was just a short walk to the hospital and with the condition that David was in, close to the hospital was the best place for us.

We moved David and Sara into the apartment and purchased a crib, high chair, and other odds and ends to get us through the next two months. There was a sofa bed in the living room for overnight guests, but I began looking for a place of my own so we could all have our privacy. Unable to find anything reasonable nearby, I kept the room at Potter's House.

Sara's parents, John and Johnie, arrived with Rachael. We were excited to see them, especially Rachael. To our surprise, Rachael didn't seem to remember her parents right away. Sara's and David's disappointment showed on their faces. Apparently, ten days was too long for a one-year-old to be away from her parents. However, after a few minutes, Rachael remembered Sara and David and began to warm up to them. We noticed changes in Rachael's vocabulary and interests. She could say "Mama," "Daddy," and "key"! To our amazement, Rachael was most interested in cars and car keys.

We settled into the life of waiting for a transplant, and we waited for David's beeper to go off. Whenever we were away from David, we carried a cellular phone and we waited.

Our days started as Rachael woke up in the morning. After breakfast, I would take Rachael out in the stroller for a walk, while David and Sara went to the hospital. Nearly every day, David had an appointment with a doctor, dietician, or physical therapist. Around noon, Rachael and I would go to the hospital cafeteria for lunch. The brand new cafeteria in the new hospital building offered a variety of healthy food and, best of all, we could walk there. Sometimes Sara joined us for lunch after dropping David off at home. David resented eating in the hospital cafeteria, so he didn't often come. He said there would be plenty of time to eat in the hospital cafeteria after his transplant, during his recovery. Convenience wasn't my only reason for eating in the hospital cafeteria. Each day, I was also hoping to run into one of David's doctors or surgeons. Our presence there would remind the doctors that David was still here in Omaha waiting for a liver.

Rachael and I had a good time in the cafeteria. When Rachael asked for watermelon or banana in her baby language, she attracted the attention of everyone around her and made them smile. It wasn't that common to see toddlers in the hospital cafeteria and strangers would stop to admire her beauty, especially her curly brown hair. Of course, all of this made me proud and eased my pain, even if just for a few moments. Each day we spent about an hour over lunch in the cafeteria and then went home to the apartment, never forgetting that we were waiting for the phone to ring with news that a liver was available for David.

Also each day, on the way home, while I pushed the stroller up the hill, I talked and sang to Rachael and watched the progress on the Lied Center. I am one person that can say that I watched the Lied Transplant Center go up right before my eyes. By the time we arrived back at the apartment, I would feel that my heart rate was up and be pleased that I'd had my exercise for the day. While Rachael took her afternoon nap, I would return to Potter's House to spend the afternoon in my room reading, sewing, or making telephone calls on the payphone in the hallway. I had an extension of the house phone in my room, but that was only for incoming calls. Radios and televisions were not allowed in the rooms at Potter's House, and I was grateful for the silence and tranquility. I also had a small, private sun porch that was no bigger than a large bay window, and I enjoyed my quiet time there, too.

I was sitting on the sun porch one afternoon when the telephone rang. My heart pounded, anticipating news of a liver, but it was only David calling to ask what time I would be returning to their apartment. Part of me wanted to ask him not to call me on the house phone, not to get my hopes up, just to tell me what time he wanted me to return. But then I remembered my blessings and realized that just to hear his voice was a joy! For months before and after his first transplant in 1981, even when he was conscious, he didn't have the energy to talk. Now he could still talk and make telephone calls. Despite my disappointment that the call was not the one I'd been waiting for, I could still be grateful that David was alive and talking!

David was no longer that 12-year-old that joked his way through his illness and recovery. He was a grown man, a husband, and a father. His life was once again being destroyed by liver failure. Once again, he was dealing with the reality that he might die if a liver didn't become available in time and, on top of that, he wasn't receiving the same level of medical care that he had received back in 1981. David had no control over what was happening to him. As a mother, I could not comfort him or keep him amused and busy as I had in 1981. He wasn't complaining, but every once in a while his anger surfaced, reminding me how much he was suffering. I knew that no matter what I did, I wouldn't be able to minimize his pain and suffering or make it go away—even for a little while—as I had in 1981.

As I was struggling with how to help David, my sister-in-law Angie was going through a similar situation with her daughter Elizabeth. Elizabeth had just been diagnosed with breast cancer. She was only 30 years old!

Our family was very close with Joe's sister Angie and her husband Pat. Angie had been pregnant with Elizabeth while I was pregnant with David. Although we lived two hours away from each other, we visited often and shared our experiences throughout our pregnancies. David and Elizabeth, born just 4 months apart, were playmates as they grew up, and Pat and Angie were a source of strength and support for us during David's first liver transplant. When they heard that David would need a second transplant, Pat and Angie shared our sorrow and continued to offer their love and support. Now they were sharing a sorrow of their own. Six months ago, Elizabeth's doctor had told her not to worry about the lump in her breast because she was too young for cancer. Now her doctors were telling her that she had an aggressive form of breast cancer that had already spread to her lymph nodes. According to Angie, Elizabeth wasn't wasting her energy complaining or wondering, "Why me?" She was taking charge of her life and gathering her strength to face surgery and massive chemotherapy. Our hearts went out to them. They lived in Arizona now. With us in Omaha, we couldn't visit each other, but we often talked on the phone. Now, when I prayed for David, I would pray for Elizabeth and her family, too.

Our meetings with Dr. Purviance were helping David, Sara, and me to understand each other. Dr. Purviance had a way of getting us to open up and talk about things without making any of us feel bad about our behavior. He let us know that, given what we were going through, our behavior and reactions were normal. Dr. Purviance also recommended a support group for liver transplant patients. The group met every Tuesday morning at 10:00 a.m. in one of the hospital conference rooms. A five-year liver transplant survivor named Bernard Goedeker, affectionately nicknamed "Bard," led the meetings.

One Tuesday morning, Sara and I took Rachael to the meeting. David was too tired to get out of bed, get dressed, and go, so it was just the three of us. It was a small group; all were transplant survivors except for one man who was waiting for a both a kidney and a liver. As Bard opened the meeting, I noticed how healthy he looked. It was hard to believe he had ever been sick a day in his life. He introduced himself and shared his story; the others then followed one by one. A woman in her late 40s introduced herself and began to speak. She was a successful liver recipient, several years posttransplant. She was upset about the rules and regulations that prevented her from contacting the family of her donor and complained about her unsuccessful efforts to find them. She continued complaining, voicing her gripes about the surgeons and the medical community. As she went on and on, we listened in silence and I thought to myself, "How soon we forget. Here she is, a healthy liver recipient living a good, healthy life. Doesn't that matter to her? How can she forget how fortunate she is, and spend all her time focusing on her complaints? None of these things are a matter of life and death!"

Finally, when it was our turn to speak, I stood up and told her that I wished we had her problems instead of our own. I told David's story and the group found it inspiring that David had lived a full life for 17 years after his first transplant. They sympathized with us and expressed interest in meeting David. I decided to ask their advice about housing. It would be nice to have a larger, more modern apartment that would still be near the hospital. They told us what we already suspected; all of the new apartment complexes were on the other side of town. The attention shifted to Rachael; some of the members commented on her beauty and others tried to engage our shy little angel in conversation. As the meeting ended, everyone wished us well and said they hoped David would receive his transplant soon and they would be able to meet him. We left the hospital knowing that this was the best place to be until we could take David home with a new liver, hopefully in about six weeks.

■   ■   ■

September 7, 1998 was Labor Day. The closer we got to that date, the more nervous we all became. Joe, Ben, Rebecca, and Dave were driving to Omaha together to spend the Labor Day weekend with us. I felt as though their lives were in danger. Here we were, hoping a liver would come for David this weekend, and the rest of my family was among the throng of holiday travelers. I prayed for everyone. They all arrived safely.

David always felt better when he had visitors. The joy of visiting with the people he loved made him set aside his problems for a while. We spent as much time as possible together, and the highlight of our weekend was a trip to the Omaha Zoo with Rachael. Although it was the highlight of our weekend, it was not without pain. Being at the zoo reminded me of visits to the zoo in happier times. Joe and I had taken our grandsons, Josh and Jacob, to the zoo in Chicago a couple times and it was now over a month since I had seen them. Today, Rachael was oblivious to everything except her delight at seeing the animals while the rest of us waited for the telephone to ring. It did ring many times that weekend, but David's beeper did not go off and none of the calls were the one for which we were hoping and praying. The long weekend passed very quickly and soon it was time to say goodbye.

Joe, Ben, Rebecca, and Dave left us on Monday morning to drive back to Chicago. After they were gone, we were overcome with disappointment. We had spent Labor Day weekend in 1981 waiting for a donor liver for David and, like this weekend, the holiday came and went with no news of a liver for David. Our disappointment this time was as overwhelming as it had been that long-ago Labor Day weekend. In some ways it was worse. Back in 1981, we knew that no other child in Pittsburgh had received a liver transplant that weekend. This time, we knew that there were other patients in Omaha who had received a liver over the weekend. We didn't know any of them; they were just numbers on the waiting list to us, but they were numbers that were ahead of David. We guessed that they were terminally ill patients who were sicker than David or who had spent more time on the waiting list.

David's first transplant had happened on September 26, 1981, almost 20 days after that first disappointing Labor Day weekend. We didn't complain. We were just thankful that David was still alive and eligible for the transplant.

Missing the rest of our family and still hoping that a liver would come for David any day, we went back to our daily routine of waiting for the phone to ring. Slowly we began to set aside our disappointment, and we set our sights on a new date. We began to hope that David would receive his second liver transplant on September 26, 1998—the same date as his first transplant in 1981.

We knew that things were vastly different now. When we had learned in June that David would need another transplant, my son Ben had used the Internet to gather the latest information on liver transplantation, the waiting list, and the distribution of organs. As David's illness progressed, Ben continued to keep us up-to-date with new developments. He told us the statistics showed that it might take up to two years on the waiting list before David received a liver. Given the state of David's health, it was hard for me to believe that David would survive that long. David was too sick to read the information that Ben provided, but the reality was that, by August 1998, there were 61,489 people waiting for an organ—11,115 of those for a liver. David was just one of 11,115 other people facing the same situation!

Ben had put all of that information in a folder and delivered it to us, but in the busy days before Rebecca's wedding, I hadn't had the time to read it all. Now, in the lonely afternoons on my sun porch at Potter's House, I read my way through the folder. The more I read, the more I worried. Given the statistics, it didn't seem possible that David would receive a liver any time soon. But we trusted Dr. Shaw and he had said "maybe by Labor Day." As time went on, we came to understand that Dr. Shaw was a surgeon with many patients and he had to treat all of his patients the same.

David finally agreed to let me contact the local newspaper, *The Omaha World-Herald*. I did it gladly because I knew that every time the subject of organ donation made the newspaper or the local television news, organ donations increased. David told the reporters that he had his hopes set on September 26th as the date for his liver transplant.

The next weekend, Joe asked David to arrange a meeting with Lori, his transplant coordinator. Joe and I met with Lori in the hospital lobby and Joe asked her some direct questions. He wanted to know when David would receive a liver. Lori explained the dire shortage of donor organs and told us that if we were in a hurry, we could go to Miami. They were doing a lot of liver transplants there; apparently they had more organs available to them. Lori then told us a little bit about the laws governing organ distribution. She said that the patients in the ICU were the first to receive the available donor organs. That got me thinking. Back in 1981, David was in a hepatic coma before his liver transplant, but still he wasn't in the ICU. How sick did a person have to be to get in the ICU? I mentioned my concerns to Lori and she explained that it didn't matter whether or not comatose patients were in the ICU; they no longer performed transplants on comatose patients. They were considered too sick to survive the surgery.

We sat in silence for a few minutes and I thought how lucky David was to receive his first transplant when he did! We later heard that their were some complaints from the transplant committee about Dr. Starzl giving a liver to a comatose patient, but Dr. Starzl's faith that David would live to play soccer again had paid off! Dr. Starzl never wrote anyone off and he wasn't afraid of controversy because he always did the right thing for the right reason. I wondered if this new policy against performing transplants on comatose patients was some kind of law or hospital policy, or if Lori was just trying to encourage David to stay healthy. I hoped it was the latter. David's weighed only 57 pounds when they wheeled him into the operating room for his first transplant and afterwards he had to fight his way back to being able to perform even the simplest of movements and tasks. I fervently hoped he wouldn't have to go through that again.

In frustration, I said to Lori, "Something should be done about this! David lost all his body fat and muscle before his first transplant, and now he is losing it again! I wish there was a law that allowed patients who have already lost everything once to move up the list when they return for a second transplant! They shouldn't have to go through all that misery twice!"

Lori looked me right in the eye and said, "What about the ones who didn't take their medication?"

I didn't answer her, but at that moment I knew we wouldn't be able to expect any sympathy from Lori. She would never be able to forgive David for choosing to participate in the study that weaned him off his medication.

The weekend ended and Joe returned home. Once again, it was just David, Sara, Rachael, and me. September 26 came and went with still no liver for David. David made an appointment with Dr. Shaw and asked me to accompany him. This was the first time we had met Dr. Shaw in his office, but as usual, David's transplant coordinator Lori was there.

"September is over. Why am I still waiting?" David wanted to know. "When will it be my turn?"

"Soon," Dr. Shaw replied. "We were thinking about you when we got a liver the other day, but the donor was 70 years old. That liver was too old for you." Dr. Shaw turned to his computer to check the waiting list for David.

My eyes scanned the walls of the office, looking for the "Super Surgeon" plaque we had given to Dr. Shaw and all the other surgeons at the 1983 reunion. There were no plaques on the walls, but I did see pictures of airplanes. Like David, Dr. Shaw was interested in flying.

Dr. Shaw turned back to us and told David, "There are only a few patients ahead of you. Unless we get a lot of critical patients, it will be your turn very soon."

David asked Dr. Shaw's opinion about something he was considering.

"Would it be better for me to go to Miami?"

Dr. Shaw was absolutely against David leaving Omaha, adamant that the best thing would be for David to continue to live in Omaha near the hospital. He explained that sometimes when they called out-of-town patients to come for a transplant, they were either unwilling or unable to come. When that happened, they looked for someone local who needed the transplant so the organ wouldn't go to waste. If David stayed in town, he would have that extra chance of receiving a transplant that someone else had refused.

"Since we never encourage any of our patients to move from their home, you will be the only one," Dr. Shaw said.

"Some patients refuse to come? How can this be?" I asked.

"Sometimes there is a wedding, a funeral, or a special family occasion that they don't want to miss," Lori explained.

"How often does something like this happen?" I wanted to know.

"Oh, every two or three months," she said.

I didn't know what to say. A picture on the wall behind Dr. Shaw caught my eye. It was a photo of Dr. Shaw with Robert Redford. I wondered how long Robert Redford's son waited for his transplant.

Once again, Lori went through the rundown. The first available liver would go to a patient in the ICU; after that, to a patient who was hospitalized; and finally, if there were no patients waiting for a liver in the ICU or the hospital, to the next person on the waiting list. We knew that they performed about one liver transplant a week in Omaha, but since David was not in the ICU or even in the hospital, he would have to wait. Part of me was happy that David wasn't in the ICU, but another part of me was sad because it meant that we would have to wait even longer here in Omaha, far away from our homes, friends, and loved ones. I didn't ask any more questions. After David and Dr. Shaw chatted a little bit about piloting airplanes, we left his office and went back to the apartment.

We didn't really want to stay in Omaha, but David felt that Dr. Shaw was the one surgeon who could and would save his life, and he was the surgeon David wanted with him when he went into the operating room. Apparently, Dr. Shaw felt the same way. His insistence that David stay in town gave us the feeling that he wanted to care for David himself, to make sure that he stayed strong, and to operate on him when the time came. So David decided to stay in Omaha, close to the transplant center.

The month of October was here. David would turn 30 on October 18, so we had something to look forward to—a birthday to celebrate. David's condition seemed fairly stable, but he wasn't smiling; the Bell's Palsy was still paralyzing part of his face. He wasn't vomiting as much, but he wasn't eating very much either. Sara prepared the recipes that the dietician suggested, but no matter what food was on the table, David stopped eating after a few bites. I could see by his face that he was losing weight, but with the fluid buildup in his abdomen, it didn't show on the scale. He had a couple of crises that took us to the emergency room, but he was quickly treated and released.

Sara's parents arrived for David's birthday and brought Sara's 91-year-old grandmother, Cora Byrd, with them. Grandma, who had survived her own battle with Non-Hodgkin's Lymphoma years earlier, was in good enough health to tolerate the drive from Michigan to Nebraska. She loved David like her own grandson and was an inspiration to all of us.

On David's birthday, as I reflected back on his 30 years of life, I realized that—like my other children—David had lived a busy and successful life. The Wilson's Disease and liver transplant had consumed only six months of his life in 1981. After that, he went back to the business of being a normal boy, and had grown into a successful adult and family man. Perhaps this crisis would only take six months and we would all bounce back just as quickly as before. That was my silent birthday wish for David, that this crisis would steal no more than six months from his life, and that he would recover as quickly and successfully as he had before.

The hot summer days were behind us and autumn was here. We had already been in Omaha two months longer than we had planned and we were still waiting for a liver. Every day I would think, "If a liver comes today, we will only be here for six more weeks. Six weeks after the transplant, we will be at home, safe and sound."

As I pushed Rachael in the stroller each day, we watched the leaves change color and fall from the trees. At Potter's House, the children carved pumpkins under the supervision of Marty and Charlene. We took Rachael, dressed like a bunny rabbit, to the mall for trick-or-treating. I couldn't believe that it was Halloween and there was still no sign of a liver for David—not even a false alarm! I was used to joking with David about his beeper. I would tell him that he should take it back and exchange it for another one, because it wasn't working. Sadly, that joke wasn't funny anymore.

The second week in November, Joe once again asked David to make an appointment with Lori. Joe would be in town on the weekend and he wanted to talk to Lori about David's status. Once again, we sat with Lori in the hospital lobby, and once again she told us about the shortage of donor organs. At one point, she looked at Joe and said, "You're big and tall, what about half of your liver for David?"

"I have a different blood type than David," Joe said.

Lori said she would look into it. The next day she called David and suggested that Joe come in for testing the next time he was in town. The tests would determine if Joe could be a living related donor for David.

The Grand Rapids Press

GES   © FRIDAY, NOVEMBER 20, 1998

In search of a
SECOND CHANCE

By Pat Shellenbarger
The Grand Rapids Press

David Yomtoob was dying. In September 1981, the 12-year-old boy from West Michigan lay in a Pittsburgh hospital in a coma, his body withered and his liver lifeless.

His last hope was a liver transplant. As he was wheeled into the operating room, his parents did not know if he would come out alive. Liver transplants still were experimental, and no one as sick as David had ever undergone the surgery and recovered.

But he did, and his case became highly celebrated, not only because it saved his life, but because it helped prove the viability of liver transplant surgery. David was the first person from Michigan to receive a liver transplant.

"For us, it was a dream come true," said his mother, Parichehr Yomtoob, who wrote a book about the

Michigan's first liver transplant recipient anxiously awaits a new organ

experience, "The Gift of Life."

"It was very difficult to believe he was going to be OK. He looked like a dead person in that bed. His heart was pumping, and that was all. We never thought he would be able to recover to a normal life."

David Yomtoob recovered completely, and in the 17 years since the surgery, he graduated from high school with honors, obtained his bachelor's degree from Western Michigan University, earned a pilot's certificate, got married and fathered a child. He is a computer software engineer for Smiths Industries in Wyoming.

He is 30 years old and recently had a house built near Lowell, but he and his family have not yet moved in.

That's because David is sick again and staying near a hospital in Omaha. His doctors say his only hope is for a second liver transplant.

■■■

David Yomtoob answered the phone in the one-

see LIVER, A4

David's story whle he was waiting for his second liver transplant.

Appendix 4

MAINTAINING AND MONITORING YOUR HEALTH WHILE WAITING

Controlling the Side Effects of End-Stage Liver Disease

(Parts reprinted with permission from the Patient and Family Guide to Liver Transplantation, developed by the pretransplant and posttransplant coordinators at the University of Miami Department of Surgery, Division of Transplantation)

There will be many crises, as the liver disease takes its toll on the body: weight loss, fatigue, jaundice, vomiting blood, bloody stools, ascites, encephalopathy, kidney failure. When possible, the patient should work with medical professionals to minimize the side effects of liver disease, as this will help to speed recovery after the transplant.

Weight loss

Weight loss occurs because the liver is unable to make normal amounts of albumin and eventually the body exhausts its stores of reserved albumin. Albumin is necessary for normal growth and development and to maintain muscle mass. When the liver is not functioning properly, it cannot convert the digested nutrients into albumin. Therefore, the body steals protein from the muscle mass, resulting in weight loss.

The liver disease patient should meet with a dietician on the transplant team to develop a diet that will minimize weight loss while on the waiting list.

Fatigue

Fatigue is a common symptom because the sick liver is unable to convert food into energy. As a result, there are down days and up days. A hopeful and happy environment can help the patient get up and out of bed and participate in a normal life.

Jaundice

Jaundice is a yellowing of the skin and the whites of the eyes. Because the sick liver cannot get rid of bile, the bile gets into the bloodstream and eventually discolors the skin and the whites of the eyes. This buildup of bile in the body also causes itching. Although there is medication to control the itching, the coloration will remain until after transplant when the new healthy liver cleanses the body of bile and other toxins.

Sometimes patients remain housebound because they are embarrassed by their yellow skin and eyes, but this is unnecessary. It will keep the patient's spirits up if they can get out of the house. They should not let jaundice inhibit them. After all, it is only temporary.

Vomiting Blood and/or Bloody Stools

Vomiting blood and/or bloody stools are a sign of internal bleeding, requiring immediate medical intervention! If you are experiencing these symptoms, call your doctor and/or go to the emergency room.

As the liver becomes damaged, liver cells die and are replaced by scar tissue. The liver becomes hard and compact. Blood that normally passes through the liver on its way from the small bowel to the heart becomes blocked. That increased pressure is called "portal hypertension." The blood backs up into the spleen and into the small vessels that drain the bottom of the esophagus. These vessels become engorged (varices) and tend to rupture, resulting in a massive bleed.

Ascites

Albumin is a protein that helps keep natural fluids in the bloodstream. When the liver is not functioning properly, it cannot convert the digested nutrients into albumin. A low albumin level contributes to the formation of ascites (fluid collection in the abdomen) and lower leg edema or swelling. The belly of a patient with ascites may resemble the belly of a pregnant woman.

The patient with ascites should consult with his/her doctor and the dietician. This condition may improve with proper diet and medications. If the fluid becomes infected (spontaneous bacterial peritonitis or SBP), antibiotics are required.

Encephalopathy

As toxins build up in the body, particularly ammonia, the patient's mental capacity diminishes and he/she may become disoriented. Patients experiencing symptoms of disorientation and mental confusion should consult their doctor. Medication may bring down the ammonia levels in the brain and restore mental capacity. If the encephalopathy is related to infection, the patient may be hospitalized so that intravenous antibiotics may be administered.

Kidney Failure

Sometimes when the liver stops working, the kidneys also stop working even though they may be perfectly healthy. This type of kidney dysfunction is called "hepatorenal syndrome." When this occurs, dialysis is necessary to keep the body free of toxins until after the transplant. In most cases, kidney function resumes soon after a successful liver transplant.

What You Can Do To Stay Healthy

Visits to the Doctor

Even if you are already on the waiting list, regular visits to the doctor and transplant center are necessary to control and treat the side effects of end-stage liver disease. Symptoms may occur with no warning, resulting in crises that disrupt the lives of patients and their families. These crises may cause feelings of fear and desperation, and with good reason. Although panic may be the initial response, it is important not to become discouraged. Remember that many of these side effects are treatable with proper care and medications, and see your medical professional regularly.

Diet and Exercise

While on the waiting list, diet and exercise are an important part of maintaining overall health. Visits to the transplant team dietician can help you develop a nutritious diet that will keep your strength up while easing some symptoms of liver disease. Some form of daily exercise or visits to the hospital gymnasium, if one is available, can help you maintain muscles mass, stay flexible, and have a swifter posttransplant recovery.

Emotional Environment

A positive emotional environment is also beneficial. Rather than dwelling on death and dying, try to find peace, joy, and humor in everyday life. Keep hope alive and remember that after transplant, you will be healthy again and can go back to a normal life.

SUNLESS
Omaha-Council Bluffs: Mostly cloudy tonight. Cloudy Wednesday, 30% chance of showers. Winds 5-12 mph tonight, 10-15 mph Wednesday.

Omaha World-Herald

35¢
AN INDEPENDENT NEWSPAPER OWNED BY EMPLOYEES

OMAHA, NEBRASKA VOL. 133, NO. 302   TUESDAY, SEPTEMBER 22, 1998   METROPOLITAN EDITION 40 PAGES

17 Years Later, Man Awaits 2nd Liver Transplant

A FAMILY WAITS: David Yomtoob, second from right, is awaiting his second liver transplant. With him many days are his father, Joe, left, his mother, Parichehr, and his wife, Sara.

RICH JANDA/THE WORLD-HERALD

BY MARY MCGRATH
WORLD-HERALD MEDICAL WRITER

As he waits out the days in a small apartment on the University of Nebraska Medical Center campus, David Yomtoob wonders if Sept. 26 might be his lucky day — maybe the day that he undergoes a liver transplant that could save his life.

After all, that was his lucky day — his transplant day — 17 years ago.

"I never thought I'd be doing this again," said Yomtoob, 29, of Lowell, Mich.

Yomtoob was a 12-year-old, sports-loving kid from Niles, Mich., in 1981 when he underwent his first liver transplant at the University of Pittsburgh

Medical Center. This was in the early years of the "modern" transplant era, which started with the introduction of cyclosporin to control organ rejection.

His first transplant made newspaper headlines in Pittsburgh and in Michigan. He played a special role in the medical community's acceptance of liver transplantation as a recognized therapy, rather than an experimental procedure.

Yomtoob's second transplant could be significant as well. It could add insight to the long-term course after liver transplants for patients, like Yomtoob, who have Wilson's disease. Wilson's is a genetic disorder that results in the buildup of damaging copper deposits in the liver and elsewhere.

Yomtoob's 1981 surgery was done by a team headed by Dr. Thomas Starzl, the country's most widely known liver-transplant surgeon, and Dr. Byers W. Shaw Jr., who then was in the transplant-surgery training program at Pittsburgh.

In 1985, Shaw brought a transplant team to the NU Medical Center to start what has become one of the busiest liver-transplant programs in the United States. It is Shaw's expertise that has brought Yomtoob and his family to Omaha.

David, his wife, Sara, and their 14-month-old daughter, Rachael, have been here since August. His mother, Parichehr Yomtoob of Chicago, also is See **TRANSPLANT** Page 2

5

LIVING RELATED DONOR
THE ULTIMATE SACRIFICE

November, 1998

1987

When my good friend Sharon Kalling heard that her sister Nancy needed a kidney, she didn't think twice. She went for the blood test, and when she found out that she was a good match she jumped for joy! Then she packed her bags, said goodbye to her husband and sons, and went to Canada to donate one of her kidneys to Nancy.

Sharon was in her forties, but an angiogram, blood tests, and x-rays showed that she was in good health and a suitable candidate for kidney donation. After the surgery, Sharon and Nancy shared a room in the hospital and tried to have some fun during their recovery. The bond between them grew stronger than ever. Sharon returned home a few weeks later, happy that she'd been able to help her sister.

Sadly, Nancy died a year and a half later as a result of complications from the diabetes she'd had since she was a child, but Sharon's kidney had given Nancy freedom from the kidney machine for the last years of her life.

She was the only living donor I knew and she was a kidney donor, not liver.

■   ■   ■

November, 1998

I went and registered Joe at the hospital so the paperwork would be done when he arrived for this blood test. I was trying to "go with the flow," but deep inside I was devastated. My pain and agony were doubled. I was terrified by the thought of having both my husband and my son in the operating room at the same time for serious and dangerous operations. And I was worried about the outcome. What if the transplant didn't work? What if both of them ended up critically ill for a long time? Joe and David would both be left with half a liver after the operation. What if the halves didn't regenerate and grow to full size, as expected? Living related donor liver transplant was still very new and experimental. Not too many had been done by 1998, so there wasn't much in the way of statistics describing the success rate for the donor or the recipient.

I had no one to blame but myself for what I was going through. I was the one who'd brought up the subject back in August when I'd volunteered part of my own liver. At the time, there was a two-year-old girl in Potter's House who'd received a portion of her mother's liver. She had returned to Omaha because of the recurring infection in her central line, an IV tube in her chest through which fluids, nutrition, and medications were administered. She was small for her age and not yet walking. Her parents were hoping that the doctors in Omaha would be able to cure her infection so she could begin eating regular food.

Doctors at the University of Chicago had started doing parent-child living donor transplants years ago. In my lifetime, I had seen many children who'd received liver transplants. None of them had this little girl's problems. I'd heard that other parent-child partial liver transplants had succeeded, but this little girl was the only recipient that I had the opportunity to meet and see on a daily basis. Given what I knew, I had to believe that a whole-liver transplant from a cadaver donor had a better result and a faster, more complete recovery than a living related donor transplant.

Recalling this little girl's experience reminded me that, even if everything went perfectly for David and Joe in the operating room, there was still the possibility of postsurgery complications. Joe and David might have to live with the complications for the rest of their lives. I was worried about this idea for another reason, too. David was not a good eater. If he received half of Joe's liver, how would the liver regenerate if he didn't eat? Was this surgery really the right thing to do when it meant taking a healthy person into the operating room for major surgery? It really didn't make sense to me, especially since I felt that we hadn't yet exhausted the alternatives. We hadn't even tried any other transplant centers.

I am not a risk-taker and what I kept coming back to was that this was a big risk! And yet, even though the outcome directly affected my life as a wife and mother, I had no control over Joe and David, both risk-takers who placed complete trust in the medical community. As the days passed, the more I thought about it, the more distracted I became. I worried that they might take David's name off the waiting list or move it down the list while we were exploring the possibility of a living related donor. I worried that Joe might be rejected because of his age and blood pressure and then Ben or Rebecca would volunteer. Ben was the one that I thought would be a perfect match. He was tall and strong and had the same blood type as David. But then what if something happened to Ben in the operating room? How could he take time off from his demanding job for a long recovery? Wouldn't he lose his job? If something happened to Ben, what would happen to his family? Ben had a wife and children. Did his responsibility lie with them, or with his sick brother?

Who could answer these questions? We were all tired of waiting in fear that David might die on the waiting list. Was living related organ donation the answer to our prayers or was it our worst nightmare? If it didn't work, we might end up with two family members on the waiting list! My imagination was running wild, and much of it was negative.

I decided to talk to Marty about it. As the director of Potter's House, she had lovingly and compassionately shared the experiences of many transplant families. What she said was very comforting: "You have no idea how many people come through these doors intending to be a donor for a loved one and just don't pass the tests."

We knew they weren't doing living related donor transplants for adult recipients in Pittsburgh, and there hadn't been any in Omaha either. If David had one, he would be the first. I started calling other transplant centers to get more information about this type of transplant. Now that my husband was involved, I needed to gather as much information and as many opinions as possible. David could not get angry with me or blame me for interfering in his life because this affected my life, too. I was beginning to believe that before we took a healthy person to the operating room and removed half the liver, we should try some other centers and exhaust all of our alternatives.

I called the University of Miami and asked to speak to Dr. Tzakis' secretary. When I got Jennie on the phone, I explained our situation, hoping and praying that Dr. Tzakis would remember David from our meeting in Pittsburgh in 1990. Jennie took my phone number and said that we would hear from Dr. Tzakis soon. He was a very busy surgeon and I wasn't so sure he would call back.

I then remembered something that Lori told us about a way to receive an organ out of turn. She told us the story of a boy on the waiting list who received an organ from another little boy in his hometown after a tragic accident left the youngster brain dead. Since they knew each other, the comatose child's family gave his liver to the other little boy from their town. When the family of the donor gives the organ directly to a person on the waiting list, it is called designated organ donation or direct donation. This was another new development. Back in 1981, designated organ donations did not exist;

organs were donated with no strings attached. Perhaps designated organ donation would be the key to David receiving a liver. Hoping to improve David's chances of receiving a designated organ, I began calling all of the newspapers in our home town and other news agencies that I thought might be interested in David's story. The more people who knew about David's plight, the better his chances would be for getting a designated liver.

I also consulted the rabbis that I knew and asked for their views on designated organ donation. I knew that rabbis visited their sick congregants in the hospital and I was hoping they might remember David the next time they visited with a family that was considering donating the organs of a loved one.

I had wanted to make these calls for some time now, but David didn't like the idea of receiving special attention. He wanted to be just another patient on the waiting list and receive his transplant when it was his turn. But now that Joe was involved, I was determined to try every avenue before sending another loved one to the operating room.

The next morning, my cell phone rang. To my surprise, Dr. Tzakis was on the phone. He remembered David and was well-briefed by his secretary on our present situation.

"Have the doctors told you that David's operation will be very difficult?" Dr. Tzakis asked.

"No," I said. "We weren't aware of that."

Dr. Tzakis explained that David's best chances would be with a whole liver transplant. A retransplant was a much more difficult operation than a first transplant because the years of built-up scar tissue made removing the failed liver a difficult and grueling operation. He invited us to visit his center in Miami so David could be evaluated and put on the waiting list there as well. I thanked Dr. Tzakis for his counsel, and explained that David was making his own decisions now and might not pay much attention to my advice.

I really appreciated the fact that Dr. Tzakis took the time to call me personally. He could have very easily referred us to one of his transplant coordinators. I was also grateful that Jennie had taken such careful note of my concerns and relayed them so completely. I knew Dr. Tzakis had the experience we needed. He had been part of Dr. Starzl's transplant team in Pittsburgh and knew all about retransplanting several years after the first transplant.

It was two weeks before Thanksgiving. Here it was, another holiday, bringing with it the possibility of more organs for the transplant centers. I told David about my telephone calls, especially the one to Dr. Tzakis in Miami, and I relayed Dr. Tzakis' invitation to come to Miami and get on the waiting list there. David flatly refused to go to Miami. Now that he knew how much Dr. Shaw wanted to be his surgeon, David wanted to return that loyalty. He would not go on the waiting list in Miami.

A few days before Thanksgiving, we met with Dr. Shaw in the clinic. When we arrived, we noticed that Lori wasn't there. She was out of town and another coordinator was substituting for her. I was so worried about the living related donor issue that I couldn't hide my feelings. Remembering that Dr. Shaw had told us that a 70-year-old donor was too old for David, I said, "You said a 70-year-old liver was too old for David, but now we are talking about a 59-year-old liver. And only half of it, at that!"

Dr. Shaw looked shocked. "Who told you that?" he asked. "We don't do partial liver transplants on adults here.[1] Let me clear this up once and for all. No one's half a liver is enough for David. David needs a whole liver."

Lori wasn't in the room to explain, so none of us said a word.

Dr. Shaw reassured us, "David, we will have a liver for you soon."

The agony of the living related donor issue was lifted from my soul! When we got up to leave, I heard the coordinator whisper in David's ear, "So, do you think we should cancel your brother's tests now?"

David nodded, and as we left the room I asked, "What was that all about?"

"Ben volunteered to get tested, too, but he asked me not to tell you because he knew you would worry," David replied, looking sheepish.

My first thought was for Laura. I wanted to put her mind at ease in case she was as devastated as I was about this possibility, and I called her as soon as I could get my hands on the phone. That done, I turned to David. I wondered if he had considered the possible consequences of Ben donating half his liver. I just had to know.

"David, what if Ben had died and you had lived?" David didn't say anything but I could tell right away that he hadn't considered this possibility. David was an optimist and didn't share my fears and worries. Ben had offered half his liver to save his brother's life, but the two brothers knew me well. They chose not to tell me, hoping they would protect me from what I was already going through.

■   ■   ■

[1] The University of Nebraska began doing adult-to-adult living donor liver transplants in 1999.

Around the same time that we were wrestling with the issues related to living related organ donation, other patients on the waiting list were doing the same, some of them with very different outcomes.

Mary Ellen and Richard Langlois

In November 1998, Mary Ellen Langlois and her husband Richard had been married for 2¹/₂ years when Richard was diagnosed with Hepatitis C, with later tests showing liver cancer. Mary Ellen and Richard had each experienced unhappy marriages and, having found love again, were a happy couple still honeymooning when they received this bad news. Richard was not ready to die at the age of 64; likewise, the thought of losing Richard was devastating to Mary Ellen. They both knew that they would fight to save Richard and preserve their new-found happiness.

Richard's diagnosis didn't come easy. The local hospital's needle biopsy was inconclusive. Later, Mary Ellen and Richard learned that the needle had missed the liver entirely. Richard's liver was failing, so they decided to go to Northwestern University Hospital in Chicago for further diagnostics and treatment. The doctors performed many tests and the results were not good. The initial diagnosis was that Richard had an inoperable tumor on his liver. He was not a good candidate for liver transplant. Without treatment, he would live for three to four months. The oncologist/hematologist described a new method of chemotherapy called interventional radiology, which used a line through the blood vessels in the thigh to deliver chemotherapy drugs directly into the liver. The chemotherapy might buy Richard some time, but since this was a new and dangerous procedure, Richard would have to be screened to see if he was a good candidate. Richard passed the tests, and Mary Ellen and Richard decided to go ahead with the interventional radiology treatments, hoping that they would shrink the tumor enough to make Richard eligible for transplant at some time in the future. Mary Ellen didn't know whether she should prepare herself for losing Richard or pin her hopes on this risky new procedure for treating inoperable liver cancer.

The treatment was painful, but Richard endured it bravely. Soon Richard's tests showed distinctly that the tumor was shrinking. That was when the doctors brought up the subject of living related organ donation. To Mary Ellen, it sounded like the answer to her prayers. A cure for Richard! The program was explained to Mary Ellen and Richard, and Mary Ellen understood that if she became Richard's donor, there were risks for her as well, including the risk that she might die or experience liver failure herself. But Mary Ellen concentrated on the positive things: Richard's liver with the cancerous tumor would be removed and 60 percent of Mary Ellen's healthy liver (the right lobe) would be put in its place. Mary Ellen's liver would regenerate and, in two to four weeks, the remaining left lobe would grow back to normal size and fill in the empty space. Doctors told Mary Ellen that the death rate among donors was 2 in 125 for the living donor transplants being performed in the U.S. at the time; but to Mary Ellen, the possibility of death from the surgery was as remote as the possibility of dying in an airplane crash. She was so overjoyed by the hope that this surgery offered for saving her husband's life and continuing her happy marriage that nothing else mattered.

Mary Ellen's mother didn't like the idea because she thought it was too great a risk, but Mary Ellen's only concern was for Richard and his recovery. Since Richard had never been put on the waiting list for a cadaver liver, Mary Ellen knew that this was the only chance for him.

Mary Ellen and Richard talked with their doctors about meeting other living donors in the area and were told that the only other living donors in Chicago were parents who had given a small portion of their liver to save their child. Mary Ellen and Richard would be the first living donor adult-to-adult liver transplant at Northwestern Memorial Hospital. There had, however, been one other such surgery at another local hospital that summer. Mary Ellen and Richard asked several times to speak to Northwestern's adult-to-child donors, but somehow the contact information never seemed to materialize. They were so wrapped up in Richard's illness, his care, and the hope this cure offered that they didn't pursue it any further.

The test results came back and showed that Mary Ellen was a perfect match, so there was nothing else to worry about. Mary Ellen had complete trust in the transplant team of experienced surgeons. Richard's pretransplant tests showed that he had two narrowed arteries in his heart, so doctors performed angioplasty to open them on August 9th to minimize the risk of heart complications during the transplant surgery.

The transplant was performed on August 25, 1999. Richard's cancerous liver was removed and Mary Ellen's right lobe, about 60 percent of her liver, was surgically removed and transplanted into Richard. After the surgery, Mary Ellen was exhausted and hallucinating from the anesthesia and painkillers. She needed a secondary procedure the next day to correct a leaking bile duct and the doctors put a stent in place to keep the duct open.

Mary Ellen was in the ICU but didn't see her husband anywhere. He wasn't in the bed next to her. The ICU staff had placed Mary Ellen and Richard in different parts of the ICU to minimize the possibility of medication mix-ups between two patients with the same last name. Mary Ellen felt that the staff was ignoring her pain and discomfort. When she complained, she was told that she wasn't the patient, her husband was! She began to feel pressure to leave the hospital. They wanted to release both Mary Ellen and Richard on August 28, just four days after the surgery. All Mary Ellen remembers is longing for sleep.

Five days after the surgery, Mary Ellen and Richard were released and moved to a furnished apartment near the hospital. The idea was that Mary Ellen, as the healthy donor, would take care of Richard during his convalescence. They had no relatives in Chicago. Richard's married son, and Mary Ellen's mother and sister had visited them in the ICU and then returned to their homes out of town.

In the apartment with Richard, Mary Ellen felt helpless because all she wanted to do was sleep. For the first two weeks one friend, Jim McLaughlin, moved in with them and made sure Richard got all his medications and went for his daily blood tests. After that, friends came to help. Each night, someone stayed over to make sure that if Richard needed something, Mary Ellen wouldn't be the only one there. Everyone always asked what they needed, but Mary Ellen was so weak and exhausted that she couldn't even tell their friends what to do for them. The hospital staff had already told Mary Ellen that she wasn't the patient, Richard was, and she felt responsible for Richard's care. She couldn't ignore the fact that she felt sick and exhausted, but she did her best to care for her ailing husband. However, the truth of the matter was that Mary Ellen had just had major abdominal surgery and 60 percent of her liver was gone. In order to recover from the surgery and have her liver regenerate and grow to normal size, she needed her rest!

Thirteen days after the surgery, the transplant clinic scheduled a news conference. Mary Ellen and Richard both participated. The media reported that the operation was a success, and a story of love, courage, and sacrifice.

It was a difficult time for the couple, especially since Richard was in and out of the hospital several times with post-surgical complications. Mary Ellen and Richard were able to return to their own home and sleep there one Saturday night, but they were back in the hospital apartment by the next night for follow-up on Mary Ellen's post-surgical complications. Three days later, Richard was back in the hospital, bleeding internally, and doctors operated to try to control the bleeding in the liver.

During this hospitalization, Richard developed a serious infection and thrombotic thrombocytopenic purpura/hemolytic uremic syndrome. The oncologist explained that Richard's new symptoms could be a side effect of either the chemotherapy treatments or the liver transplant. Mary Ellen visited Richard as much as she was allowed to in the ICU. For a month, Richard was on a respirator and not often conscious. Then, on Sunday, October 24, Richard woke up. He recognized Mary Ellen and was happy to see her alive and healthy, but he was frustrated. He was on the respirator and couldn't talk, write, or communicate with Mary Ellen in any way. The next day, Richard's health began to decline, but he was a fighter and didn't give up easily. Over the next few days, the doctors did what they could, but they slowly lost control over Richard's bleeding and infection. Richard died on October 28, 1999.

After the loss of her husband, recovery was a struggle for Mary Ellen. Hope had given her the courage to undergo the operation and then sustained her through the difficult months afterwards. Now that Richard was gone, so was her hope, and in its place was grief. Mary Ellen returned to work on November 22, 1999, the Monday before Thanksgiving.

Today, four years later, Mary Ellen has been diagnosed with a bone marrow disorder that, although she was already showing symptoms then, went undiagnosed at the time of the transplant. She wonders now if predonor testing shouldn't be more rigorous than the cursory testing (blood type, EKG, chest x-ray) she received. She feels that if she had known she had this destructive bone marrow disease, her decision would have been very different.

Mary Ellen has never fully recovered the energy and strength that she had before the operation. Perhaps that energy and strength is the part of her that was buried with Richard. Ironically, the autopsy of Richard's diseased liver showed that the interventional radiology treatments were working and that the large inoperable tumor in Richard's liver was already gone at the time of the living donor transplant.

The Reverend Gary Graf and Miguel Zavala

The Reverend Gary Graf is the pastor of Holy Family Catholic Church, a parish of about 4,000 members in Waukegan, Illinois. In March 2002, when Miguel Zavala, a 48-year-old factory worker, told his pastor that he would die in six months without a liver transplant, Reverend Graf unhesitatingly offered to donate part of his own liver.

Zavala was suffering from primary sclerosing cholangitis, a rare disease that causes inflammation and scarring of the bile duct. Eventually the bile duct narrows and the resulting accumulation of bile in the liver leads to cirrhosis and liver failure. Miguel had been on the waiting list for 18 months and was slowly dying. By sharing his story with his pastor, Miguel was hoping for prayer and emotional support and perhaps to remind the priest of the desperate need for organ donors in case he was in the position to counsel families considering donating the organs of a loved one. He never expected the priest to offer part of his own liver.

Miguel's brother Eliseo was also a match, but Reverend Graf persuaded him to bow out, telling him, "I can't let you do it. You are the father of four. I'll do it." He later explained to a reporter that one of the benefits of celibacy was that he didn't have a wife and children to worry about in case he didn't survive the surgery. The Reverend Graf was tested and found to be a match for Zavala and on Wednesday, April 17, the transplant surgery was performed. By Thursday, Reverend Graf and Zavala were off the respirators and held a news conference. By the following Tuesday, they were talking and joking with reporters.

Reverend Graf stayed six days in the hospital, longer than the average donor because he had fluid in his lungs which had to be drained before his release. Looking back on the event, Reverend Graf admitted that the surgery was much more involved than he expected and took a lot out of him. It took him eight weeks to recuperate and for five months after the surgery, he had problems with insomnia. He wished that he'd been more prepared physically for what was to come. He compared it to a person that runs in a marathon without training for it ahead of time. Although Miguel Zavala has had to return to the hospital several times for treatment, Reverend Graf's recovery has been free of major complications.

Auxiliary Bishop Jerome E. Listecki of the Chicago Archdiocese told reporters that he wasn't surprised by Reverend Graf's sacrifice. He said he was privileged to share the priesthood with Gary Graf because if there was ever anything he could do for a parishioner, he would do it, and that this behavior was typical of good priests.

Today, both the recipient and the donor are living normal, healthy lives.

Laura and Joan Odom

Laura Odom's sister-in-law, Joan Odom, was suffering from primary biliary cirrhosis (PBC), which had damaged the bile ducts in her liver. The liver bile ducts are the exit routes used by the bile that helps digest fat and get rid of waste. When the ducts are damaged, bile backs up in the liver and gradually destroys the vital organ.

Like most patients suffering from liver failure, Joan was jaundiced, her skin itched, she had muscle cramps, and some days she just couldn't get out of bed. Her name was on the waiting list for a liver transplant, but she was dying. Joan had seven children and it was becoming increasingly hard to care for them. If she died, they would be left without a mother. It was devastating to think that she might not be around to see them grow to adulthood.

The average wait for a liver was over two years long. In 2001, 1,975 people in Joan's situation had died while awaiting a liver transplant. Joan and Laura both knew that Joan's chances of receiving a new liver in time were much slimmer than the likelihood that she would die on the waiting list. Laura didn't think she could bear to watch her sister-in-law die. Laura had four children of her own and her heart ached whenever she thought about Joan and her children. She wanted to see Joan active, healthy, happy, and looking forward to the future again.

Waiting for a donor liver was frustrating and discouraging. What if Joan died before her name came up on the waiting list? Laura became pregnant with her fifth child but felt like she couldn't enjoy her pregnancy, her children, her life, or her health until Joan was healthy, too; she offered to donate part of her liver to Joan. Of course, Joan refused and the doctors wouldn't even consider a pregnant woman as a living donor. After the birth of her baby, Laura watched as Joan's health deteriorated even more and felt that she had to do something to help her sister-in-law. So, once *again, Laura offered to donate part of her liver to Joan and this time she pushed and cajoled until Joan agreed.*

Laura's mother, a nurse, came from Florida for Laura's surgery and accompanied Laura to her presurgical appointment two days before the operation. Her mom was worried and asked many questions about the death rate of living donors, postsurgical complications, and the quality of life Laura could expect after the operation. Her mom listened carefully to all of the explanations, but Laura wasn't worried. She didn't give the negatives a second thought. Ever since Joan had agreed to the surgery, Laura had been experiencing a wonderful sense of peace and serenity. She didn't even consider the possibility that something might go wrong; she just had faith that everything would be all right. The doctors liked her positive attitude.

Two days later, on a summer day in June 2002, Laura Odom smiled bravely and, after saying "I love you" to each of her family members, she was wheeled into the operating room. When she woke up after the operation, Joan was not there. Laura found out that Joan's room was down the hall. As soon as she had permission to get up and walk, she went to Joan's room to visit with her.

Laura only spent a day and a half in the hospital after the operation that removed the larger half of her liver and transplanted it into Joan. On the day she was released, her mom picked her up from the hospital and took her home. Laura was a little apprehensive about going home so soon and would have liked to stay a couple extra days, but the doctors said her vital signs were good and there was no need to remain in the hospital. They said she would recover just fine at home, but shouldn't lift her five-month- old baby during the first month or she would risk hernia.

Living donors are required to take four to six weeks off work after surgery to rest and recover while the liver regenerates, but Laura had three small children, ages five, three, and five months, at home. Laura's mom went back to Florida one week after her surgery and her husband's time off from work also ended all-too-soon. When her husband John went back to work, Laura resumed caring for the family.

John felt torn between his recovering wife at home and his responsibilities at work. He helped Laura as much as he could, but he was holding down a full-time day job and a part-time job on evenings and weekends to make ends meet. Each day, Laura alone had the responsibility for dressing and feeding the children, making bottles, changing countless diapers, keeping the children amused, comforting them when they cried, and preparing dinner at the end of a long day. Rarely did the children all nap at the same time, and there were many times when Laura's incision bled and oozed. She was physically and emotionally exhausted, yet at night, she was unable to rest. Insomnia kept her awake.

The doctors at Northwestern wanted her to return for a six-week postoperative checkup, but there were just too many obstacles. Laura didn't have anyone to stay with the children, didn't have the strength and energy to travel all that way alone, and didn't have a car during the day. The transplant coordinator called to check on Laura and expressed concern over her physical and mental condition, but offered no solutions for getting Laura to the post-op exam that she needed.

Just as Laura felt she was beginning to recover some of her physical strength, she began having emotional problems. She found that she was crying all the time, but had no idea whether it was related to her recent surgery or was just delayed post-partum depression. By September, Laura's local doctor had become very concerned and contacted the doctors at Northwestern on her behalf. This time, the transplant coordinator called and urged Laura to return to Northwestern for both a physical checkup and to see their psychiatrist—something they had never suggested before, not even prior to the surgery.

By this time, Laura's physical and emotional problems had taken their toll on John as well and he'd lost his job. So they packed up the kids and returned to Northwestern for Laura's evaluations. The psychiatrist prescribed medication and therapy, and eventually Laura's melancholy lifted and her life got back to normal.

Laura feels that if there is a message in her story, it is "Prepare, prepare, prepare for your recovery! Make sure you can get the rest you need to heal. Having a baby at 44, followed by the transplant surgery, left me totally drained physically and emotionally. But having said all that, I would still do it again!"

Joan's recovery took a different path. She was so sick after the surgery that there was no doubt she would need full-time care. Luckily, her husband was able to stay by her side and care for her and her seven children took care of each other. She had to return to the hospital a few times for postsurgical complications, including a stomach infection that required careful monitoring. Nine months later, she was doing fine. She now says that she can never repay her sister-in-law Laura for the gift of life and hopes that God will bless her hundred-fold.

■   ■   ■

Dr. Shaw was emphatic that David needed a whole liver, and there was no room for debate on this issue. With the agony of the living related donor issue lifted, my thoughts turned to our Thanksgiving Day gathering. Ben, Laura, Josh, and Jacob were coming from Chicago to Omaha for the holiday, and Joe was driving out with Rebecca and Dave. We were all invited to have Thanksgiving dinner with Laura's brother, Rick Esper, at his apartment on the other side of town.

In other years, we had celebrated the family holiday with joy and togetherness, turkey, and a lot of good food. Rick was a single man, so Laura was preparing the food in Chicago and bringing it along, and I would cook the turkey at David and Sara's apartment. What I thought would be a simple Thanksgiving meal turned out to be a beautiful and fancy feast! Laura's side dishes, salads, mashed potatoes, rolls, pies, and desserts covered the countertops in the kitchen. Ben and Laura had even brought card table and chairs, extra china, crystal and silver. It was another wonderful Thanksgiving, just like the ones we'd celebrated in years past, except that Laura, Ben, and Rick were our hosts.

For the first time since Rebecca's wedding, we were all together. The joy of seeing Josh and Jacob after four months brought tears to my eyes. They were as active and playful as always, and looked like they'd grown taller since I'd seen them last.

The day after Thanksgiving we exchanged our holiday gifts. The living room of David and Sara's apartment was filled with wrapped packages in all shapes and sizes. After the gifts were opened, Ben and Laura set up the card table outside for Josh, Jacob, and Rachael to play with their toys. It was a warm and sunny day. While everyone was busy with their gifts, I took a good look at Joe. He had tried to participate in everything this weekend with his usual enthusiasm, but he looked tired. He didn't have the same energetic glow that he usually did. He had a demanding job as school superintendent of Hawthorn District 73. In addition, this year they were in the process of building a new Junior High School. Joe was attending a lot of extra meetings, taking care of the house, and shouldering all of my usual responsibilities. On weekends, he was either driving or flying to Omaha to be with us. He hardly had time to rest and was suffering from a cold that had not improved much over the last several weeks. He told me that he was too tired most days to walk on the treadmill, so he wasn't getting his exercise anymore either. But like David, Joe was an optimist. Rather than complain, he believed that soon everything would be fine.

With David's first transplant, while I stayed with David in the hospital, my mother and Joe's mother took care of Joe and the kids at home. Now, Joe was coming home to an empty house. After such a hectic summer and fall, I felt that Joe might need me more at home than David needed me here in Omaha. David's condition was stable and his encephalopathy had cleared up. He had Sara and Rachael with him, and he was able to drive himself the two blocks to the hospital for his appointments with the doctors. Sara had met several people in the support group and at Potter's House who were willing to help. Elaine Dietrich, a two-year posttransplant liver recipient, volunteered to take care of Rachael if there was an emergency. When the call for David's liver transplant came, Joe and I could be back there in a matter of hours. In the meantime, Joe and I could always come to Omaha together on weekends. I decided to return home.

It was difficult saying goodbye to David and Sara, and especially Rachael. Rachael and I had been near-constant companions for months. We'd had a lot of good times together and had grown very attached to one other. As we were leaving, I remembered the special moments like when she wanted her own key chain. She didn't want just any old keys; she wanted the key that turned the ignition in the car. She refused every key chain we offered, until I finally made a copy of the car key for her. On cold days, when we couldn't play outside, I put her in my car behind the wheel and she could play there for a half hour or more, turning the knobs and pressing the buttons. Every time she succeeded in turning something on or off, her eyes sparkled with joy. She wanted to drive more than anything. And not a kiddy car, she wanted to drive a real car! Whenever I would ask if she was ready to go back in the apartment, she was emphatic. "NO! NO!" she would cry, and it would take me a while to convince her that it was time for lunch or that she had to get back in her car seat.

I will always remember the expression on her face when we said goodbye. She was standing in front of the apartment holding two balloons, one in each hand. She was dressed in her party dress and looked older than her 18 months. I tried to hold back my tears and not show my pain, so that saying goodbye was just like every other day when I said goodbye to her before returning to Potter's House, but my heart ached for her. She was too young to understand that I was leaving for a long time and that we wouldn't spend our days together anymore. I knew that she had grown as attached to me as I was to her. I wondered if she would miss our daily lunches together and the friendly faces that sought us out each day in the cafeteria. I hoped that Sara would have the time to continue some of our daily rituals, especially the cafeteria lunches, because Rachael was a people person and enjoyed the company of our cafeteria friends. Maybe these little rituals would ease the transition of my departure.

Appendix 5

LIVING RELATED ORGAN DONATION

A Brief History

Living donor organ transplants began in the 1950's with kidney donation from one identical twin to the other. These living donor kidney transplants generally had a good outcome, and soon branched out to include non-twin kidney donations as well.

The first living donor liver transplant was from an adult to a child performed in Australia in 1989[1]. That same year, the first successful living donor liver transplant in the U.S. was performed at the University of Chicago. In this operation, a mother donated a small portion of her liver to her sick child.

The procedure is now common at major pediatric centers. Pediatric living donor liver transplant surgery (parent to child) has helped many families with sick children. With parent-to-child donation, surgery can be scheduled according the child's need for transplant, so parents are spared the agony of watching their child suffer from the ravages of advanced liver failure. Since only a small portion of the parent's liver is needed, this type of living donor surgery has been very successful and has not resulted in severe liver damage or death for the parent donor.

Adult-to-adult living donor liver transplants began in 1995[2] and in 2001, 514 such procedures were performed in the United States. Many surgeons didn't like the idea of taking a healthy person into the operating room to remove a good part of their liver to help a sick person. They felt that it violated a basic tenet of the Hippocratic oath to "First, do no harm." However, the success of the surgery encouraged many transplant surgeons who might have harbored reservations to start living donor programs in their own centers. With about 2,000 liver patients on the waiting list dying each year, liv-

---

[1] International Association of Living Donors, Inc.
[2] International Association of Living Donors, Inc.

ing donor liver transplants were one way to help address dire shortage of cadaver livers.

Problems with Donor Care

Some transplant surgeons view living donor liver transplant as a life-saving procedure and concentrate their efforts on their patients, the recipients. They treat the care of the living donor as a secondary concern, perhaps without even realizing it.

Transplant centers that were already doing live donor kidney transplants had some experience caring for living donors. But staff members at other transplant centers were used to receiving cadaver donor livers in coolers, and were unprepared for the full implications of receiving a donor liver that had a living, breathing, healthy human being attached to it. This was undoubtedly the reason behind the negligence that caused donor deaths at some centers.

A hospital staff trained to care for the liver recipient doesn't necessarily have experience caring for living donors and may not know what to do with them. The prevailing opinion seems to be that the living donor is a healthy person and if they survive the surgery, they should be able to go home and get on with their lives. In some cases, living donors are released just a day or two after the major abdominal surgery that removes about half of their liver and they receive little or no follow-up care. Reasons for the lack of aftercare may be related, in some cases, to insurance coverage. If the cost of the living donor transplant is being covered by the recipient's insurance company, then the recipient is the patient, not the donor, so services may be limited for the donor.

The Recipient's Perspective

When making the decision whether to accept the offer of a living organ donation, the patient's mind may be clouded from the side effects of liver failure. The months or even years spent waiting for an organ on the waiting list have left them frustrated and desperate, and they may not be thinking clearly. Influenced by the complete trust they have placed in their surgical team, the liver patient may be unable to realistically consider the very real risks to their living donor and may never even entertain the idea that a living donor risks death as a result of their surgery. The end-stage liver patient is just sick, tired of being sick, and looking to put an end to their pain and suffering.

Living Donors: The Unsung Heroes

In our society, many people opt not to sign organ donor cards and many others refuse to donate the organs of their loved ones after death. The shortage of cadaver organs is so dire that the medical community is researching substitutes, like the artificial heart and pig organs. You read a great deal about these efforts in the media, yet you don't often hear about the healthy people who risk major surgery and give up parts of their own bodies to help friends and loved ones in desperate circumstances. The living donors are truly unsung heroes.

I had the opportunity to talk personally to each of the three living donors whose stories are related in Chapter 5. Mary Ellen was a career woman and a newlywed. Laura was a wife and the mother of five children, her youngest just five months old. Reverend Graf was the pastor of a 4,000-member Catholic parish. They were three very different people living completely different lives, yet I was struck by the similarities in their characters, their motives for donating part of themselves, their attitudes toward the recipients, and the trust they placed in their doctors and the efficacy of today's medical procedures. I even found similarities in their experiences with recovery. Here are some of their remarkable similarities in spirit:

1. They could not just stand by idly and watch the recipient suffer and die on the waiting list when they knew they had the power to intervene and save a life.
2. They felt healthy, strong, and confident that they would be able to recover quickly from surgery.
3. They were each interested in meeting other living donors, but none of them pursued it since they had already made up their minds.
4. Their primary concern was not for their own health or safety, but whether they would be a good match for the recipient.
5. Their immediate family members had reservations or were against the surgery, but were unable to sway them from their conviction.
6. They were aware of the donor fatality statistics, but they were sure they would be one of the survivors.
7. After the surgery, they were overwhelmed by pain and fatigue. They felt the surgery was much more involved and their recovery much longer than they expected.
8. If they had the chance to go back, they would do it again,

but would wish to be better informed and more prepared.

9. If they found themselves in the position of needing a liver transplant, they would not accept a donation from a living donor.

10. They are each living a normal life at one to four years post surgery, but none have recovered the same level of strength and energy that they enjoyed before the surgery.

11. They prefer not to talk about the great gift that they gave, unless it is in the context of helping others. They don't see themselves as heroes and are embarrassed when others view them as heroic. They treat their great act of kindness as if it were something as simple as helping an old person to cross the street.

Survival Statistics

Several deaths of living donors have been reported in the media and one liver donor ended up on the waiting list for a transplant herself. Many donors have experienced serious complications and/or lengthy recoveries. However, transplant doctors are steadfast in their assertions that the risks and expectations are clearly laid out for potential donors. They say that those who volunteer to be a living donor are usually so strongly motivated that the message doesn't always sink in.

The number of partial liver transplants from living donors being performed in the United States each year is rapidly increasing. This has some doctors worried. They say that to truly understand the risks and benefits of adult-to-adult living donor transplants, information about complications and outcomes must be recorded and tracked in a central registry. Other doctors have proposed that a regulator be appointed to certify hospitals before they are allowed to do live donor liver transplants in adults. This proposal was put forth in the New England Journal of Medicine in April 2002.

Today, in 2003, there really isn't enough information available to provide accurate statistics, but the death rate of living donors, initially estimated at one percent, has now been raised to two to three percent.[1] See these websites for more information on living donor transplants:

- www.unos.org
- www.optn.org
- www.transplantliving.org

---

[1] American Medical News, www.amednews.com, 4/8/2002

American Society of Transplant Surgeons' Position Paper on Adult-to-Adult Living Donor Liver Transplantation

(Reprinted from the American Society of Transplant Surgeons Web site, www.ASTS.org, with permission from the ASTS)

Introduction

Liver transplantation is a proven therapy for end-stage liver disease from a wide variety of etiologies. As the clinical results of liver transplantation have improved and the indications have broadened, the numbers of patients awaiting transplantation have continued to outstrip the supply of cadaveric liver donors. Currently there are approximately 13,000 patients listed in the United States for liver transplant, and in 1998, there were approximately 4,500 liver transplants performed. Approximately 1,300 patients died waiting. The gap continues to widen. In addition, with waiting times lengthening, more patients become critically ill prior to receiving a liver transplant, resulting in poorer clinical outcomes.

Historical Perspective

The practice of using living solid organ donors began in the early days of renal transplantation, before immunosuppression was developed. The earliest renal transplants were performed between identical twins, one of whom had developed chronic renal failure. The remarkable success of this early work, coupled with the development of potent immunosuppressive agents and techniques, led to the extension of donor selection to include other related donors, and then eventually to emotionally-related living donors.

Throughout the development of this therapeutic endeavor, the central theme remained a deep commitment to the health and safety of the donor. Living donor surgery remains the only area of medicine and surgery in which a major operation is performed on an individual for whom it is not medically indicated. The risk for the donor is balanced by the great benefit to be received by the transplant recipient, as well as the donor's psychological benefit.

The record of living donor kidney transplantation in the U.S. has been acceptable for the relative lack of morbidity and mortality in the donor population and the excellent short- and long-term results in the recipients. The recent development of laparoscopic donor nephrectomy appears to have further decreased the morbidity of the operation and made it more acceptable to the potential donor.

In the past, the gap between demand and supply of cadaver livers for transplantation was most acute for children. Today, however, with the widening application and excellent results of cadaveric split liver transplantation (introduced in 1987) and living related liver transplantation (introduced in 1990), children less commonly die on the waiting list.

Although living donor liver transplantation was first applied only in elective cases in an attempt to minimize the amount of situational coercion, there is now a wide acceptance of its use for children with fulminate liver failure.

Living donor liver transplantation in children involves the removal of an adult donor's left lateral segment (segments II and III). The donor operation has been associated with a low and acceptable risk of complications; however, donor deaths have been reported. Technical problems with the recipient's hepatic artery and the bile duct, common in the early experience, have decreased with greater experience. Results of segmental transplantation in children, either from cadaveric or living donors, have now been shown to be comparable to results with whole organ transplants. Experience in children has highlighted the advantages of living donor liver transplantation, which are as follows:

1. The ability to do the operation electively.
2. The ability to optimize the recipient's condition pre-transplant.
3. Shortened preservation time for the donor liver.
4. The option to do a pretransplant crossmatch between donor and recipient.
5. Increase in availability of cadaver livers for the remainder of the pool.

The continued shortage of cadaver livers in the face of a growing list of recipients plus the advantages of the living donor liver transplant has led to the introduction of living donor liver transplantation to adults.

Adult-to-adult living donor liver transplantation involves the use of either a full left or right hepatic lobe. Successful resection of a right or left lobe suitable for transplantation requires skill and experience. This, coupled with the overriding issue of preserving the donor's health and welfare, makes the undertaking the most challenging one in medicine and surgery.

Right lobectomy represents an approximately 60% resection of hepatic mass and has been associated in the surgical literature with mortality rates of approximately 5%. This rate would be unacceptable for living donation. Recent experience, however, suggests that donor morbidity and mortality will be lower.

For adult-to-adult living donor liver transplantation techniques to be developed and expanded to their full potential, specific guidelines for donor and recipient selection, center criteria, and the best approach to obtaining informed consent are suggested.

Risk to the Donor

Early experience with adult-to-adult living donor liver transplantation has demonstrated that the operation can be performed with a low morbidity and mortality. Results are preliminary, however, and deaths have occurred. At present, there is insufficient information to accurately assign risk for the donor.

When compared to left lateral segmentectomy as performed for pediatric liver transplantation, a formal right or left lobectomy is a more formidable procedure that puts the donor at greater risk. The risks to the donor include:

1. Risks associated with any surgical procedure, e.g. bleeding, infection, anesthetic complications, etc.
2. The possibility that the donor will be left with insufficient hepatic function.
3. The possibility of biliary complications, both in the early and late postoperative periods.
4. The risks associated with blood transfusion.
5. Unknown, long-term risks associated with major hepatic resection.

Whether adult-to-adult living donor liver transplantation will become a widely applicable option for the patient in need of liver transplantation depends largely on the demonstration that the donor procedure is generally safe.

Guidelines for Donor Selection and Evaluation

1. Potential donors should be healthy individuals who are carefully evaluated and approved by a multidisciplinary team that includes hepatologists and surgeons to assure that they can tolerate the procedure.
2. Potential donors should undergo evaluation to assure that they fully understand the procedure and associated risks.
3. Potential donors must be of legal age and have sufficient intellectual ability to understand the procedure and give informed consent.
4. Potential donors should be emotionally related to the recipient.
5. Potential donors who are felt or known to be coerced must be excluded.
6. Potential donors need to have the ability and willingness to comply with long-term follow-up.

Recipient Criteria

The following recipient criteria are suggested:

1. Recipients need to be medically suitable for liver transplantation by standard criteria of the transplant center.
2. Recipients need to understand and accept that the donation will put the donor at significant risk.

While it may not be possible to firmly state that adult-to-adult living donor liver transplantation should not be done in situations in which the recipient has a poor chance of overall survival, the added risk to the donor must be balanced with a realistic estimate of the chances of success.

Center Criteria

Centers preparing to perform adult-to-adult living donor liver transplantation should undergo careful institutional planning that demonstrates the following:

1. Consideration of the significant risks of the procedure to the donor.
2. Establishment of an appropriate informed consent process.
3. Surgical expertise in liver transplantation and hepatobiliary surgery.

4. An existing need for living donation versus cadaveric dona-
    tion as shown by insufficient cadaver organs for transplan-
    tation resulting in potentially avoidable deaths on the wait-
    ing list.
5. Adequate resources: e.g., multiple surgical teams, adequate
    operating room resources and institutional support.
6. Ongoing oversight.

Consent

Because of the lack of data, accurate risk assessment for the donor is currently not possible. Informed consent for the procedure should contain ele-
ments as listed below:

1. The risk of death during or after the operation.
2. The risk of liver failure resulting in the need for
    transplantation.
3. The risk of life-threatening infection resulting from the
    operation.
4. The risk of blood-borne infection acquired through
    transfusion.
5. The risk of temporary or permanent disability.
6. The ability to withdraw from participation at any time prior
    to surgery.

Registry

The ASTS should implement a national registry for all living donor liver
transplant procedures.

Summary

Living donor transplantation in children has proven to be safe and effective for both donors and recipients and has helped to make death on the
waiting list a less common event. Since its introduction in 1990, many of the
technical and ethical issues have been addressed and the procedure is generally applied.

The development of left or right hepatic lobectomy for adult-to-adult
living donor liver transplantation has been slower. Because of the ongoing
shortage of cadaver livers suitable for transplantation, adult-to-adult living

donor liver transplantation has been undertaken at a number of centers. While early results appear encouraging, sufficient data is not available to ascertain donor morbidity and mortality rates. There is general consensus that the health and safety of the donor is and must remain central to living organ donation.

The practice guidelines put forth here are intended to underscore this issue as well as provide a mechanism to document outcomes as the area develops.

Figure 1:   Resection of Donor Liver in Adult-to-Adult Living Donor Transplant, drawing by Evangelos Misiakos M.D, 2003

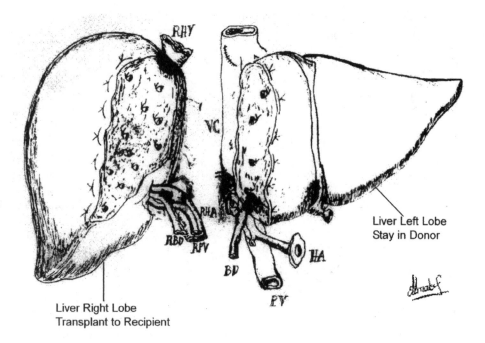

Liver Left Lobe
Stay in Donor

Liver Right Lobe
Transplant to Recipient

LEGEND

RHV: Right Hepatic Vein   BD: Left Bile Duct
RHA: Right Hepatic Artery   PN: Left Portal Vein
RPV: Right Portal Vein   HA: Left Hepatic Artery
RBD: Right Bile Duct

Questions to Ask if You're Considering Donation ©

(Taken from Living Donors Online!, www.livingdonor.org, a Web site maintained by the International Association of Living Organ Donors, Inc. Reprinted with permission from the National Kidney Foundation.)©

In the event you are considering donation—whether for a child or adult—here are some questions you'll want to answer for yourself:

- How do I feel about organ donation in general?
- Does my religion have a position on organ donation?
- How long a wait might there be for a cadaveric donation? (Durations vary by state in the U.S.)
- What impact, if any, will donation likely have on my relationship with the recipient? My family members? Friends?
- Who else might be considered as a donor? How might we mutually agree on who should be considered first?
- Do I have the financial resources available to cover time off from work for testing, surgery, and recovery?
- Am I prepared to deal with the possible outcomes of the donation such as rejection of the organ, pain, and even death?
- Am I comfortable with my motives for donation? Do I expect some sort of compensation or payback for donating?
- Do I feel sufficiently informed to make an educated decision?
- Am I up to it physically? Are there current aspects of my health that I know should keep me from donating?
- Do I have a "support network"—family and friends—to help me through this process, or am I going it alone?
- How will I feel if I am rejected as a consequence of the screening process?

You also need to be prepared for the possibility that you will not qualify as a donor, which can be emotionally taxing to a parent if the recipient is your child. Various liver transplant centers report 50 to70 percent of potential donors are not accepted.

Ultimately, the decision whether or not to donate rests with you alone. However, there are resources available to you to help you through the process. It is now becoming standard practice for a transplantation team to include a social worker or counselor. This person may interview you, asking questions similar to those above, in an effort to assess your emotional and financial preparedness for living donation. This interview can be a time to explore your feelings with an independent third party.

You might also consider reaching out to family members, close friends, a religious or spiritual guide, or someone who has gone through this process.

There are reasons not to donate. The financial strain may be too great. You might feel you're being pressured into it. Your own motives may be misguided. If you decide against donation, consider working with the transplant coordinator for a graceful way of backing out. There's no reason to be ashamed, especially if you've had the opportunity to educate yourself and think through the issues.

The Screening Process for Living Donors©

(Information taken from Living Donors Online!, www.livingdonor.org, a Web site maintained by the International Association of Living Organ Donors, Inc. Reprinted with permission from the National Kidney Foundation.)

As a potential living liver donor, you'll get a thorough and in-depth assessment of your health. It's your health that is of utmost importance to the transplant team. What they want to know is that:

- Your blood and tissue types are compatible with the recipient.
- You are healthy enough to withstand major surgery and recover completely.
- You have a healthy liver.

With these three primary goals in mind, donor candidates are medically evaluated as follows.

Blood and Tissue Compatibility

1. Blood type:

The first step is to determine your blood type. There are four blood types designated by the presence or absence of two antigens—the A antigen and the B antigen. Blood type A means you have the A antigen. Type B means you have the B antigen. Type AB means you have both antigens. Type O means you have neither antigen.

You must have a blood type compatible with the recipient or you will not be able to donate. Here is who can donate to whom:

- Type A can donate to types A and AB.
- Type B can donate to types B and AB.
- Type AB can donate to type AB.
- Type O can donate to types A, B, AB, and O.

The blood type is determined by drawing your blood and testing it.

2. Tissue type:

Whether tissue typing is done appears to vary; some transplant centers mention it and others don't. Tissue compatibility looks at the match of human leukocyte antigens (HLA). Your antigens are determined by drawing blood and testing it. A similar test is run for the recipient, and the antigens are compared. The closer the match, the better, because the recipient is less likely to reject the donated organ. However, developments in anti-rejection drugs have made tissue matching less important.

3. Cross-matching:

The third blood test is an important one. Cross-matching is a further testing of antigen compatibility. In this test, white blood cells from you are mixed with blood from the recipient. If the white blood cells are attacked and die, then the cross-match is "positive," which rules you out as a potential donor. It means the recipient is "sensitized" to you—the recipient has antibodies to some of your antigens, so his/her immune system would turn on the donated organ. If the cross-match is negative, you are compatible with the recipient.

Your General Health

At some point in the screening process, you will have a complete physical exam. When this occurs varies. You will share your medical history and possibly have a series of tests, such as a chest x-ray, electrocardiogram, blood tests, urine tests, and so on. Female donor candidates may also undergo a gynecological exam, pregnancy test, and mammogram. The purpose of the exam is to ensure you don't have any health conditions that would rule you out as a donor.

In the case of liver donation, there are specific health criteria for potential donors. The criteria depends on the transplant center, but here's a list of considerations:

- No heart, renal, or liver problems or abnormalities.
- No history of deep vein thrombosis or history of bleeding problems.

- Negative for Hepatitis B and C and for HIV.
- No history of diabetes.
- No prior liver surgery.
- No alcoholism or frequent and heavy alcohol intake.
- No history of cancer.
- No psychiatric illness under treatment.
- Your height and weight compared to the recipient is appropriate.
- There may be an age limit. One center places it at 45, another at 60. Check with your transplant team.

The Health of Your Liver

Following a general assessment of your health, the testing focuses on the integrity of your liver with these tests:

1. Hepatic angiogram:

This test identifies the blood vessels of the liver. The procedure is done in a hospital and is relatively invasive. For this test, you will change into a hospital gown and lay on a gurney. A dye is injected into an artery—some people feel pain or heat temporarily after the dye is released—and X-rays are taken to determine the mapping of your liver's blood vessels. After this test, you are required to remain immobile for several hours. Because the test was done via an artery, the physician wants to be absolutely sure the wound is completely healed before you leave.

2. Computed tomography (CT) angiography:

The test, commonly called a CT scan, is a sophisticated form of X-ray. In this case, a dye is injected into a vein, you lay flat on a table, and the table moves through a special machine shaped like a giant doughnut. The machine projects a thin x-ray beam through your body and measures the output. The dye helps give more contrast to the blood vessels making them easier to identify. A computer takes the information from the x-ray scan and, using sophisticated mathematics, generates a three-dimensional image of your liver and surrounding anatomy.

The information from these tests is used by the surgeon to determine the anatomy of your liver and to decide which lobe is best for donation. Because these tests use x-rays, female donor candidates should inform the medical technician if you are pregnant or think you're pregnant. Also, the tests use a dye to which some people may have an allergic reaction. Let the technician know if you have had allergic reactions in the past, especially to iodine.

Other Assessments

Depending on hospital guidelines and transplant team protocol, there may be other assessments, such as psychological and financial reviews:

1. A social worker or psychiatrist may evaluate your state of mind.

What are your motives? What is your relationship to the recipient? Are you committed to donation or were you pressured? This interview is an opportunity to explore any concerns you have about donation. Often the transplant team will arrange to give you an out without embarrassment if you decide donation isn't for you.

2. You may also be asked about financial considerations.

Can you get off work for testing, surgery, and recovery? Medical expenses are covered by the medical insurance of the recipient, but lost wages are not. What kind of paid sick leave and vacation do you have from your employer? Do you have other financial resources available if you need them? Do you need help raising money?

6

THE DESIGNATED DONOR
DIRECT DONATION

November, 1998

The drive home was uneventful. We rode with Rebecca and her husband Dave. After three months of being separated from the family, it was fun just to be in the car with them. Even on the ride home I was waiting for my cell phone to ring. I was happy to be returning home and sleeping in my own bed again but, at the same time, I was ready to turn around and go back to Omaha if a call came saying that there was a liver for David. My heart ached for David and Sara who were still in Omaha; they had never spent even a single night in their brand new home, which stood empty and dark in Lowell, Michigan.

When I arrived home, I could see that not much had changed. Joe had kept the house clean and the plants watered. The inside of the house was just the way I'd left it after Rebecca and Dave's wedding. The tulle and silk flowers were still draped from the banister of the second floor staircase. The flower arrangements that we'd brought home from the wedding were still drying on the dining room table. I was still surrounded by all the signs of the happy wedding we'd celebrated in August. I decided that I would pack everything away, except the tulle and silk flowers on the banister. I would leave those until David received his liver transplant.

I looked outside. All of the flowers I'd planted to decorate the outside of the house for the wedding were now frozen. Winter was on its way. Two seasons had passed and David was still on the waiting list for a liver. We were grateful that David was still alive—that was all.

We established a routine for keeping in touch with David and Sara. Each evening, we called them on the telephone and reassured them that when a liver came for David, we would be on the next flight to Omaha. We visited them on weekends, taking turns with Sara's parents. We wanted to give them as much support as possible so that David would have the will to stay alive until a liver came.

Every time we arrived in Omaha, we had to prepare ourselves to find David thinner and more jaundiced. We looked forward to the joy of seeing Rachael, and tried to appreciate the fact that David was still alive and standing on his own two feet instead of in a hospital bed attached to life-support equipment.

We celebrated New Year's Eve with David and Sara in the tiny apartment in Omaha. I wondered where we would all be next year at this time. It started snowing the day after New Year's Day, and all of a sudden, it was time for us to return home. David took Sara outside to talk to her for a few moments and when they returned, David insisted that I stay in Omaha for a few weeks. I agreed and Joe left for home without me.

The Blizzard of 1999 commenced. There was snow everywhere! We bought a snowsuit and sled for Rachael and towed her around outside the apartment. We laughed that one of our old jokes was hitting pretty close to home. We had joked about buying snow tires for Rachael's stroller to get us through the Omaha winter. Now we were using a sled, instead of a stroller, to transport Rachael to and from the hospital cafeteria and support group meetings!

At one of the support group meetings, we heard about a girl on the waiting list whose parents we had met. After going home for her brother's wedding, she was called for a transplant. She returned to Omaha, missing the wedding, but receiving the transplant that she so desperately needed. Although she didn't bounce back as quickly as expected, she eventually recovered and returned home. We could relate to this family, planning a wedding for one child while the other was on the waiting list for a transplant! At the support group, we also found out that the man waiting for both a liver and kidney transplant died of a stroke before receiving the transplants. That was very sad for all of us, but especially for David, even though he hadn't met the man. We also heard a rumor that one of the reasons for the organ shortage in Omaha was that people in Omaha were more reluctant to donate their organs than the people in other large U.S. cities.[1] I didn't know if this was true, but I did know that the hospital had plenty of programs to educate and encourage the public to sign their organ donor cards.

By this time, the Lied Transplant Center I had watched being built for months was finally finished, and there were celebrations for its grand opening. The center was divided into 14 floors, with two floors consisting of 44 patient residences devoted to cooperative care, four floors designated solely for research, and other floors set aside for patient care and education. Touted

[1] In 2002, Nebraska passed legislation allowing people who signed the backs of their Drivers' Licenses to become organ donors without permission from the next of kin.

as the first facility in the world devoted entirely to transplantation, with patient care, education, and research all under one roof, this state-of-the-art building was a dream for any transplant patient. In the beautiful lobby on the first floor there was even a playhouse for children that Rachael just loved!

The two cooperative care floors of the building were designed for hospital patients who have a friend or loved one to stay with them 24 hours a day and assist in their medical care. There were training classes and hands-on practice sessions for the care partner who stayed with the patient in a suite of two rooms divided by a glass door. Each room in the suite had its own television and VCR. The patient and care partner could choose to eat meals in their suite or in a centrally located dining room with other patients and their care partners, or even in the hospital cafeteria for a change of pace. Before building the Lied Center, the University of Nebraska had experimented with the cooperative care idea in the hospital, setting up a series of suites for transplant patients with care partners, and using the nurses' station to provide education and support for the care partners. They found that it was an excellent idea that cost much less than a regular hospital room, especially for transplant patients who required months of care to recuperate from the complicated surgery.

It sounded like a dream to me! In 1981, I stayed with David in the hospital 24 hours a day, sleeping on a rented rollaway bed in his hospital room, and taking showers in the nurses' bathroom. Back then, it was unusual to have someone living in the hospital with the patient, even a parent with a sick child, and some of the nurses were intimidated by my presence. I knew that some of the nurses resented having me there, but until someone asked me to leave, I was determined to stay with David, to keep him company, give him emotional support, and hopefully be a source of strength for him. Before the transplant, he was at first so sick that he had no energy and then he fell into a coma. After the transplant, he was like a newborn. He had to relearn everything: how to hold his head up, sit, crawl, and walk; how to talk, eat, and even control his bowels and bladder. As a mother, I couldn't leave him alone in the hospital helpless like that. Life in the hospital was neither comfortable nor convenient for me during that long two months, and I am still amazed by the strength that I had back then. I know that it was God that gave me the strength because I prayed for it all the time, and He had answered my prayers.

While the Lied Center was going up, David and Sara often mused that maybe David would be the first patient in the Cooperative Care unit. Now the Lied Center was finished and David was still on the waiting list on the day that Sara, Rachael, and I visited the new building.

As we left, I told Sara that the Cooperative Care unit would have been my dream in Pittsburgh. It would have been wonderful to be near my son, participate in his care, and at the same time have a comfortable bed to sleep in, convenient showers, and meals brought to the room. In Pittsburgh, I missed many meals because I was busy with David, waiting for a doctor to visit his room, or just not hungry during the hours that the cafeteria was open.

Sara said that she didn't know how she would be able to take care of David around the clock as his care partner and also take care of Rachael at the same time. I understood her concerns because I had been faced with same dilemma. I'd had to choose between going home with my husband and staying in Omaha with my sick son. I told her that I would be here for them, and we would share the responsibility when the time came. From that point forward, I began splitting my time between Omaha and Chicago, spending two weeks with David and Sara, then two weeks at home with Joe.

By some miracle, I was at home when Joe experienced chest pains on Sunday, January 24. Pain that felt like indigestion was preventing Joe from falling asleep and around 11 p.m., he took a nitroglycerin tablet. He had just passed a cardiogram two days before at the doctor's office and the stress test was scheduled for the coming Wednesday. Joe didn't think his pain was a sign of major problems and he was too embarrassed to let me call 911 or take him to the emergency room, so I called his doctor. The doctor insisted that we call 911, and Joe relented. The ambulance arrived to transport Joe to the nearest hospital, which was a small local hospital that we'd never been to before. Joe was given blood thinners en route. At the hospital, tests showed some dead blood cells in his blood, which could mean a blockage or narrowing of a heart artery. Joe was kept in bed and we were told that he would have to stay there until a coronary angiogram could be performed. An x-ray dye would be injected into the arteries and the x-ray would show whether there was a narrowing or blockage of the arteries. Joe was moved to the ICU and I sat with him on a chair in his room. I couldn't believe what was happening. I was mentally prepared to stay in a hospital room with David through his transplant and recovery, but here I was instead with Joe in the hospital for chest pain, hundreds of miles away from David.

We didn't know any of the doctors in this small local hospital. On Monday morning a cardiologist arrived, hands stuffed deep in his pockets, to explain everything to us. Joe agreed to an angiogram and it was scheduled for Tuesday morning. Shortly after the test was done, while Joe was still in recovery, the cardiologist arrived with another doctor and explained that one of Joe's arteries had narrowed due to plaque buildup. Joe would need angioplasty to reopen the artery. A specially designed balloon catheter would be inserted into the artery and then inflated to reopen the blocked passage. Since this hospital did not have the equipment for angioplasty, Joe would be moved to a larger hospital and the procedure would be performed later in the week, most likely Friday. Until then Joe would have to stay in bed.

Joe waited all day for the doctors to return with the specifics of his testing and transportation to the other hospital, but neither one returned. When the cardiologist returned the next day, Joe asked if the schedule could be moved forward so he could get out of the hospital and get on with is life. The cardiologist's attitude was cold and he didn't seem to care about Joe's concerns. He also refused to consult with Joe's internist who was on staff at the larger hospital where Joe was to have the angioplasty. The cardiologist seemed very insecure, and when he finally removed his hands from his pockets, I noticed that they were shaking. Given his shaky hands, we were fortunate that the angiograms had been successful. I guessed that it must have been the other doctor who performed the testing procedures.

We didn't like the idea of keeping Joe in the ICU for three days among patients with infectious diseases, so I called the cardiologist who was scheduled to perform Joe's stress test on Wednesday. I needed to cancel the appointment (since Joe was obviously in no condition to undergo a stress test) and I also wanted to get another opinion. To our surprise, this cardiologist could get us into the larger hospital much sooner. We wouldn't have to wait until Friday, when the partner of the doctor with shaky hands was available. Now the question was how to get out of this hospital. We couldn't just walk out because this could be dangerous for Joe. We would have to call an ambulance. It would be hard to explain why we were leaving this hospital that was working so hard to correct Joe's narrowed artery. The nursing staff was wonderful; some of them even recognized Joe because they had children in the Hawthorn schools where Joe was superintendent.

I called our internist and explained the situation to her. To my relief, she said she would make the necessary arrangements to move Joe to the larger hospital where she was on staff. As soon as the word was out that we were leaving the hospital, some staffers from the personnel department stopped in to ask if we were pleased with the care that Joe was receiving in their hospital. We really couldn't complain about the nurses; they were doing a great job. We just said that we wanted Joe to have the angioplasty as soon as possible and we preferred to have the procedure performed in a larger hospital. The staff prepared Joe's medical records and the ambulance arrived that afternoon to transport him.

By the next day, Joe was settled in his new surroundings. Our internist stopped in to examine Joe and told us that she had arranged for a cardiologist to see him later in the day. Our internist was a young woman we knew well. She immediately put my mind at ease by telling me that this cardiologist was the only one she would permit to treat her own father.

The cardiologist was also a young woman. She examined Joe, reviewed all of his medical records thoroughly, and, the next day, performed the angioplasty. We returned home one day after the procedure with souvenirs—computer-generated pictures of the arteries around Joe's heart before and after the angioplasty. In a couple days, life was back to normal.

Throughout Joe's heart ordeal, we had been in touch with David on a daily basis. We told David's story in both hospital emergency rooms and ICUs. We also put copies of the newspaper articles about David in the nurses' lounge in both hospitals. We found that the medical professionals in both hospitals were well-informed about the shortage of organs, and several of them wore a special pin to promote organ donation. Through it all, we never stopped worrying about David. We were desperate to hear that a liver had been located for him.

As soon as Joe was able, we returned to Omaha. We had only been away a couple of weeks, but things had changed while we were gone. David's physical therapy sessions had been discontinued. He was told, "Now that you know how to exercise, you can use your pass for the University Gym and exercise on your own." The physical therapy sessions had been David's only contact with recent transplant recipients. Seeing these other transplant patients on the road to recovery had been David's inspiration, keeping his hope alive that soon his turn would come. Joe and I were disappointed about this new development, but could only guess that David's insurance had stopped paying for the physical therapy sessions.

David tried using the gym to continue his exercise sessions, but on some days it would take him hours to complete the repetitions of a simple exercise. With no one to encourage him and urge him on when he felt tired, he took frequent rest breaks and sometimes fell asleep on the couch at the gym while resting.

By February, I had established a routine. I would spend two weeks at home with Joe, then two weeks in Omaha with David, Sara, and Rachael. David was seeing his doctor once a month, with trips to the emergency room in between to manage the crises brought on by his liver failure. During my weeks in Omaha, Sara, Rachael and I attended the support group meetings whenever we could. The faces were usually the same, but at one of the February meetings, we learned the sad news that Bard, the dynamic leader of our support group, had developed a cancerous tumor in his liver. The surgeons were hoping the tumor could be removed surgically. We also heard that Walter Payton, a famous football player, had been put on the waiting list for a liver at the Mayo Clinic. His liver disease was explained as a stricture of the bile duct. We began to see him on all the television talk shows and we could see that he had lost a lot of weight. When he appeared on the Larry King Live talk show and they began taking calls from viewers, I tried very hard to get through. I wanted to explain the possibility of direct organ donation to Mr. Payton and to the viewing public. With all the publicity Walter Payton was getting, I felt there was a good possibility that he might receive a designated organ from someone in Chicago. Knowing that they could save Walter Payton's life with a direct donation might be a strong motivating factor for someone considering donating a loved one's organs. Unfortunately, my call did not get through. But I later learned that Walter Payton, like David, preferred to wait his turn and did not wish to receive special treatment.

Unless you were hospitalized in critical condition in the ICU, the waiting list operated on a "first come, first serve" basis. David was living a miserable life and seemed to be heading for a slow, miserable death. Without a dramatic change in David's condition that required hospitalization and landed him in the ICU still healthy enough to be a good candidate, there was a very good chance that he might die while waiting his turn. David's liver disease hadn't landed him in the ICU back in 1981, either. While most Wilson's Disease patients who presented with liver failure died in two or three days, David had lived six months. Even when he was in a coma, he stayed in a regular hospital room, not critical enough to require the ICU. I was worried that the same thing might happen this time, except that now they no longer operated on comatose patients. Dr. Shaw wanted to fulfill David's wish and be his transplant surgeon, but despite our hopes and Dr. Shaw's encouragement, David's turn just wasn't coming up. I had to believe that there were others ahead of David on the list that had been waiting months or even years longer.[1] UNOS closely supervised the transplant centers, and everyone knew that centers that flouted the laws could be closed

---

[1] In 2004, the organ placement process changed. See Appendix 3B

down. We told all of our friends and relatives about direct donation and hoped that a designated liver would save David's life.

■   ■   ■

The phone rang. It was my husband's niece Diane calling from Los Angeles. She told us about the relative of a friend, a young woman who had just been pronounced brain dead. The 30-year-old woman was of average size and her blood type was O-positive—the same blood type as David! Diane was wondering what, if anything, she should do. I explained that one of the doctors or a representative from the Organ Procurement Office should approach the family and broach the subject of organ donation. If they were receptive, then perhaps someone could talk to them about David. Diane's husband Simon and her son Bobby were both doctors, and Diane said that one of them would follow up on this potential donor for David.

When I hung up the phone, I reminded myself not to get my hopes up too much. Even though this woman was a perfect match, her family might not be interested in organ donation. And even though David was sick and tired of being sick, he might not agree to accept a designated organ.

Joe and I approached David cautiously with the news and, as I suspected, he did not like the idea of accepting an organ out of turn. Joe and I reasoned with him. We explained that the woman's family might not know much about organ donation and that unless they knew of someone who needed an organ, they might not otherwise consider donating. To them, David was like a "friend of a friend." If they agreed to donate a liver for David, they might also donate other organs and save other lives.

David finally agreed and said he would accept a designated liver from the woman in California, but disappointment followed shortly thereafter. Diane reported that both Simon and Bobby tried to contact the doctors caring for this young woman. They were told that the family of the patient was in no condition to consider organ donation. The patient's husband was distraught and grief-stricken and her mother was in denial. The mother was having trouble accepting the concept of brain death and wanted to take her daughter home with her and care for her until she awakened. The hospital had no policy governing whether or how to approach families under these circumstances. Despite the efforts of Simon, Bobby, and Diane, the hospital decided that it would be best not to raise the subject of organ donation with this family. I was tempted to fly to Los Angeles and talk to the family myself, but I knew that when I was face-to-face with the woman's mother, I wouldn't be able to get the words out of my mouth. I still felt the same way I'd felt back in 1981, when I met David's donor in the Pittsburgh ICU: I had a dying son, they had a dying daughter the same age and blood type, and we were both praying for a miracle. Who was I to try to tell a mother that her child was not going to wake up? I was waiting for the angel that would save my son's life, but no matter how desperate I was for David, I just couldn't do that.

I did the same thing that I did in 1981. I prayed for the patient and her family, and I put the rest in God's hands. Diane, Bobby, Simon, Joe, and I had done everything we could reasonably do. If God meant for David to have this liver, then it would happen, just as it had in Pittsburgh in 1981.

A few days later, we knew that this wasn't going to be David's time. We heard that the young woman in California had died without anyone approaching her family about the subject of organ donation. She had taken all of her organs to the grave. Even though we were disappointed, I still felt that direct organ donation was a good concept and it was only a matter of time before we started hearing more about it.

■　■　■

2001

In the summer 2001, Anna Esparza was all over the news in Chicago. Anna's parents were undocumented immigrants and 11-year-old Anna needed a liver transplant. The local hospital did not put her on the waiting list for a transplant because Anna's parents did not have medical insurance. Medicaid was not an option either because Anna was not an American citizen. Without someone to pay for the procedure, which might cost upwards of half a million dollars, Anna would die. A Hispanic reporter took up her cause and told her story on television, on the radio, and in the newspaper. One Hispanic neighborhood had a block party to raise money for Anna's transplant and other neighborhoods soon followed suit. Anna's fund began to grow. Then, Dr. Andreas Tzakis, the head of the liver transplant team at the University of Miami, heard Anna's story. Dr. Tzakis invited Anna to come to Miami to be evaluated and put on the waiting list at his center. When the reporters tracked Dr. Tzakis down and asked who would pay for the transplant, his answer was: "First we will take care of Anna, then we will worry about the finances."

Anna's fund grew steadily throughout the summer, fed by the nickels and dimes collected at block parties in the Hispanic community. Then, just before August, a Hispanic family that had met Anna and supported the fundraising efforts had their own tragedy. Their 17-year-old son was declared brain dead after a tragic accident.

People were saying that the 17-year-old had talked to Anna during one of the fundrais-
ers and encouraged her, telling her, "Hang in there. Everything will be okay soon."
When the subject of organ donation was raised with the boy's parents, they remem-
bered Anna and their son's encouraging words to her. They asked for his liver to be
given to Anna. Incredibly, blood tests showed that everything matched except the
liver's size; it was too big for Anna. When this was reported to Dr. Tzakis in Miami,
he said that Anna would do just fine with half the liver and he had another patient
that would benefit from the other half. On August 1, 2001, the liver was flown to
Jackson Memorial Hospital in Miami where surgery was performed. Half of the liver
went to Anna and the other half was transplanted into a 49-year-old woman from
the waiting list there. Two lives were saved!

During Anna's recovery, the fundraising continued until enough money was
raised to pay for all of Anna's transplant expenses. A few months after the operation,
Anna returned home, went back to school, and started a normal life.

When I met Anna in January 2002, she looked great and she expressed her grat-
itude for the people who had raised money and to everyone else who helped to make
her transplant possible. She was especially grateful to Dr. Tzakis and the transplant
team in Miami but, most of all, she was thankful for the family that had donated a
liver directly to her. She hoped that she would some day be able to meet them so that
she could thank them in person.

■   ■   ■

Our disappointment for David didn't last long. We had been careful not
to get our hopes for the designated liver too high. If that had been the right
liver for David, God would have shown us the way. Instead, he sent us
inspiration that reinforced our belief that miracles do happen.

We heard the true story of two sisters. One sister needed a liver and a
kidney in one part of the country, so the other one was flying across country
to donate one of her kidneys to her sister. On the airplane, the healthy sister
struck up a conversation with the man next to her. She found that the man
was on his way to bury his nephew, who had been pronounced brain dead
after a tragic accident. She, in turn, shared the reason for her travel. The man
realized that donor organs must be in extremely short supply if this woman
was flying across the country to become a living donor! He asked about the
possibility of donating his nephew's organs to save the woman's sister, if it
wasn't too late. The two seatmates used the AirPhone on the plane and
found that it wasn't too late—the man's nephew was still connected to life
support. They got the ball rolling on tests that would determine whether the

man's nephew was a good match for the woman's sister and by the time the airplane landed, all the arrangements were made! The man's nephew became an organ donor for the sister of the woman who was sitting next to him on the airplane.

In a few weeks, we saw the recipient and her sister on television along with the uncle of the donor. The recipient looked healthy and vibrant as she publicly thanked the man who had donated his nephew's organs.

Stories like this kept our hopes high and reinforced our belief in miracles. If it wasn't David's time to die, his salvation might come in the most unexpected of ways.

Appendix 6

THE DONOR

The Shortage of Donor Organs

Seventeen people die each day while waiting for an organ, and every 13 minutes a new name is added to the national waiting list for organs. The shortage of organs is so desperate that as of early 2004, nearly 84,000 people were waiting for an organ. These numbers are ever-increasing. There are organizations all over the country that educate the public about the importance of organ donation and the desperate need for donors. These campaigns have resulted in more than 80,000 cadaveric donors over the years, but thousands of potential donors still take their organs to the grave.

As this UNOS graph[1] shows, the demand for organs has risen sharply, while the number of organ donors has remained relatively constant:

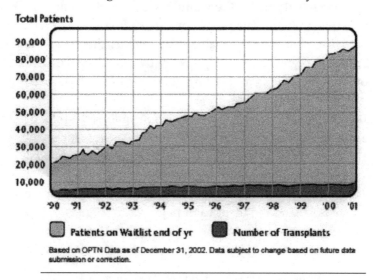

Total Patients

Patients on Waitlist end of yr   Number of Transplants

Based on OPTN Data as of December 31, 2002. Data subject to change based on future data submission or correction.

---

[1] © 2003 United Network for Organ Sharing. All rights reserved "Help Save a Life: Promote Organ Donation," United Network for Organ Sharing, http://www.unos.org/helpSaveALife/promoteOrganDonation/. (1/6/2004).

Out of a potential 15,000 deceased, brain-dead organ donors each year, on average no more than 50 percent of those families from whom donation is requested agree to donate.[2] When you consider that not all families of potential donors are approached to request organ donation, the percentage of actual cadaver organ donors falls significantly below 50 percent.

No one knows exactly why the number of actual donors is so low compared to the number of potential donors. Sometimes hospitals fail to approach the family of a potential donor; other times, the family simply declines. In any case, the efficacy of our organ donation policies is being hotly debated in the medical community right now. Some say current organ donation policies are costing up to 6,000 American lives per year, and that by the time policies are reformed, more Americans will die than died in the entire Vietnam War!

Right now, there are only two motivations for donating the organs of a loved one after brain death has occurred:

1. Honoring the stated wishes of the loved one to become an organ donor after death.

2. Altruism – an unselfish concern for the welfare of others in which the family chooses to save the lives of others so that something good will come out of their tragedy and grief.

Unfortunately, in the cases of many potential organ donors, these reasons are not proving to be motivation enough. The medical community that watches its patients dying on the waiting list year after year is looking for solutions to this problem. The people on the waiting list are also desperate. If you ask dying people on the waiting list whether they are willing to pay for the lifesaving organs they need, most of them will say yes, even though they know that the buying and selling of body parts sounds gruesome and some may think it is immoral.

In 2002, the American Medical Association endorsed a pilot program to examine the advisability of providing incentives for supplying organs. UNOS and the American Society of Transplant Surgeons have also made similar proposals. One popular suggestion proposes offering a few thousand dollars to offset the funeral costs of the deceased donor. However, there is some fierce opposition to the idea of payment for organs. The American College of Surgeons and the National Kidney Foundation have both come out against the idea of providing any form of payment as incentive.

[2] URREA; UNOS. 2002 Annual Report of the U.S. Organ Procurement and Transplantation Network and the Scientific Registry of Transplant Recipients: Transplant Data 1992-2001 [Internet]. Rockville (MD): HHS/HRSA/OSP/DOT; 2003 [modified 2003 Feb 18; cited 2004 Jan 6]. Available from: http://www.optn.org/data/annualReport.asp

So far, no one has suggested providing financial incentives to living donors. In fact, one of the biggest problems with the existing system is illustrated by the data below: because of the shortage of cadaver organ donors, more and more living people are choosing to assume the very real risks associated with living donor surgery to become organ donors for loved ones!

Donors Recovered in the U.S. by Donor Type[3]

Donors Recovered : January 1, 1988 - October 31, 2003
Based on OPTN data as of December 26, 2003
Data subject to change based on future data submission or correction.

		2003	2002	2001	2000	1999	1998	1997	1996
TO DATE ALL DONORS	**144,372**	9,845	12,805	12,638	11,855	10,825	10,351	9,530	9,197
DECADE DONORS	**82,536**	4,804	6,187	6,080	5,985	5,824	5,794	5,478	5,416
LIVING DONORS	**61,836**	5,041	6,618	6,558	5,870	5,001	4,557	4,052	3,781

	1995	1994	1993	1992	1991	1990	1989	1988
ALL DONORS	8,850	8,201	7,766	7,092	6,951	6,633	5,929	5,904
DECEASED DONORS	5,362	5,099	4,861	4,520	4,526	4,509	4,011	4,080
LIVING DONORS	3,488	3,102	2,905	2,572	2,425	2,124	1,918	1,824

The Family's Perspective

Donors are people in good health who have died suddenly, often through accidents, and have been declared "brain dead." In this condition, brain function has permanently ceased but the heart and lungs continue to function with the use of artificial life supports.

When medical personnel treat a patient, they don't think of the patient in terms of organ donation. To the best of their ability, medical professionals use their skills to save the patient's life and preserve his/her quality of life. When that is impossible, doctors run all the necessary tests and exhaust all resources to be sure the patient will never be able to breathe on his/her own, before declaring him/her brain dead.

When a patient is pronounced brain dead, it usually comes as a complete shock to the family. A family member who only a short time ago was healthy, active, and enjoying life is suddenly hospitalized after a gunshot wound, bad asthma attack, or tragic accident. The person might look so per-

[3] © 2003 United Networrk for Organ Sharing. All rights reserved. "National Data," The Organ Procuredment and Transplantation Network.
<http://www.optn.org/latestData/rptData.asp>(1/6/2004)

fectly healthy and peaceful lying in bed with a respirator breathing for them and stimulating their heart to beat that it can be extremely difficult for families with no experience or understanding of brain death to accept this diagnosis. Their instinct is that if they just take the patient home to an environment of tranquility, love, and comfort, the comatose patient will eventually regain consciousness and reclaim their former life. How can they agree to donate organs when they are still waiting for their loved one to sit up and open their eyes?

That is why it is so important for the subject of brain death to be discussed at home during good times when everyone is healthy. After researching the facts and making an informed decision, parents should discuss their wishes regarding brain death, life support, and organ donation with their children and share the reasons for their decisions. Adult children should be encouraged to do the same for themselves. It is extremely difficult for grief-stricken family members to make major decisions of this nature without knowing the wishes of their loved one. Religious ethical teachings, laws governing death and burial, and modern conventions provide a framework for grieving relatives to get through the loss of a loved one. However, deciding when to remove a loved one from life support and whether to donate his/her organs—these are much more personal decisions that families must decide for themselves.

Direct Donation or Designated Donors

Sometimes when a family member is on the waiting list, another member of the same family dies in a tragic accident and becomes an organ donor. Years ago, a father was on the waiting list for a heart transplant when his daughter died in a car accident. Upon her death, the daughter became an organ donor. Since she was a good match for her father, her heart was donated directly to her father out of turn and his wait was over.

In a community that is praying for or raising funds for a patient on the waiting list, the publicity that this patient receives may allow him to receive an organ out of turn. When a member of the community dies in a tragic accident and becomes an organ donor, the family may remember the patient on the waiting list and wish to donate the organs to someone that they know. If it is a good match, then the person who is designated as the organ recipient may receive his transplant out of turn, as happened to Anna Esparza as described earlier in Chapter 6.

Twenty years ago, this was not possible. Families that donated the organs of a loved one donated them with no strings attached. However, laws have changed. Now, the next of kin can designate or directly give the organ to someone they know on the waiting list. From our experience, we know that in many cases the next of kin may never be asked to donate the organs of a deceased loved one, but families should know that they have the right to make a direct donation.

Recipients who receive a direct donation should not feel guilty about receiving an organ out of turn simply because there is a good possibility that the family of the organ donor may never have considered organ donation at all if not for hearing the story of the patient to whom they donated the organ.

Myth and Fact about Becoming an Organ Donor

(Reprinted from the Coalition on Donation Web site, www.shareyourlife.org, with permission from UNOS)

Myth: If emergency room doctors know you're an organ donor, they won't work as hard to save you.

Fact: If you are sick or injured and admitted to the hospital, the number one priority is to save your life. Organ donation can only be considered if you die and after your family has been consulted.

Myth: When you're waiting for a transplant, your financial status or celebrity status is as important as your medical status.

Fact: When you are on the transplant waiting list for a donor organ, what really counts is the severity of your illness, time spent waiting, blood type, and other important medical information.

Myth: Having "organ donor" noted on your driver's license or carrying a donor card is all you have to do to become a donor.

Fact: While a signed donor card and a driver's license with an organ donor designation are legal documents, organ and tissue donation is always discussed with family members prior to the donation. To ensure that your family understands your wishes, it is important that you share your decision to "donate LIFE."

Myth: I am 60 years old. I am too old to be a donor.

Fact: People of all ages and medical histories should consider themselves potential donors. Your medical condition at the time of death will determine what organs and tissue can be donated.

Myth: My family will be charged for donating my organs.

Fact: There is no cost to the donor's family or estate for organ and tissue donation. Funeral costs remain the responsibility of the family. At this time, there is no national registry of organ and tissue donors. Even if you have documented your wishes, be sure you have told your family you want to donate LIFE!

Understanding Brain Death

(Reprinted from "Understanding Brain Death," a one-page resource that provides an explanation to patients' families on the definition and meaning of brain death, with permission from UNOS)

There are two ways to pronounce death. It may be pronounced when a person's heart stops beating or when the brain stops functioning.

The brain cannot survive without oxygen. Brain death occurs when blood and the oxygen it carries cannot flow to the brain. Without blood and oxygen, the brain dies. When the brain dies, the person cannot move, breathe, think, or feel. Pain and suffering cease.

Brain death is death, and cannot be reversed. The heart can continue to beat for a while as the ventilator (breathing machine) provides oxygen to the body. It may look as if the person is sleeping because the ventilator fills the lungs with oxygen and helps keep the skin color normal and warm. But they are not sleeping.

Many tests are performed by the doctor to determine if brain death has occurred. Most or all of these tests take place at the person's bed-side. If the tests prove that brain death has occurred, the person is pronounced dead. The doctor then records the time of death while the person is still on the ventilator and their heart is still beating.

It is important that you understand brain death so that you can make important decisions as needed about your loved one. More questions may arise when talking with family or friends. Be sure to discuss any concerns with your loved one's doctors or nurses.

Legal Issues Surrounding Cadaveric Organ Donation

(Reprinted from Vital Connections, Donation and Transplantation...The Critical Link, the United Network for Organ Sharing, Health Resources and Services Administration, American College of Emergency Physicians, 1996, with permission from UNOS)

The laws surrounding organ procurement and transplantation have evolved to support the medical advances taking place in the surgical arena. Thus, statutory and regulatory systems have been developed to accommodate the donation process. These systems are designed to ensure that a sound, rational process is in place to offer protection to the referring physician, donor, donor family, transplant recipients, and the procurement and transplantation network. There are three medical-legal areas pertinent to the emergency physician's role in organ donation:

- Facilitating the determination of death.
- Expediting the consent process for donation.
- Understanding your routine inquiry/required request laws.

Determining Brain Death

Historically, death was synonymous with the cessation of heartbeat and respiration. Today, however, the diagnosis of death has become more complex due to advances in medicine and the ability to artificially maintain cardiopulmonary function through the use of medication and technology. In 1959, a group of French neurophysiologists coined the phrase "coma depasse" (beyond coma) to describe a patient had who lost all brain and brainstem function.

Through the early 1960s, interest in the concept of brain death as determined by neurologic criteria continued to grow. In 1968, a year after the first heart transplant, the Ad Hoc Committee on Brain Death of the Harvard Medical School released its set of criteria for the determination of the condition they called irreversible coma, cerebral death, or brain death. Since the publication of the Harvard Criteria, numerous groups have restudied the issue of brain death. These reports include:

- *The NIH Collaborative Study, 1977*
- *The British Criteria, 1979*
- *The President's Commission for the Study of Ethical Problems in Medicine and Biomedical and Behavioral Research: Guidelines for the Determination of Death, 1981*
- *The Task Force for the Determination of Brain Death in Children, 1987*

Currently, most organ donors are declared dead by neurologic criteria. For a determination of brain death to be made, established criteria must be met. Every state has adopted some type of statutory or judicial citation that defines death. The Uniform Determination of Death Act, promulgated in 1980, was the model utilized by most states when brain death legislation was enacted. The law states: "An individual is dead if the individual sustains irreversible cessation of circulatory and respiratory functions or all functions of the entire brain and brainstem....A determination of death must be made in accordance with generally accepted medical standards."

In addition, most hospitals have brain-death protocols in place that delineate the specific tests required to determine brain death. These may include apnea testing, EEGs, computer tomography scans, or blood-flow studies.

State laws do vary with respect to brain death. Some state laws require religious tolerance to accommodate those who for religious reasons seek a cardiac death determination.

Brain death is a medically and legally valid declaration of death and is defined as the complete and irreversible loss of all brain and brainstem functions. The concept of brain death is difficult for families and sometimes health professionals to understand. The following criteria are used in determining brain death in accordance with the President's Commission of the Study of Ethical Problems in Medicine and Biomedical and Behavioral Research.

Brain death is determined by:

- A known etiology.
- The exclusion of reversible conditions (e.g., hypothermia, drug intoxication or metabolic abnormalities).
- The clinical examination of the patient demonstrating: absence of cerebral functioning, spontaneous movements, brainstem reflexes, and spontaneous respirations.
- Confirmatory tests (e.g., EEG, cerebral angiography) may be performed in conjunction with a clinical exam but may not be necessary under hospital policy.

When brain death is diagnosed, the patient should be declared dead and appropriate documentation should be made in the patient's record including the methodology of the diagnosis, date and time of the death, and the physician's signature.

Obtaining Consent for Donation

The Uniform Anatomical Gift Act (UAGA) of 1968, amended in 1987, established the legal framework for organ and tissue donation. All states have enacted some form of the UAGA.

The UAGA provides individuals the right to document their wish to give anatomic gifts during their lifetimes. Examples of these documents include a properly executed driver's license or donor card.

The UAGA also defines those persons who may authorize a gift of all or part of the decedent's body in the event that the deceased individual has not made a decision regarding donation prior to death. General legal guidelines for obtaining any medical consent must be followed in this situation.

In order of legal priority, the following persons may consent to anatomical donation:

1. Spouse of the decedent.
2. Adult son or daughter of the decedent.
3. Parent of the decedent.
4. Adult brother or sister of the decedent.
5. Grandparent of the decedent.
6. Guardian of the decedent at the time of death.
7. Any other person authorized to dispose of the remains.

Once consent for donation is given, the procurement coordinator obtains written consent or recorded telephonic consent for each donated organ and/or tissue to be recovered. The written documentation is signed by the next of kin, when present, and witnessed by two individuals. A copy of the consent form will become part of the permanent hospital record.

The Patient Self-Determination Act of 1990 ensures that a patient's right to self-determined healthcare decisions be communicated and protected. Instruments for these decisions include living wills, durable powers of attorney, and advance care medical directives. Through these legal documents, individuals can record their wishes regarding organ and tissue donation.

Contemporary Jewish Positions on Organ Donation and Transplantation

(Reprinted from Organ Donation and Transplantation, Congregation Study Program Guide #9, Spring 1997, pages 6-7, with permission from the Department of Jewish Family Concerns, Union for Reform Judaism, New York, NY)

The mood of contemporary Judaism, across the denominational line, favors organ donation and transplantation. Indeed, it has become for many, a modern mitzvah. The basis for this belief is rooted in the value of saving a life (p'kuach nefesh). Strengthened by the developments in modern medical technology, the acceptance of organ donation and transplantation has been affirmed by modern Judaism.

There have been a variety of responsa issued by the Central Conference of American Rabbis, Reform Judaism (CCAR) dealing with many aspects of the donation issue. Indeed, they were an important foundation in the creation of the UAHC "Matan Chaiim" project. The selections reproduced here outline a timeline that notes the CCAR's involvement in the issue over several decades. The 1968 Freehof Responsa "Surgical Transplants" set the groundwork for subsequent CCAR deliberations and developed interesting and exciting interpretations that dealt with deriving benefit from organs of the dead and the conflict between honoring the dead and the thrust to save a life.

This same discussion, enhanced by the progress of technology and informed by the heightened awareness of the issue, is witnessed in a recent report of the Committee on Jewish Law and Standards of the Rabbinical Assembly (Conservative Judaism). Rabbi Joseph H. Prouser developed a teshuvah entitled: "Chesed or Chiyuv? The Obligation to Preserve Life and the Question of Post-Mortem Organ Donation." Published in December 1995, this document also traces the Jewish value and textual approach to our issue. It likewise concludes that organ donation becomes a modern mitzvah bringing various types of healing to both donor family and recipient.

The issue of not burying the donated organs with the dead body (an often-heard concern and a popular misconception as to why Judaism would not favor donation) is discussed by Prouser in a note from the former Chief Rabbi of Israel, Isser Yehuda Unterman: "As to the question of burial, Rabbi Unterman discusses only the particular organs or tissue being transplanted. In this regard, he considers transplanted tissue to be restored to life and thus not requiring burial with the donor's remains."

Likewise, the overriding belief in the saving of life also drives the contemporary Orthodox community to support organ donation and transplantation. As seen in the CCAR and Rabbinical Assembly pieces, texts underscore the saving of life as a basic theological foundation for the Orthodox community. These positions also reflect the growth of medical technology and the impact of that technology on Judaism's reinterpretation of the definition of death. The Rabbinical Council of America (Orthodox) approved organ donation as this modern mitzvah to save a life in a landmark decision in 1991. The decision noted that "no halachic barriers exist to donation of the deceased if they are harvested in accord with the highest standard of dignity and propriety....Vital organs such as heart and liver may be donated after the patient has been declared dead by a competent neurologist based upon the clinical and/or radiological evidence....Since organs that can be life saving may be donated, the family is urged to do so. When human life can be saved, it must be saved....The halacha therefore looks with great favor on those who facilitate that procurement of life-saving organ donations."

An examination of the following selections will show the interesting similarity amongst contemporary Jewish scholars across denominational lines in calling organ donation and transplantation the modern mitzvah that it has become. At the foundation for it all remains the belief in the saving of life. Embracing it all is Judaism's willingness to understand that in the growth of medical technology, we can find the tools to make real the belief.

Determination of Death

(Reprinted from Organ Donation and Transplantation, Congregation Study/Program Guide #9, Spring 1997, pages 30-31; with permission from the Department of Jewish Family Concerns, Union for Reform Judaism, New York, NY)

Finally, there was a greater reluctance in the early years of the transplant era to mandate (indeed, to allow) donation due to fears regarding determination of the donor's death. Using brain death as a medical, much less halachic, determinant of death dates only to the twenty-second World Medical Assembly held in 1968. Brain death is defined as "permanent functional death of the centers in the brain that control the breathing, papillary, and other vital reflexes." Rabbinic proponents of such a definition of death, that is, the total cessation of brain and brain-stem activity, as indicated (among other diagnostic methods) by an isoelectric or "flat" electroencephalogram (EEG), include Rabbis Seymour Siegel, Eliot Dorff, Avram Reisner, and David Golinkin, all of the Rabbinical Assembly; and Rabbi Moshe Tendler, a preeminent Orthodox authority on Jewish medical ethics as well as the Chief Rabbinate of Israel.

All rabbinic authorities agree that the classic definition of death in Judaism is the absence of

> *spontaneous respiration in a patient with no*
> *other signs of life… Brain death is a criterion for*
> *confirming death in a patient who already has*
> *irreversible absence of spontaneous respiration.*

It should be noted that the determination of brain death is often made while the deceased appears to be breathing and to have a pulse due to the use of a mechanical respirator. Where brain death is determined, these misleading data in no way constitute life. Quite to the contrary, "it might be forbidden to continue artificial means of 'life' in these conditions, since it would, in fact, be halanat harnet, a delay in burying a dead person."

Writing in 1975, Rabbi Jakobovits pointedly discusses the implications of this issue:

> *The question of defining the moment of death*
> *with precision has been rendered both more diffi-*
> *cult and more critically acute by… the demand*
> *for viable cadaver organs for transplant purpos-*
> *es. The lapse of only a few minutes may spell the*
> *difference between success and failure in such*
> *operations; on the other hand, the premature*
> *removal of organs from the dying may hasten*
> *death and constitute murder.*

Greater familiarity with the practice of transplantation, as well as a broader medical and rabbinic literature on determination of death and brain death, has largely eliminated this concern. Prevalent premodern fears of "use death" are no longer compelling. The final moments of the donor's life are safeguarded by requirements that two physicians certify death, and that these physicians not be involved in the transplant procedure.

A Sampling of Views of the World's Religions on Organ Donation and Transplantation

(Reprinted from Organ Donation and Transplantation, Congregation Study/Program Guide #9, Spring 1997, pages 56-64, with permission from the Department of Jewish Family Concerns, Union for Reform Judaism, New York, NY)

When death visits, it can call attention to the importance of the spiritual dimension of life. When faced with the trauma of a loved one's death and the decision of organ and tissue donation, the question often arises, "What does my religious tradition believe about organ and tissue donation?" Recent surveys indicate that less than 10 percent of those surveyed were aware of their religious group's doctrine or position regarding organ and tissue donation. As a result, the decision maker often looks to his or her parish clergyperson or hospital chaplain for an informed answer.

Religious groups have been on both the "cutting-edge" of biomedical ethics and on the "slow-to-accept" end of the issue. No one person, or even an assembly of religious representatives, can speak for numerous religious groups. The connectional religious groups appear more likely to have official positions on subjects such as organ and tissue donation. The free-Church traditions champion the idea that no group can usurp the autonomy of the local congregation. Thus, the religious group's official resolution is not binding on the local congregation or individual persons. It is, therefore, difficult to state an official position for some of the nation's larger religious groups. Research shows, however, that the vast majority of religious groups do support organ and tissue donation and transplantation so long as it does not impede the life or hasten the death of the donor.

Research into the positions of various religious groups reveals the underlying attitude that unless the group has taken action to prohibit organ or tissue donation and transplantation, it is usually assumed that such donation is permissible. It is encouraged as a charitable act that saves and/or enhances life; therefore, it requires no action on the part of the religious group. Although this is a passive approach to affirming organ and tissue donation and transplantation, it seems to be the position of a large segment of the religious community. Some groups have taken a more proactive stance in recent years, feeling that a resolution or adopted position encourages people to seriously consider the matter and plan accordingly. This segment appears to be increasing in number with only a few religious groups actively opposing organ and tissue donation and transplantation.

Each congregational clergyperson is encouraged to research his or her religious group's tradition and position on organ and tissue donation and transplantation, as well as on other biomedical ethical issues. In addition, each parish clergyperson should keep abreast of any new resolutions or positions adopted at his or her religious group's national assembly. The group's position is subject to change in any given year. It is important to be informed, since the family member suddenly faced with making a decision concerning organ and tissue donation of a loved one may be depending on the clergy to know the position held by his or her religious group. Inability to make an informed decision could leave the family member with a feeling of guilt regardless of the decision he or she may make.

The following summary statements concerning the various religious groups' positions on organ and tissue donation and transplantation may be of assistance to you. Perhaps you can help your religious group adopt a more clearly defined position. A pro-active position does, indeed, help clarify a group's attitude on the subject. Your knowledge and action may alleviate the suffering of the thousands of people who die annually due to a lack of available donor organs and tissues while a multitude of healthy organs are being buried every day. This dilemma is within itself an ethical issue.

AME & AME ZION (African Methodist Episcopal)

Organ and tissue donation is viewed as an act of neighborly love and charity by these denominations. They encourage all members to support donation as a way of helping others.

AMISH

The Amish will consent to transplantation if they believe it is for the well-being of the transplant recipient. John Hostetler, world renowned authority on Amish religion and professor of anthropology at Temple University in Philadelphia, says in his book, Amish Society, "The Amish believe that since God created the human body, it is God who heals. However, nothing in the Amish understanding of the Bible forbids them from using modern medical services, including surgery, hospitalization, dental work, anesthesia, blood transfusions, or immunization."

ASSEMBLY OF GOD

The Church has no official policy regarding organ and tissue donation. The decision to donate is left up to the individual. Donation is highly supported by the denomination.

BAPTIST

Though Baptists generally believe that organ and tissue donation and transplantation are ultimately matters of personal conscience, the nation's largest protestant denomination, the Southern Baptist Convention, adopted a resolution in 1988 encouraging physicians to request organ donation in appropriate circumstances and to "encourage volunteerism regarding organ donations in the spirit of stewardship, compassion for the needs of others, and alleviating suffering." Other Baptist groups have supported organ and tissue donation as an act of charity and leave the decision to donate up to the individual.

BRETHREN

While no official position has been taken by the Brethren denominations, according to Pastor Mike Smith, there is a consensus among the national Fellowship of Grace Brethren that organ and tissue donation is a charitable act so long as it does not impede the life or hasten the death of the donor or does not come from an unborn child.

BUDDHISM

Buddhists believe that organ and tissue donation is a matter of individual conscience and place high value on acts of compassion. Reverend Gyomay Masao, president and founder of the Buddhist Temple of Chicago, says, "We honor those people who donate their bodies and organs to the advancement of medical science and to saving lives." The importance of letting loved ones know your wishes is stressed.

CATHOLICISM

Catholics view organ and tissue donation as an act of charity and love. Transplants are morally and ethically acceptable to the Vatican. According to Father Leroy Wickowski, Director of the Office of Health Affairs of the Archdiocese of Chicago, "We encourage donation as an act of charity. It is something good that can result from tragedy and a way for families to find comfort by helping others." Pope John Paul II has stated, "The Catholic Church would promote the fact that there is a need for organ donors and that Christians should accept this as a 'challenge to their generosity and fraternal love' so long as ethical principles are followed."

CHRISTIAN CHURCH *(Disciples of Christ)*

The Christian Church encourages organ and tissue donation, stating that we were created for God's glory and for sharing God's love. A 1985 resolution, adopted by the General Assembly, encourages "members of the Christian Church (Disciples of Christ) to enroll as organ donors and prayerfully support those who have received an organ transplant."

CHRISTIAN SCIENCE

The Church of Christ, Scientist does not have a specific position regarding organ donation. According to the First Church of Christ, Scientist in Boston, Christian Scientists normally rely on spiritual instead of medical means of healing. They are free, however, to choose whatever form of medical treatment they desire—including transplant. The question of organ and tissue donation is an individual decision.

EPISCOPAL

The Episcopal Church passed a resolution in 1982 that recognizes the life-giving benefits of organ, blood, and tissue donation. All Christians are encouraged to become organ, blood and tissue donors "as part of their ministry to others in the name of Christ, who gave his life that we may have life in its fullness."

GREEK ORTHODOX

According to Reverend Dr. Milton Efthimiou, Director of the Department of Church and Society for the Greek Orthodox Church of North and South America, "The Greek Orthodox Church is not opposed to organ donation as long as the organs and tissue in questions are used to better human life, i.e., for transplantation or for research that will lead to improvements in the treatment and prevention of disease."

GYPSIES

Gypsies are a people of different ethnic groups without a formalized religion. They share common folk beliefs and tend to be opposed to organ donation. Their opposition is connected with their beliefs about the afterlife. Traditional belief contends that for one year after death the soul retraces its steps. Thus, the body must remain intact because the soul maintains its physical shape.

HINDUISM

According to the Hindu Temple Society of North America, Hindus are not prohibited by religious law from donating their organs, considering this act an individual decision. H.L. Trivedi, in Transplantation Proceedings, states that, "Hindu mythology has stories in which the parts of the human body are used for the benefit of other humans and society. There is nothing in the Hindu religion indicating that parts of humans, dead or alive, cannot be used to alleviate the suffering of other humans."

INDEPENDENT CONSERVATIVE EVANGELICAL

Generally, Evangelicals have no opposition to organ and tissue donation. Each church is autonomous and leaves the decision to donate up to the individual.

ISLAM

The religion of Islam believes in the principle of saving human lives. According to A. Sachedina in his Transplantation Proceedings' (1990) article, Islamic Views on Organ Transplantation, "the majority of the Muslim scholars belonging to various schools of Islamic law have invoked the principle of priority of saving human life and have permitted the organ transplant as a necessity to procure that noble end."

JEHOVAH'S WITNESSES

According to the Watch Tower Society, Jehovah's Witnesses believe donation is a matter of individual decision. Jehovah's Witnesses are often assumed to be opposed to donation because of their belief against blood transfusion. However, this merely means that all blood must be removed from the organs and tissues before being transplanted.

JUDAISM

All four branches of Judaism (Orthodox, Conservative, Reform, and Reconstructionist) support and encourage donation. According to Orthodox Rabbi Moshes Tendler, Chairman of the Biology Department of Yeshiva University in New York City and Chairman of the Bioethics Commission of the Rabbinical Council of America, "If one is in the position to donate an organ and to save another's life, it's obligatory to do so, even if the donor never knows who the beneficiary will be. The basic principle of Jewish ethics—'the infinite worth of the human being'—also includes donation of corneas, since eyesight restoration is considered a life-saving operation." In 1991, the Rabbinical Council of America (Orthodox) approved organ donations as permissible, and even required, from brain-dead patients. The Reform movement looks upon the transplant program favorably and Rabbi Richard Address, Director of the Union of American Hebrew Congregations Bio-Ethics Committee and Committee on Older Adults, states that "Judaic Responsa materials provide a positive approach and, by-and-large, the North American Reform Jewish community approves of transplantation."

LUTHERAN

In 1984, the Lutheran Church in America passed a resolution stating that donation contributes to the well-being of humanity and can be "an expression of sacrificial love for a neighbor in need." They call on members to consider donating organs and to make any necessary family and legal arrangements, including the use of a signed donor card.

MENNONITE

Mennonites have no formal position on donation, but are not opposed to it. They believe the decision to donate is up to the individual and/or his or her family.

MORAVIAN

The Moravian Church has made no statement addressing organ and tissue donation or transplantation. Robert E. Sawyer, President, Provincial Elders Conference, Moravian Church of America, Southern Province, states, "There is nothing in our doctrine or policy that would prevent a Moravian pastor from assisting a family in making a decision to donate or not to donate an organ." It is, therefore a matter of individual choice.

MORMON CHURCH *(Church of Jesus Christ of Latter-Day Saints)*

The Church of Jesus Christ of Latter-Day Saints believes that the decision to donate is an individual one made in conjunction with family, medical personnel, and prayer. They do not oppose donation.

PENTECOSTAL

Pentecostals believe that the decision to donate should be left up to the individual.

PRESBYTERIAN

Presbyterians encourage and support donation. They respect a person's right to make decisions regarding his or her own body.

SEVENTH-DAY ADVENTIST

Donation and transplantation are strongly encouraged by Seventh-Day Adventists. They have many transplant hospitals, including Loma Linda in California. Loma Linda specializes in pediatric heart transplantation.

SHINTO

In Shinto, the dead body is considered to be impure and dangerous, and thus quite powerful. "In folk belief context, injuring a dead body is a serious crime," according to E. Namihira in his article, Shinto Concept Concerning the Dead Human Body. "To this day it is difficult to obtain consent from bereaved families for organ donation or dissection for medical education or pathological anatomy."

The Japanese regard them all in the sense of injuring a dead body. Families are often concerned that they not injure the itai, the relationship between the dead person and the bereaved people.

SOCIETY OF FRIENDS *(Quakers)*

Organ and tissue donation is believed to be an individual decision. The Society of Friends does not have an official position on donation.

UNITARIAN UNIVERSALIST

Organ and tissue donation is widely supported by Unitarian Universalists. They view it as an act of love and selfless giving.

UNITED CHURCH OF CHRIST

Reverend Jay Lintner, Director, Washington Office of the United Church of Christ Office for Church in Society, states, "United Church of Christ people, churches and agencies are extremely and overwhelmingly supportive of organ sharing. The General Synod has never spoken to this issue because, in general, the Synod speaks on more controversial issues, and there is no controversy about organ sharing, just as there is no controversy about blood donation in the denomination. While the General Synod has never spoken about blood donation, blood donation rooms have been set up at several General Synods. Similarly, any organized effort to get the General Synod delegates or individual churches to sign organ donation cards would meet with generally positive responses.

UNITED METHODIST

The United Methodist Church issued a policy statement regarding organ and tissue donation. In it, they state that, "The United Methodist Church recognizes the life-giving benefits of organ and tissue donation, and thereby encourages all Christians to become organ and tissue donors by signing and carrying cards or driver's licenses, attesting to their commitment of such organs upon their death, to those in need, as a part of their ministry to others in the name of Christ, who gave his life that we might have life in its fullness." A 1992 resolution states, "Donation is to be encouraged, assuming appropriate safeguards against hastening death and determination of death by reliable criteria." The resolution further states, "Pastoral-care persons should be willing to explore these options as a normal part of conversation with patients and their families."

7

WAITING FOR THE PHONE TO RING

March, 1999

David was deteriorating both mentally and physically. And he was literally climbing the walls. It was a game that he played with Rachael. David would count to three, then he and Rachael would jump on the couch and try to climb the wall. Of course, Rachael was faster than David. I wondered why David had made up this senseless game. I hoped that it was David's sarcastic side surfacing to poke fun at his depressing situation—sick and cooped-up for months in a little apartment, waiting for something that always seemed to be just around the corner, but never came. The alternative was that it was just a silly game and that his mental faculties had deteriorated so much that he was doing senseless, silly things that he never would have done if he was healthy.

Since there was no reason to get up in the morning, David often stayed in bed until the middle of the afternoon. Dr. Purviance thought that David might be depressed and suggested, with spring just around the corner, David might be better off waiting at home in Michigan. The winter was over, so the brutal snowstorms that would slow or prevent travel between Michigan and Nebraska were no longer a threat. David made an appointment to discuss this with Dr. McCashland and Dr. Shaw. The appointment was for Thursday, April 1, the first day of the Jewish holiday of Passover.

Passover is a celebration of the time God helped Moses free the Jews from the slavery of Pharaoh in ancient Egypt. This important event is commemorated annually with a special dinner, the Seder.

I went home for the last two weeks of March, assuring David that Joe and I would return in time to celebrate Passover and accompany him to his appointment on the first of April. I was exhausted when I went to bed at home in Chicago on March 19, but I couldn't get to sleep. As I prayed for David and the rest of our family, I thought how wonderful it would be if we only knew the date of David's transplant. Our lives would be so much easier if only we had a date to look forward to. I was almost asleep when the number 275 popped into my head. All night, during my sleep, I kept hearing this number. When I woke up in the morning, this number—275—once again popped into my head.

I kept asking myself, "275 days from when? Could it be 275 days from the date of the diagnosis? Or 275 days from the date David was put on the waiting list? Or 275 days from today—the day that I dreamed the number?" To me, the most logical interpretation was 275 days from today. I did a little calculation and came up with December 18. I didn't like it; it was too far away. I put the date on the calendar and tried to forget about it, but that date stayed in the back of my mind.

I went on to plan for Passover. We decided to celebrate Passover one week early in Chicago with Ben and his family, Rebecca and Dave, and my friend Sharon and her family. Then we would celebrate Passover again in Omaha on the actual eve of Passover with David, Sara, and Rachael. The next day, Joe and I would accompany David to his meeting with the doctors.

As always, we cleaned the house, and cooked and cooked and cooked. In the evening, we gathered with Sharon and her family as we had for the past 21 years. Gathering around the Passover table without David reminded me of Passover 1981. David had become jaundiced the day before Passover and when we gathered the next day around Sharon's Passover table, it was without David. He had stayed at home, too ill to join us. Now, 18 years later, David was jaundiced and suffering from liver failure and once again, was not among us as we celebrated Passover. Not only were we missing David, now we were missing Sara and Rachael, too. I silently vowed that next year we would all be together around the Passover table. I had promised myself the same thing in 1981 and it had worked; we were all together for Passover 1982. In 1981 and 1982, my mother had been with us, but this year she was in Israel with my sisters and brother. I was grateful that she was healthy. This is how we were able to tolerate being away from each other for years at a time. As long as we were both healthy, we knew we would see each other again.

If I'd had the power to see a year into the future to Passover 2000, I would have been discouraged. But as it was, I was certain that in a year's time, David would be healthy again, and who knew? Maybe my mother would be here with us, too.

After our Passover celebration ended and everyone went home, I thought ahead to our upcoming celebration in Omaha and the meeting with David's doctors. I hoped Dr. Shaw would give his approval for David to return home. David and Sara would be more comfortable in their new home, and the joy of living in the house they had built together might ease their pain and suffering for awhile and help to lift David's depression. They would also be less than an hour away from Sara's family. This would be easier on Sara in some ways, and harder on her in others. We had recently learned that Johnie's cancer was back, and while it would be comforting to Sara to be close enough to help her mom through this difficult time, she might also feel torn between the responsibilities of caring for a sick husband, caring for her sick mother, and trying to raise a child.

Johnie's doctors were planning a new treatment for her. We all knew that Sara's grandmother had battled the same form of non-Hodgkin's lymphoma years ago and won, so we were hopeful that Johnie's battle would have a similarly successful outcome.

Two days before Passover, I was once again cooking the Seder meal. Joe and I were going to take the food to Omaha to celebrate with David and Sara. We were planning to leave first thing in the next morning. As we were getting ready for bed, Joe began to have chest pains. Out the door we went to the emergency room! By now, we knew the ropes. Joe would have to stay in the hospital for at least 24 hours.

The next day, the test results did not show any signs of heart attack. We had learned the last time that when blockages cause a heart attack, heart cells die and are released into the bloodstream. Those dead heart cells are detectable in the blood samples taken by the doctor while the patient is having chest pains. Joe's blood tests did not show any dead heart cells. The next day, as Joe's cardiologist prepared to release him from the hospital, he strongly advised Joe to take it easy. Joe felt good, so we decided to head for Omaha and check into a hotel along the way when we got tired. At least we would be there for tomorrow's meeting with Dr. Shaw.

Rebecca, who had been at the hospital with us, came home with me and helped me pack the car. I picked Joe up from the hospital and we drove for a few hours before stopping for the night. The next morning we woke up early and by 9:00 a.m. we were at David's apartment. One hour later, we were with David and Dr. McCashland in the examining room at the liver clinic. Dr. McCashland examined David, and then paged Dr. Shaw. Dr. Shaw arrived dressed in surgical garb and I guessed that he must have come straight from the operating room. He looked tired. David, who was sitting on the examining table, had the only seat in the room. So Dr. Shaw sat down on the floor, leaned against the wall, and listened as Dr. McCashland described David's condition.

Dr. McCashland reported that David was in stable physical condition. He was no longer suffering from the infections he'd had when he arrived in Omaha, and there was no need for him to be hospitalized. There was, however, some concern about David's mental state. Dr. Purviance felt David was depressed and was recommending that they consider sending David home to his wait for a liver there. David had been in Omaha for eight months and Dr. Purviance thought that going home might improve David's emotional state. When Dr. McCashland stopped talking, there was total silence in the room. Even Rachael was silent. All eyes turned to Dr. Shaw, waiting for his reaction.

Dr. Shaw was quiet. He ran his fingers through his hair. It was clear that he was having a hard time reaching a decision. I guessed that he didn't want to let David go. He wanted to be the one to operate on David, give him a new liver, and send him home healthy, happy, and looking forward to the rest of his life. He did not want to send David home thin, jaundiced, depressed, and looking forward to all the complications of liver failure. That would be like defeat. When Dr. Shaw spoke, we could hear the disappointment in his voice. "If all of you think David should go home, he should go home."

The verdict was in. We said some quick goodbyes and left the clinic. David was like an inmate whose prison term had been suddenly cut short. We went back to the apartment to plan for David's return home. It would be like moving again; during the eight months they'd been in Omaha, David, Sara, and Rachael had accumulated books, housewares, toys, and clothing. But we couldn't start packing yet; we still had to celebrate Passover.

Our Passover Seder this time was small—just the five of us. Rachael enjoyed the food and the songs. The next day we prepared to attend Friday services at Temple Israel. Since arriving in Omaha, we'd attended High Holy Day services there and went to Friday services whenever we could. Rachael was a little young for the temple's preschool classes, but we took her anyway. She enjoyed the music, songs, crafts, and she especially enjoyed being with the other children. By coincidence, the cantor at the temple, Jennifer G. Blum, had been a student cantor at the Temple Beth El in South Bend where we had worshiped years ago and where David had had his Bar Mitzvah after his first transplant. Jennifer, Rabbi Aryeh Azriel, and Rabbi Debbie S. Stiel were all concerned about David's condition. David's name was on the list of people that they prayed for during each service when the congregation sang the Mi Shebeirakh, the prayers for healing. They had also held a special healing service for David and the other ailing congregants. Tonight, they were dedicating the service to promoting organ donation and David was invited to give the sermon. The Reform Movement, the Union of American Hebrew Congregations, had embraced and begun promoting organ donation years ago, but we were still moved by the kindness and personal concern shown by the leaders and members of Temple Israel.

We arrived 20 minutes before the service was to start. Rachael looked very pretty in her new spring dress and white patent leather shoes. As Rachael's shoes clickety-clacked on the shiny floor of the temple hall, she got more and more excited. The shoes reminded her of the tap shoes she had seen a little girl wearing on the Teletubbies show. She wanted to do a tap dance. I didn't think she would be able to sit still during the service so I took her to the babysitting room. There was a babysitter in the room, but no other children so I stayed with her during the service and missed David's sermon.

Rachael and I rejoined Joe, David, and Sara at the reception following the service, where Sara and Joe filled me in. They told me that during his speech, David spoke quietly and was emotional. He told the story of his first transplant, and the triumphant Bar Mitzvah that followed. I knew it was hard for David to make that speech; being up on the bima (altar) reminded him of his Bar Mitzvah, just five months after his first transplant. After David's speech, the rabbi discussed the ethics of organ donation. She said that organ donation was a mitzvah, or good deed, because it saved human lives that would otherwise be lost. At the end of the service, everyone prayed for the sick and especially for David.

Rabbi Stiel continued the theme of organ donation at the reception. She did a great job! She had an informational sheet with statistics showing the numbers on the waiting list, pencils from the Omaha organ procurement office, and organ donation lapel pins. She had also prepared a 110-page bound book on the bioethics of organ donation for each family! Everyone was wonderful and it wasn't easy to say goodbye to this kind, thoughtful group that was giving us so much support. We promised we would return to the temple when we returned to Omaha for David's transplant.

On the drive back to the apartment, I switched gears and started focusing on the task ahead. Moving wouldn't be easy; David was as sick as ever. There was no joy in our hearts.

Loading the moving van was a problem. Joe was not allowed to lift because of his heart problem and David was in no condition to lift. We decided to hire movers and tried Two Men and a Truck, but they weren't available on such short notice. Neither were any of the other movers we called. None of us were interested in staying another week in Omaha, so we decided to call Potter's House to see if the teenagers in Charlene's extended family group would like to make a little extra money. Unfortunately, Charlene and her group weren't there; they were all at Disneyworld under the auspices of the Make-A-Wish Foundation. That left Sara and me.

We joked that since we couldn't get Two Men and a Truck, our movers would have to be "Two Women and a Baby." We bought small boxes, packed them lightly, and loaded the van. It wasn't easy to say goodbye to the volunteers at University House. When we returned the key to the apartment, they expressed their concern for David and volunteered to keep Rachael's crib and high chair in storage until we returned for David's transplant. They reminded us that a liver might be found for David while we were making the trip home and then we would have to turn around and come right back. It had happened before!

The drive home was uneventful and we arrived in Chicago on Sunday. We stopped at Laura and Ben's house for dinner, and Rachael, Josh, and Jacob played in the yard. David barely had enough energy to help Rachael down the slide. David, Sara, and Rachael then spent the night at our house, and the next day Sara's parents arrived to help them with the last leg of their journey. After lunch, John and Johnie drove David, Sara, and Rachael to their new home in Lowell, Michigan.

With all of us back in our own homes and no longer shuttling back and forth between Omaha and Chicago, we could try to pretend that everything was normal. But the reality was that David could get sicker at any moment. Without the transplant, he would die. And every time we heard the phone ring, it could mean that there was a liver for David.

As we waited and waited for the phone to ring, I tried to make sense of it all. The fact that they let David go home might mean that he was much lower on the Omaha waiting list than we'd thought. Maybe he was in the middle of the list, instead of near the top like we'd thought. He'd been on the waiting list for almost a year and it might be another year or more before his turn came. I decided that I couldn't dwell on it; at least David was home among his friends and family.

David and Sara spent the spring and summer of 1999 working on their new house. Sara unpacked boxes and David concentrated on the yard, which needed grass and landscaping. Of the three evergreens planted by the developer, one was dead, one had been stolen, and one was still alive. Even though it was a wooded lot, it still needed a lot of work and it seemed to give David a reason to get up in the morning. He ordered topsoil and bought the materials to seed the yard. He tried to do a little every day, but with so little energy it wasn't long before he was back in the house to rest.

People with chronic liver failure can divide their days into normal days and down days. On normal days, they are able to get out of bed and live a normal, but slow, life. On down days, they just can't get out of bed. As the disease progresses, there are more down days than normal days.

David had always been quite single-minded and determined when he had a goal that he wanted to accomplish, so I wasn't too surprised to see that, in spite of his physical limitations, he seemed to be making some progress on the yard. The topsoil arrived full of rocks and it was backbreaking work to pull them out. It was a four-hour drive for us, but Joe and I visited often and always spent some time helping David with whatever yard project he was currently working on. We tried to pretend that David was okay and everything was normal, but that only worked until we actually saw him. It was always a shock to see him a little thinner and a little more jaundiced than before. That was the reality that we couldn't run away from.

We all attended a friend's wedding. It was a happy occasion, but David looked very thin in his suit. He tried to dance with Sara and Rachael, but I could see that he was much slower. I thought about how he had danced at Rebecca's wedding nine months ago and could see a big difference. There was an ice sculpture on the buffet table and every time we looked at it, it was a little smaller—it was melting away. It occurred to me that the same thing was happening to David. Every time I saw him, he was a little smaller. We were waiting our way through the days, trying to live genuinely, to be interested in our work, look forward to celebrations, and find joy in life. After this wedding, we would look forward to Josh's and Rachael's birthdays in June, then to Sara's and Joe's birthdays in July. We could keep busy during the days but we couldn't forget, even for a minute, that David was on the waiting list. We might have to leave on a moment's notice for Omaha or Pittsburgh, or even for Lowell, if David had a medical crisis.

We were always "on call" for David. Whenever he had a medical crisis and needed to be hospitalized in Grand Rapids, I went to stay with Rachael who was two years old and interested in everything. I would bring Rachael to the hospital to visit David and we would ride the elevators, go to the gift shop, and of course, eat in the cafeteria. David would be spending a great deal of time in the hospital and I didn't want it to seem like a scary place to Rachael, so I tried my best to make it seem like a fun and friendly place to her.

I had been asking David to make an appointment with Nancy, his coordinator in Pittsburgh, so he could get a checkup and meet the transplant team in Pittsburgh. David's answer was always that the Pittsburgh team was reviewing the blood test results and reports sent by his local doctor and they already knew how sick he was. David said that when the time came (meaning, when they called him to come for a transplant), he would meet everyone. David knew that I was keeping in touch with Dr. Jorge Reyes in Pittsburgh. I would call and leave a message for his secretary; Dr. Reyes would then call me back and I would update him on David's situation. Dr. Reyes gave us valuable advice and his care and concern for David meant a lot to us. David had complete trust in the Pittsburgh team led by Dr. John J. Fung. Dr. Fung had received his training as a transplant surgeon from Dr. Starzl and later took Dr. Starzl's place in the operating room when he retired. That was good enough for David!

We then got the bad news that David's medical insurance would no longer be covering Sara and Rachael's medical expenses; he had been off work for so long that their coverage was expiring. David decided to return to work. In order to reinstate their coverage, he had to work full-time, but his employers agreed to allow David to pick his own hours as long as he finished his assignments on time. David tried to put in his hours. He would drag himself to work at odd times of the day and night, but it was taking a toll on him. After two weeks he quit working, but he had worked long enough to reinstate Sara and Rachael's insurance coverage.

When friends and relatives who'd read my first book called to see how I was doing, they always asked if I was crying in the shower at night as I did during David's first transplant ordeal. I told them that I was not. At the time of David's first transplant, liver transplantation was so new that we didn't know whether the transplant operation would save David's life or not. Now, 17 years later, I knew that David would be healthy and normal after his transplant, so I didn't feel hopeless. It was just the uncertainty over when David would get a liver that was ruining our lives. Every morning we told ourselves "today will be the day," and every night we went to bed hoping that the call would come in the middle of the night.

Still, life couldn't stand still until the day of David's transplant arrived, so with the help of my children, I planned a surprise party for Joe's 60th birthday. All the guests knew that if the call for David's transplant came before the party, the party would be cancelled because Joe and I would be in either Pittsburgh or Omaha. If the call came on the day of the party or during the party, our plan was to have Ben, Laura, Rebecca, and Dave entertain the guests since the food would be prepared and the house already decorated. We narrowed the guest list down to friends who lived in town to avoid inconveniencing anyone with a last-minute cancellation. Everyone understood the situation.

Although we got through the birthday party with no sign of a liver for David—not even a false alarm—we were ready to go at a moment's notice with a list of the things that we would throw into a suitcase when the call came. Now we were praying every night for strength for all of us, especially for David.

Shortly after the birthday party, I traveled with Joe to one of his annual education conferences in Buffalo, New York. After the conference, our group decided to visit Niagara Falls. We went along even though we had been to Niagara Falls many times before with our children. Every time we had relatives visit from outside the U.S. we brought them to Niagara Falls because it is such a wonder. The last time we'd been to the falls was 1994, the year that David and Sara married. After the wedding, we brought my sisters and my mother. I had many good memories of Niagara Falls.

This time, we arrived in the afternoon. I looked up and I saw a beautiful rainbow that spanned from one side of the falls to the other. It was the largest, brightest rainbow I'd ever seen. I felt that this was a sign from God, that He was answering my prayers. I prayed every night and asked for a sign that everything was going to be alright, and this was the answer He sent. There are many stories about rainbows, but the one that I've always liked says that a rainbow is God's signature as He shows his presence to us. It says that a beautiful rainbow is God's way of telling us that everything will be beautiful. As I watched the rainbow, I felt that I was seeing God's signature and that now I should believe that everything would be alright for David.

We weren't the only ones worried about David. Relatives came from all over to visit him. David's cousin Danny came from Los Angeles, and Joe and I brought my nephew Ofer to visit David in August. Ofer lived in Israel and was in the U.S. on business. He wanted to see David before returning to Israel. It was my birthday, so Sara baked a cake. Rachael loved birthday parties and we celebrated my birthday as if everything was normal and David wasn't sick. But we were still all waiting for the phone to ring.

Appendix 7

HOW TO CHOOSE A GOOD DOCTOR AND BE A GOOD PATIENT

Choosing the Right Doctor

Doctors are human beings who've been through medical school. In medical school, they learned about illnesses and the medications that cure those illnesses. Like us, they are human beings who occasionally make mistakes and forget things. As in other professions, some doctors are very good at the practice of medicine, and others are not quite as good. It is better to invest the time in finding a good doctor while you are healthy and establish a track record with him/her, than to wait until you are ill and may not have the time to make a careful selection. So, how can we tell the good ones from the not-so-good ones?

It may be helpful to ask your neighbors, friends, and coworkers if they have a doctor that they admire and trust and to listen to their reasons for recommending him/her. Whether you decide to accept a recommendation or you find yourself looking through the phone book, you should always check the doctor's medical track record and accreditation. One helpful website is www.questionabledoctors.org. If everything seems to be in order, a phone call to the doctor's office is the next step.

You can often learn a lot about the atmosphere in the doctor's office just by talking to the staff on the telephone. When you call, ask the nurse about the doctor's background, policies, areas of specialization, and bedside manner. You may even want to ask whether the doctor frequently runs late! If your conversation with the nurse meets with your satisfaction, make an appointment for a consultation with the doctor. Here are some qualities to look for:

- *Good Listening Skills:* A doctor with good listening skills will actively listen when the patient relates symptoms of illness and pain, and will ask questions to assist in diagnosis instead of doing all the talking and/or relying solely on tests.

- **Good Communication Skills:** A doctor with good communication skills will take the time to explain tests, procedures, and therapies to the patient. When a diagnosis is reached, the doctor will explain it thoroughly, using pictures or drawings as necessary. When medications are indicated, the doctor will explain what the medication is for, how to administer it, and what side effects to watch for.

- **Doesn't Patronize:** A good doctor can be an effective communicator without talking down to his/her patients.

- **Leaves Time for Questions:** A good doctor will want to make sure that the patient is comfortable with the information that has been communicated, and will schedule appointments with enough time to allow the patient to ask questions. In fact, a good doctor will encourage patients to ask questions and will not appear rushed or impatient when these concerns are voiced.

- **Is Available:** Doctors who care about their patients are available to meet their needs at all times, whether through communication with a competent nurse or partner, in person, or over the phone. A responsible doctor will make arrangements for patients' medical needs to be met outside regular office hours as well. Doctors that do not have a partner on call and cannot be reached within a reasonable amount of time are doctors that we don't want!

- **Puts Patients First:** A good doctor puts his patients' health before his/her own financial gain. A good doctor doesn't base his medical recommendations on the depth of the patient's insurance company's pockets, nor does he push a particular prescription company's brand-name medications or insist that diagnostic tests be performed at a specific laboratory.

- **Treats a Patient as a Person, Not a Diagnosis:** Doctors who treat their patients with friendliness and compassion see their patients as a human being first , not just a "case" or a diagnosis. Similarly, a doctor who treats patients with respect will also have a staff and nurses who treat patients with respect.

- **Willing to Send You to a Specialist:** A responsible doctor will send you to a specialist as soon as they realize your condition is one that they can't treat. In fact, the doctors with the most knowledge and expertise are often the same ones that are humble and down-to-earth.

- **Stresses Prevention:** A good doctor not only educates patients about illness, but also teaches them how to prevent illness.

Being a Good Patient

It is easy to become intimidated in the doctor's office if the doctor doesn't put you at ease. Again, a doctor you are uneasy with is a doctor you don't want. If you've already taken the time to find a doctor you are comfortable with, you're halfway there! Once you've found a good doctor, it's important to remember the other half of the equation: to have a positive medical experience, it helps to be a good patient! Here are some tips for being a good patient:

- **Take care of your body.** Even if we never liked biology in school, we should be knowledgeable about our own body and how our lifestyle affects it. We should take responsibility for the condition of our body by learning about and following the principles of good diet and exercise.

- **Ask the right questions.** Asking the right questions insures that we get the right answers! One good question to ask the doctor is, "What would you do if you were experiencing what I am experiencing?" A doctor who answers this question carefully will put himself/herself in the patient's position and will provide the same advice he would give to a member of his/her own family. Another good question is, "What other sources can you recommend where I can get more information on this condition, treatment, or medication?"

- **Be an active participant in the treatment process.** A good patient will learn as much as possible about his/her illness and become an active participant in the treatment process. To be an active participant, we must follow our doctor's advice, accept responsibility for understanding our diagnosis, educate ourselves about our medications/therapies, know what effect medications are supposed to have, watch for side effects, and ask questions when we need more information.

- **Communicate changes in condition/symptoms.** Of course, once we've become an active participant in our treatment process, we must also communicate any changes in our symptoms to the doctor and be persistent about getting an answer, whether in person or over the telephone, if things just don't seem right.

- **Don't be afraid to get a second opinion.** If we are uncomfortable with our healthcare provider, our treatment, or our progress, we must not hesitate to seek another opinion. Ultimately, we are responsible for our own health and for finding a doctor who is willing to help us get the care that we need.

Why Problems Occur

Some people sit passively during their appointment with the doctor. They assume the doctor has read the questionnaire they filled out in the waiting room, and they wait meekly for a diagnosis. These patients take their medications unquestioningly, follow doctor's orders, and do not feel the need to communicate or request any extra information.

Poor communication between doctors and patients is responsible for all sorts of problems. For example, many people became addicted to pain pills or tranquilizers in the Sixties, not knowing that these medications only treated symptoms and were not a cure for their headaches or anxiety. They never asked questions, and their doctors never offered this information. Other problems caused by poor communication include:

- misdiagnoses because symptoms were not related or were not listened to;
- improper administration of medication because instructions were not clear or were not written down; and
- serious complications because side effects were not reported or did not reach the doctor.

The list could go on and on. Better communication between doctors and patients would go a long way toward preventing many malpractice lawsuits.

Most patients who bring lawsuits for reasons other than death or permanent physical damage are profoundly disappointed with their doctors. Many of them hold doctors in such high esteem that they assume their doctor knows everything and can cure anything. When this doesn't happen, their high expectations are dashed and they respond with a lawsuit.

Patients who have a good relationship with their doctor realize that doctors are human and fallible. These people are less likely to sue. When doctors are friendly and compassionate and patients are active participants in their treatment, patients can accept that the doctor did everything within his/her power to help them.

8

THIRD TRANSPLANT CENTER

Northwestern University
August, 1999

During the summer, Joe and I watched a documentary on television about living related organ donation. It was about a wife who donated half her liver to save her husband's life. This couple was older than the one we had seen the year before, and both husband and wife had survived the surgeries which had taken place at Northwestern University in Chicago. David also saw the program and called us. Once again, he was excited about the idea of living related organ donation and wanted to go for tests. This time, he asked me if I would be a donor for him. He only wanted me to be tested, not Ben or Joe. We called and made an appointment for September 30.

This was a real change of heart for David. A year ago, I'd asked him to come to Chicago and get his name on the waiting lists at the four transplant centers here. Since Joe and I had a four-bedroom house, it wouldn't be difficult for David to be on the waiting list here in Chicago. If David needed to stay close by, he, Sara, and Rachael could stay with us while he waited for the transplant. However, David had refused. He wasn't sure his insurance would be accepted at all the transplant centers and he also wanted a surgeon who had worked closely with Dr. Starzl. Dr. Shaw in Omaha and Dr. Fung in Pittsburgh were the only two surgeons he was willing to consider. When the transplant coordinator explained that surgeons often traveled for lectures and conferences and that David's preferred surgeon might be out of town when a liver became available, David agreed to accept other members of Dr. Shaw's or Dr. Fung's team, but only reluctantly.

Now he wanted to go to Northwestern University in Chicago and be considered for a type of surgery for which—as two experienced transplant surgeons had already told him—he was not a good candidate. I could only think that he must be desperate, sick and tired of being sick, and just wanting to put an end to this waiting game. I didn't think the surgeons at Northwestern would accept David as a candidate but I went along with it anyway, thinking that this new idea might give David some hope for awhile. Who knew? Maybe while we were looking into living related liver donation at Northwestern, they would find a donor liver for David.

September was a difficult month. Sara's mom Johnie was still struggling with non-Hodgkin's lymphoma. The conventional cancer treatments hadn't worked and she was now scheduled to have a bone marrow transplant at the University of Michigan. The idea was to take out her bone marrow, give her massive doses of chemotherapy to kill the cancer, and then return her bone marrow so that it could rebuild her immune system. Now we had two people in the family who needed a lifesaving transplant! But at least Johnie had a date. I think Johnie felt bad for David because he didn't have a date on which to pin his hopes.

When I first arrived in the U.S. in 1962, I communicated with my mom in Israel through weekly letters. Thirty-seven years later, to everyone's amazement, we were still writing to each other weekly. Every Monday I wrote a letter to her, and then looked forward to Friday when I would receive a letter from her. If something unusual happened and I was unable to write on Monday, I would call to tell her my letter would be late so she wouldn't worry or make unnecessary trips to her mailbox.

While I was pregnant with each of my children, I wrote to Mom about the progress of the pregnancy. After the children were born, I reported the first smile, the first steps, their first words, and how we spent our days. Whenever something special or interesting happened, I made a mental note to include the news in my next letter to Mom. Now that my children were grown, I was sharing the special events that happened in their lives as well as my own.

Mom was coping with a slow-growing cancer, but she didn't like to dwell on it. In a letter at the end of July, Mom shared an interesting story with me, but did not mention her illness. In August, she described my sister Dalia's surprise birthday party. Our letters to each other were never unpleasant. We never complained; we just shared the interesting things that had happened in our lives since the last letter. We didn't hide things from each other, but we tried to save the bad news for when we got together in person, or after the events were over. Neither one of us wanted the other to worry.

Mom knew about David's Wilson's Disease and his first transplant; she'd been here to help us through the ordeal. Now she knew that David was sick again and would need another transplant. Like us, she was hopeful and sure that everything would be all right, that it was just a matter of time. Now, every time I called her, the first words out of her mouth were,

"Have they located a liver for David?" The hardest thing for me was to tell her, "No, we are still waiting."

I'd always believed in the power of prayer. Mom had fostered that belief in us by praying for us. On the night before a big exam, she saw to it that we studied hard. Then she would say, "Get a good night's sleep, and I'll pray that you do well on the test tomorrow." Of course, it always worked because we'd studied hard and gotten a good night's sleep, but we also felt that Mom's prayers had something to do with our success. So whenever we needed a little extra help, we always asked Mom to pray for us.

When I'd first told Mom that David was sick again, she went to her Rabbi and asked him for a special prayer for David. The Rabbi gave her a piece of paper with a prayer[1] printed on it. He told Mom that David should carry the prayer with him at all times and recite Psalm 91[2] from his prayer book every evening. Mom sent the prayer paper to me and I made copies. I then sent the original to David along with the instructions to recite Psalm 91 daily.

In early September, my sister Sima, a nurse by profession, called from Israel to tell me about Mom's last checkup. The x-rays showed that her cancer had spread to her lungs and liver. It was hard for me to accept this, so I tried not to think about it. I was hoping for a miracle—that she would soon be okay.

When I called Mom, she told me that she was nauseated and didn't have much of an appetite. She said, "Now I know how David feels." Just a week later, my sister again called to tell me that Mom was in the hospital because she was dehydrated and vomiting. I asked my nephew Ofer to give Mom a hug and kiss for me when he visited her in the hospital. Ofer did more than that. He took his digital camera and computer to the hospital and photographed Mom, taped her voice, and sent the picture and recording to me within moments over the Internet. Thanks to technology, I could see and hear Mom even though she was thousands of miles away! David and Ben printed the pictures and saved the recording for me.

Mom spoke for only 30 seconds in the recording, but she mentioned David's name three times. She said, "I hope David is doing okay. I am praying for David's health. Some day all of this will come to an end." Then she said, "David came here, gave me a hug and a kiss, and took my picture." I think she meant to say "Ofer," but "David" is what came out of her mouth. Mom was as consumed with worry about David as I was.

---

[1] See Appendix 11 for text of the prayers my mom sent

[2] See Appendix 11 for text of Psalm 91

In the pictures, Mom didn't look like herself at all. She'd lost a lot of weight and the expression in her eyes showed how much she was suffering. "This can't be true," I thought to myself. As I put the picture on my desk, I thought about the last time I'd seen Mom, a year and a half ago. I tried to be hopeful, thinking that her condition would improve and she would go on to live another year or more. After all, her cancer was slow-growing. I promised myself that after David's transplant, I would go to Israel to visit Mom again and, as always, we would stay together in her condo and do some of her favorite activities. Mom liked to do needlework and make patchwork quilts; she had made a needlework picture and patchwork quilt for me and each of the children. I would bring some fabric squares with me and Mom and I could make a quilt together. I went on and on making plans for my next visit with Mom, hoping I wasn't deluding myself.

That night was the eve of Yom Kippur. For Jews, Yom Kippur, the Day of Atonement, is the holiest day of the year. On this day, we forgive and are forgiven. We went to services at our temple. During a quiet moment, when the Rabbi had stopped speaking and the cantor hadn't yet started singing, Ben leaned over and whispered in my ear, "Don't you want to go see your mother?"

"You heard what she said," I replied. "She said she would be upset if I left David to go to her. My responsibility is here with David." I took my handkerchief out of my purse so my tears wouldn't fall on the prayer book.

"It doesn't matter what she said," Ben answered. "Do you want to see her?"

I shook my head yes.

"We'll take care of David," Ben said. "I'll go with Dad to Omaha or Pittsburgh if a liver comes while you're away."

I tried to stop crying. For a minute, I was proud that I'd succeeded in raising my children the way that my mother had raised me. We could talk about anything and express our feelings and opinions freely. Ben knew me well enough to know how much I loved my mother and needed to see her. When he first started to walk, he would make the daily trips to the mailbox with me and ask me what I was looking for in the box. One of the first words he learned was nomeh, which means "letter." He met my mother for the first time when he was five years old. It was Mom's first trip to the U.S. That summer, he had to share me not only with his nine-month-old brother David, but also with my mom. He did it without any complaint; even then, he understood how important my mother was in my life.

Now, 30 years later, as a grown man and father of two, Ben was suffering in silence for all of us. That was why he'd offered half of his liver to

David without thinking about the risk. He just wanted the whole ordeal to be over and to put an end to all of our pain and suffering.

Yom Kippur went by as usual. We fasted, we forgave everyone who'd caused us pain in the last year, and we asked for God's forgiveness for our own transgressions. As always, we ended the day praying for the health and longevity of everyone we knew. We prayed that God would inscribe our names and the names of our loved ones in the Book of Life, and we accepted that God's will would decide who should live and who should die in the coming year. Our prayers always reminded us that we should pray like everything depended on God and act like everything depended on us. I hoped that our prayers would bring us peace and tranquility as we spoke to God of our pain.

I went to bed praying for both Mom and David, for their improved strength and health, and I asked God to guide us through all of this. That night, I had a dream that seemed very real. It was 1969—the summer of Mom's first trip to the United States. I was making breakfast in the kitchen of our house in Niles, Michigan. The sun streamed through the large glass sliding door into the middle of the room. My mom entered, fresh from her shower with damp hair. She liked to sit in front of the sunny window to dry her hair. She was sixty years old and her hair had turned gray, but she used hair color to get it back to the dark, shiny black of her youth. During the day, she pinned her hair up in the back, but in the early morning, until her hair dried, she let it hang on her shoulders. It gleamed in the sun. In my dream, she held nine-month-old David on her lap and he was fascinated with her hair, wrapping his hands in it and playing with it. Everything was as lovely as it was in 1969, but then I suddenly noticed that my mom was dressed entirely in black! In the Middle Eastern culture, dressing in all black is a sign of mourning and shows that the wearer is grieving. After my father passed away in 1957, my mother, sisters, and I had dressed in black for an entire year. Ever since then, I'd hated the color; thankfully, I hadn't had to wear it since then. I thought that Mom must be telling me it was time for her to die. But then why was she holding David?

I woke up and realized that my beautiful dream had turned into a nightmare. My mom and David were both dying, and there was nothing I could do about it! I began to cry for the happy days that were gone and the darker days that I knew were coming, and I knew Ben was right. I had to go see my mother. I tried to think of an excuse so she wouldn't be upset with me for leaving David. I decided to tell her that I was coming to Israel to go to the Wailing Wall in Jerusalem to pray for David.

When I was growing up in Iran, one of the pictures on the wall in our home stood out. It was a picture of a stone wall with a group of people facing it. When I asked my father about the wall, he told me that it was the western wall of the temple that King Solomon built in Jerusalem on top of the mountain. It had been around since Biblical times, but now we were not allowed to go there. Even so, the Jewish people around the world had not lost hope. They were hoping and praying that some day they would be allowed to return to this holy place. My father visited Israel frequently after the independence, but only half of Jerusalem was part of the state of Israel. Then, in 1967 when Egypt, Syria, and Jordan attacked Israel hoping to take over the small country, Israel fought hard to defend the country. In the Six-Day War, Israeli people not only defended their country, they also won the other half of Jerusalem, which included the Wailing Wall.[1] Tears came to my eyes when I saw television footage of Jews returning freely to the Wailing Wall for the first time in years.

I called my brother Menacheh and asked him to prepare Mom for my visit and get her approval. Mom agreed that I should come to the Wailing Wall to pray for David, and I made arrangements for my four-day trip to Israel. I would return in time for our September 30 appointment at Northwestern University, when I would be evaluated as a living related donor for David. The plane trip seemed to take forever, but it was only two hours from Chicago to New York and twelve hours over the ocean. Even though I'd purchased my ticket at the last minute, I was able to get a window seat on the jumbo jet. When the doors of the plane shut, I realized that I would have all three seats to myself. By moving the armrests, I had enough space to lie down and sleep. I wasn't sleepy, so I tried to prepare myself for what might be ahead. I thought about past trips and what a joy it was to see my mother waiting for me with a bouquet of flowers at the gate. Now she was 90 years old and we were lucky to have had her with us for so long, healthy in mind, body, and spirit. I reminded myself that no one lives forever and I remembered a young woman I met on one of my past trips to Israel.

---

[1] The Wailing Wall is the western wall of the holy temple built by King Solomon on top of the mountain in Jerusalem. The temple was the center of the spiritual world, serving both Jews and non-Jews. The temple mount, also called Mount Moriah, is the spot where Abraham bound Isaac, and where Jacob dreamt of a ladder reaching to heaven. While the temple stood, Jews from around the area would make the pilgrimage to Jerusalem three times each year. The temple was destroyed by Titus in 68 C.E., but the western wall still stands. After the temple's destruction, the sages prophesied that the Divine Presence would never leave the western wall. That is why, even during the 1900 year exile, Jews would travel to Jerusalem at great expense and danger, just to pray at the wall. There, they would pour their hearts out to God, beseeching him for Jewish redemption. And today, Jews still flock to the western wall, placing their prayer notes in cracks and holes in the wall, asking God to hear and answer their prayers.

She was crying on the plane. When I asked her why she was crying, she told me that her mom was dying and she was on her way to see her for the last time. I felt deep compassion for her and knew that one day it would be my turn to make the same trip. Now here I was, years later, and I couldn't believe or accept it either.

Morning arrived without sleep. Our plane landed at the Tel Aviv airport and the moment I had been both anticipating and dreading had arrived. Menacheh and Edna were waiting for me. They knew I was despairing, so they said we would go straight to the hospital. I tried to pretend everything was okay, but I just couldn't believe I would be seeing my mother in the hospital. When we arrived, I noticed that she looked very thin and could hardly keep her eyes open. She couldn't even manage a sitting position, so we raised the head of her bed. I showed her all the pictures I'd brought for her and told her all about our lives while she listened quietly. At lunch time, the portable buffet arrived but all that Mom wanted was some soup. I had fed her only a few spoonfuls before she didn't want any more. I showed her the jar of peanut butter I'd brought for her; it had been one of her favorite foods when she'd visited us in the States. She refused it, as well as the sour cherry preserves that I made every year and we all loved. When she asked me to take the beautiful new robe I'd brought for her to my sister's house, I was near tears. She was really sick and she knew it. She would not be getting out of bed so she didn't need a new robe. I tried to hold back my tears because I knew it would upset her to see me crying. For the first time, I didn't want her to know my feelings. I tried to stay calm, but part of me wanted to tell her that this was not the time to die. She couldn't die now, with David so sick. I needed her around to tell me that everything would be fine. I needed her around to celebrate David's recovery as we had in 1981 with his Bar Mitzvah, and in 1994 with his wedding. But I knew that wasn't fair. She had no control over what was happening to her, and I wanted her to see that I was brave and able to handle everything.

During one of her past visits to the U.S., we had talked about life and death. She'd told me that we shouldn't cry when she was gone because she'd lived a wonderful and full life. She even told us we should not sit Shiva, the seven days of mourning required when a loved one passes away. If we did ignore her wishes and sit Shiva, she wanted us to laugh and joke and celebrate the happy times we'd shared. She told me that she prayed that when it was her time to go, it would be a sudden and unexpected death. She didn't want to burden any of us by being sick in bed. When she told me these things, I started to cry. She said, "I'm not dead yet. I told all the other children these same things, but they didn't cry. Why are you crying?" My answer was simple. They were all living in Israel, around Mom every day. They couldn't imagine what their lives would be like without her around. But I already knew what it was like. Living in the U.S., I didn't have Mom around for holidays, or just your everyday good days and bad days. I think she understood.

After the soup, Mom reminded us that it was time for us to go home and have lunch. As we left the hospital, I realized how tired I was from the long flight. Edna had prepared a nice lunch of rice, chicken, and salad. For the first time, all of us siblings were together without our spouses. My three sisters, my brother, and I sat down to lunch. I had no appetite, but I knew Edna wouldn't let me get away without eating something at the midday meal, the most important meal of the day in that culture. I also didn't feel that it would be right to refuse the food that she'd worked so hard to prepare. It seemed strange for us all to be sitting around the table in Edna's house without my mother. "This is just the beginning," I told myself while I forced myself to eat. "We have to get used to this."

While we ate, we talked about our mother and shared our good memories. When it was my turn, I suddenly realized that each of us was talking about a different person. She had treated each one of us differently. "How can it be that the same woman loved each one of us differently?" I marveled. I wished that she was with us to explain it to us, but I knew that even if she'd been here, she would have been silent. She was a very good listener, and it made me cherish the 37 years of letters that I had at home even more. In those letters, she'd shared more of herself and her feelings with me than she had with the others who'd lived with her every day. Even though we were physically separated by an ocean and thousands of miles, I realized that I was much closer to my mother than my brother and sisters.

After lunch and a short rest, we went back to the hospital. Her first and only words for me were, "When are you going to Kotel (the Wailing Wall)?" I told her I would go soon and, as always, we talked and she listened until dinner time. Dinner for Mom was a few spoons of an oatmeal-like soup. Then she fell asleep. I returned home with Edna. I was pleased that she'd invited me to stay with her. There was no way I could have stayed in my mother's condominium without her there.

Two days later, Edna and I went to the Wailing Wall together. We got out of the cab at the gates to Jerusalem. We would have to walk the rest of the way. It was a beautiful, warm day and as we walked with the throng, I realized that it wasn't just any day. It was the holiday of Sukkoth and there were people everywhere.

Sukkoth, described in the Bible as the Feast of Tabernacles, is a pilgrimage festival. It was celebrated until 70 C.E. by a mass pilgrimage to the temple in Jerusalem. Sukkoth is also a time when we remember the mass exodus of the Jews from Egypt, and a celebration of Harvest. Today, the Jews celebrate this holiday by building huts like the ancient farmers built and lived in during harvest time. And, if at all possible, they go to Jerusalem to worship at the Wailing Wall.

I was about 50 feet from the wall, but every square foot between me and the wall was packed with people either moving toward or away from the wall. I looked at my sister in dismay. She knew that I didn't like crowds and would do everything in my power to avoid getting caught up in them. "What do you want to do?" she asked. I didn't have a choice. I had come so far and now I was so close. I knew I had to make my way through the crowd to put my prayer note in the wall and pray there. Edna took her notebook out and I wrote my prayers. I asked for health and strength for my mother, David, and all of our family, and put my prayers together with a copy of the special prayer that my mother had sent for David a few weeks ago. Then I started to make my way toward the wall. There were people all around me, but it was strangely silent. They all shared my same mood. My sister whispered in my ear, "You keep going. I'll follow you." As I continued to make my way toward the wall, I heard in my head the voice of our Rabbi speaking the words we heard often during the High Holy Days: "Our Father, our King, hear our voices and all of our prayers."

As I moved closer, step by step, I felt like I was in a huge outdoor sanctuary surrounded by peaceful people. Amazingly, there was no pushing, no shoving, and it seemed as though everyone felt the presence of God watching from the temple mount as I did. Finally, there I was near the front of the crowd, with only one person between me and the wall. I was hot and tired. I'd seen many women put their hands on the wall or lay their head on the wall as they prayed. I'd never done that before nor had I ever felt the desire to do such a thing on the many past occasions when I'd visited the wall. Today, I felt compelled to touch the wall. As I whispered my prayers, the woman in front of me heard my prayers and moved away from the wall to make room for me.

The wall was cool and comforting against my head on that warm afternoon. I looked for somewhere to put my prayer note in the wall, but all the holes and cracks were packed with the prayers of others. I found a small shelf where a stone had once been, but had long since fallen out. I placed my prayer there, then turned around and left the wall to make room for the people waiting behind me. We retreated from the wall and the crowd as slowly and peacefully as we'd arrived. We bought some bottled water and souvenirs and began to look for a cab to take us back to Edna's house.

On the sidewalk, I tripped and lost my balance. Afraid that I was about to fall flat on my face, I put out my hands to protect myself and managed to protect my face. I got up off the ground with my sister's help and realized that I hadn't broken any bones or sustained a major injury. When I looked up, there was an old woman in front of me who looked just like my grandmother had years ago. She looked deep into my eyes and said, "Your prayers have been answered." I thanked her shakily and looked around for the cause of my fall. There was a low metal fence that separated the sidewalk from the street, presumably to protect pedestrians. Part of it had come loose and was sticking out into the walkway and I had tripped over it. I shook the dust off my clothes. Even though I was dressed in white, the dust brushed off easily. I thought about what the old woman had said and decided that it was a positive sign.

Not finding a cab, we decided to take the bus. We sat down in back with a mother and her teenagers and struck up a conversation. I told them about David and the mitzvah of organ donation and the trip went by quickly. A few hours later, we were back at the hospital with Mom. I proudly told her how we'd accomplished our goal of visiting the Wailing Wall to pray for her and David. She shook her head, indicating that she didn't need "get well" prayers; she was ready to go. By her bedside, my mom had the cards that my children had sent, wishing her well. My grandson Jacob had sent her some beads to let her know that he was praying for her and she kept those in the drawer next to her bed.

Early the next morning, we arrived at the hospital just as the nurse was bringing my mom from the shower. The nurse settled my mom in the recliner on the sun porch and, once again, we were alone in the sun. She looked weak and had trouble holding her head up. I felt that this might be the last time we would be alone together. For once, I was speechless and Mom filled in with the words. She said she wished she had been able to come to Rebecca's wedding. I reassured her and told her that I wished she'd been there, too. I said I wished I had had more time with her and that I could have done more for her. That was our last conversation.

Then the nurse arrived and put my mother back in bed. As Mom closed her eyes, I realized that her cancer wasn't killing her as fast as food deprivation was. She had an IV for fluids and oxygen so she could breathe comfortably, but she had refused force feeding and all other sources of nutrition.

She didn't want to prolong the death process because she was ready to go. Her condition worsened the next day and I changed my flight home so I could stay an extra day with her. I spent another day at her bedside, feeding her as much as she would eat and talking to her. Every once in a while, I asked her if she wanted me to stop and be quiet, but she let me know with a squeeze of the hand that she wanted me to continue. All too soon, it was time to say goodbye to her and to my brother and sisters. As I prepared to leave, they expressed their concern about living related organ donation. They wanted to know if I was really going to go into the operating room and give half of my liver to David. I told them yes; I would do that for David.

I gave my mom one last kiss and felt her soft skin under my lips. I tried to be brave, to let her think that I was strong and could handle everything. There were no tears. At the door, I turned and looked back at Mom. I knew it would be the last time I would see my mother alive. I wished I could lift her from the bed like a baby, take her home with me, and care of her myself until her last moments arrived. It was an unrealistic thought, but at that moment, I wanted that more than anything. I knew that part of me was still in denial and that, in spite of my show of bravery, there was still much pain ahead.

Edna and Menacheh drove me to the airport. By coincidence, I had the same seat on the airplane that I'd had on the arriving flight. Once again, I didn't sleep a wink; my thoughts were on my mother and David. I arrived home late Wednesday night. David, Sara, and Rachael had arrived in Chicago earlier in the day and were already asleep in bed.

Our appointment was early the next morning at Northwestern University. We dropped Rachael off at Ben and Laura's house where Laura would watch her until we returned from our appointment late in the day. Rachael liked Laura and always looked forward to playing with her cousins Josh and Jacob.

At the hospital, we met with the director of Northwestern's Liver Transplant Program, Dr. Michael Abecassis, and with the team gastroenterologist. Both doctors were young and enthusiastic. As they told us about their backgrounds, we learned that Dr. Abecassis had spent time in Pittsburgh and trained with the Pittsburgh team. They explained their program and told us they would need both an MRI and a CT scan of David. I would have to be evaluated by a doctor that was not part of the Northwestern team. They needed an impartial opinion about whether I was a suitable donor; they wanted me to see a doctor that was unfamiliar with David's case to avoid the possibility that concern for David's condition might influence the outcome of my evaluation. They also knew that transplant surgeons who are used to receiving cadaver livers in coolers aren't used to thinking about the welfare of a living donor. In the case of living related organ donation, the donor needs to be able to live a normal life after the operation, making it crucial that the decision be considered very carefully from both a medical and a personal standpoint. The doctors ordered tests and x-rays for David and a blood test for me, and we made an appointment to return the following month when all the results would be in.

David and Sara stayed with us and for several days went back and forth to Northwestern for David's tests. I finished writing a letter to my mother that I'd begun on the plane ride home from Israel. I wrote about the airplane trip and my arrival home, but this time I didn't mail it. I faxed it to the hospital where my mother was staying and called my sister Sima to ask her to watch for it and to read it to Mom when it arrived. Sima told me that our mother hadn't opened her eyes since I'd left. The doctors were saying she was in a coma, so reading the letter was useless. Several days later, when I talked with Sima again, I learned that the night after our last telephone conversation, Sima had a dream about our mother. In the dream, our mother asked Sima why she hadn't read my letter to her. So first thing the next morning, Sima went to the hospital and read my letter to Mom, even though she couldn't tell whether Mom was hearing and understanding. I thanked Sima. Personally, I believe that comatose patients can hear and understand, but they are just too weak to respond. I think Mom heard her.

It was October and we had three birthdays to celebrate: Jacob's, Laura's and David's. I tried to concentrate on the birthdays rather than dwelling on Mom's declining health and David's position on the waiting list. I was keeping in touch with my sisters by telephone and there weren't any changes in Mom's condition. She was slowly dying and there was nothing any of us could do.

We celebrated the birthdays. David was turning 31. We tried to smile and celebrate, but seeing David's small face and shrunken body made it difficult to celebrate. Last year, I'd been sure that David would be healthy and back to normal by now, but that hadn't happened. There had been at least one transplant per week in both Omaha and Pittsburgh, but it just wasn't David's turn yet. We wondered whether all the others who'd received livers in the last year were sicker than David and needed the livers more.

On October 21, news from Israel arrived. I received a phone call from my sister saying that they'd been asked to come to Mom's bedside at the hospital and were leaving at once. I hung up the phone and waited. I still had hope that Mom would come out of the coma and thought maybe that was why they were all going to the hospital. Several hours passed and I was still waiting for good news. When I couldn't wait any longer, I began calling all of my siblings in Israel but got no answer at any of their homes. Finally, I tried my niece Ilana and found her husband Shmouel at home. Shmouel told me that my mother had passed away and that my brother and sisters were planning her funeral.

Since we'd left the Middle East and settled in the U.S., Joe and I knew that we would never be able to attend the funerals of friends and loved ones living in other countries. In the Jewish faith, funerals must take place as soon as possible—usually before sundown on the day of the death. Several hours just weren't enough to get to a funeral half way around the world. This was an unspoken understanding between us, our parents, and our siblings. Since we'd moved to the U.S., Joe's father, Joe's sister Faroch, and my brother Nader had died. We didn't go to their funerals, but we'd attended services at the temple and held a memorial service for each of them in our house. Our children and our friends had attended.

In Israel, I knew my brothers and sisters would sit Shiva for my mother in her home, as is the custom of Jews around the world. They would hold morning and afternoon prayer services and their children and friends would drop by and talk about my mother, remembering the good times and the bad times. They would talk about her and cry, and then talk some more, until they could talk about her without crying. They would spend seven days in her house, returning to their own homes at night. This way, they would get used to coming to her house without having her there. I knew that my place was here in the United States. Not just because of David's illness, but also because my children would be mourning their Grandma's death and we all needed to be together.

Joe and I planned a memorial service for my mother on the upcoming Sunday. Yards of tulle and silk flower decorations from Rebecca's wedding still draped the second floor banister. Back in December, I had decided to leave them in place until David received a successful liver transplant. Now, a whole year after Rebecca's wedding, David still didn't have a transplant and we were preparing to mourn the death of my mother. We certainly didn't need those types of decorations now. We would have to take them down early.

On Sunday, friends and relatives arrived for the memorial service. My close friend Sharon and her husband David drove the three hours from Niles. Donna and Will Phillips, from Southfield, Michigan, were in Chicago for a convention and delayed their return to stay for the service. We were so close that I thought of Sharon and Donna as my "American sisters." They knew my mother from her visits to the U.S. and they had been fond of her.

Rabbi Lisa Green of the North Shore Congregation Israel in Glencoe, Illinois officiated at the memorial service. I had written a eulogy for my mother, and Rabbi Lisa read it beautifully. Then Ben shared his memories of his grandmother. David volunteered to read the 23rd Psalm from his prayer book. David's skeletal body was lost in his suit and as he read the psalm, I had the horrifying vision that he was reading it from the grave at his own funeral. David began crying, and we all cried with him.

Josh and Jacob were solemn and well-behaved, and perhaps a little unsettled to see so many adults in tears. We had hired a babysitter for Rachael, who took her up to the playroom during the service. Somehow, Rachael had the feeling that something unusual and serious was going on in the living room and the sitter's invitation to play with the toys did not completely hold her attention. Every once in a while, she peeked down at us from the top of the stairway just to see what was going on.

Rebecca could not stop crying and so did not speak about her grandmother. Rebecca's tears reminded me of my mother's words about the special bond between her and Rebecca. "I feel very close to her," she used to say. "Rebecca is a very special granddaughter to me. We have spent a lot of time together." That was true. In the spring and summer of 1981, while I was tending to David in the hospital, my mom and Rebecca were together. Joe's mom also joined them for a few months, but it was my mother that Rebecca looked to for comfort while I was gone. My mother was like a second mother to Rebecca during that first monumental crisis in our lives. After that, there was always a special bond between them. The hardest thing of all was that now, 18 years later, we were revisiting all of those dark days and nights but Mom would not be here to see us through this crisis.

In Jewish tradition, mourners end the funeral service by throwing dirt into the grave because it helps mourners to accept the reality of their loved one's death. Joe and I wanted to bring this symbolism into my mother's service. We supplied roses and the rabbi asked everyone to leave the petals on a silver tray that we had placed in front of Mom's picture.

After the service, David had a few bites of dinner then went upstairs to bed. He hadn't talked much to anyone at the service and just didn't seem to be himself. Around 9:00 p.m., after everyone was gone, David came downstairs and rested on the sofa. As I put the food away and picked up the house, I thought about my parents' deaths and how my life had changed over the years. By midnight, I was ready to go to bed. I tried waking David up to go up to bed, but he didn't respond. Even as a child, he hated to be awakened from a sound sleep, so I got a blanket and covered him up. He pushed the blanket away angrily. "Well, at least he's not in a coma," I thought and decided not to worry about him.

Early the next morning, Sara woke me and told me that David was behaving strangely. Sara had brought Rachael downstairs for breakfast and found David in the utility room holding onto the washing machine. He didn't know how to get back to the family room or the bedroom. Sara helped him back to the family room and seated him on the sofa. Now she didn't know what to do with him. I got out of bed and went downstairs to see David. I could barely communicate with him and I guessed that he was experiencing symptoms of encephalopathy. They seemed to be pretty severe.

We called 911 and Sara followed the ambulance to the local hospital. I stayed home with Rachael. As David was being examined, Sara told the doctor that David was a patient at Northwestern, and the doctor immediately made arrangements to have David transported there. David was already registered at Northwestern and doctors were reviewing the results of the tests they had performed on David's first visit. We felt better knowing that David's care would be managed by a transplant center that was familiar with his case.

I called Joe to let him know what was going on and he told me that when he left for work that morning, David was already in the utility room. When Joe asked David what he was doing there, he said he was looking for his vomit. David sometimes had a wry sense of humor so Joe assumed David was joking, said goodbye, and left the house. Sara later told me that David had been vomiting off and on the previous week.

In the ambulance on the way to Northwestern, the paramedic asked David his birth date and David responded with the date of his first liver transplant, September 26, 1981. At the hospital, doctors diagnosed David with encephalopathy and end-stage liver disease, and also found signs of infection. David was admitted and started on medication that would reduce the ammonia levels in his blood and tests were ordered to find the source of his infection.

I had passed tests showing that my blood type matched David's O-positive blood type, and my liver was in good condition. Those were the first steps toward becoming a living donor. Now, I scheduled the next round of tests to see if I was physically fit enough to donate half my liver to David.

There was no time to mourn my mother. David was teetering on the brink and needed all of us. Before the day was out, we decided that Sara would return to the hospital in the morning to sit with David, and I would take care of Rachael. In the afternoon, I would bring Rachael to the hospital during visiting hours, and while she visited with David, I would go for my tests.

After lunch the next day, Rachael and I drove to the hospital. Normally, she napped after lunch, so I played a soothing cassette, hoping she would sleep during the hour-long drive. That was not to be. For a little girl that loves cars, Chicago's freeways were like an automobile showroom! She looked at all of the cars and trucks and commented on all of them. I was fascinated with her interest and joined the conversation. As I drove, we speculated on the purpose, destination, and cargo of the vehicles on the road.

All of a sudden she stopped talking, and began to sing along with one of the songs on the cassette:

> *The bear went over the mountain,*
> *The bear went over the mountain,*
> *The bear went over the mountain*
> *To see what he could see.*
> *And all that he could see,*
> *And all that he could see,*
> *Was the other side of the mountain,*
> *The other side of the mountain*
> *The other side of the mountain,*
> *Was all that he could see.*

The lyrics reminded me of a saying we had in our native language, "Wherever you go, the sky is the same color." Interpreted pessimistically, it implies that it is futile to strive for change in the hope of finding happiness or a better life, because everywhere you go will be the same. I was glad that children didn't think too much about the meaning behind the lyrics; they were more interested in the rhymes and rhythms. The song was over and Rachael wanted me to play it again. As the bear went over the mountain again, we exited the freeway and I saw a sign for the Marriott Hotel. We had been to this hotel in 1982 for the meeting of the American Association for the Study of Liver Disease, where David had been presented as an example of a successful liver recipient. Remembering how David had surprised the 1,500 doctors by running down the aisle and up onto the stage reminded me of happier times and brought hope that lifted my spirits.

Northwestern Hospital and Medical Center is an impressive building that occupies an entire block of downtown Chicago. The first time we entered, we couldn't help but notice how different it was from the hospitals we were used to. Each floor has a large, beautiful lobby, and mahogany-paneled interiors with indirect lighting exuding warmth and elegance.

When we pulled into the hospital parking lot, Rachael was excited about seeing her mom and dad, and also because the hospital had become a fun place for her. Rachael enjoyed riding elevators. And when the elevator door opened with a "ding" to take us up to David's tenth floor room, Rachael smiled.

We knew that the doctors were considering a feeding tube for David, so at home that morning I had taped a plastic tube to the nose of one of Rachael's dolls. If David had a feeding tube in his nose when we entered the room, I didn't want Rachael to be upset; I wanted her to understand what a feeding tube was all about.

To our surprise, there was no feeding tube in David's nose. David and Sara explained the prognosis that the doctors had delivered that morning. They were giving David intravenous antibiotics for the infection that was causing the encephalopathy. Due to the severity of David's liver failure, the doctors thought that David would be in the ICU by the end of the week and his failing condition would put him at the top of the waiting list. In the ICU, David would have a good chance of getting a cadaver liver. If they were unable to find a cadaver liver, it would be up to me. My tests today would determine whether I would become the living donor for David.

Today, David looked normal and alert. I left Rachael with David and Sara, and went to my appointment. I was prepared for the physical and felt confident that I would pass since I didn't have any major illnesses.

The physical exam was brief. Afterwards, the doctor asked me to sit down and began asking questions about my life. He wanted to know how I was spending my days now that my children were grown and I wasn't employed outside the house. I answered honestly. I told him that I was taking care of the house and now that David was hospitalized, I was also caring for Rachael whenever I was needed. I told him that I had just finished planning my daughter's wedding and also had several volunteer organizations that I supported.

"Who takes care of you?" he asked.

"No one. I've never needed anyone to take care of me. I have always taken care of myself," I replied.

"But who takes care of you when you get sick?" he persisted.

"No one. I've never been that sick before," I smiled.

I'd been healthy all my life. Even as a little girl, I'd never had any major illnesses. As an adult, I'd had three natural childbirths, some minor surgery here and there, but I'd never needed anyone to care for me. During minor illnesses and after the delivery of my three children, my husband helped me when he got home from work. When the kids were older, they helped with chores around the house when I was sick, but I was never sick for long. My expectations for this liver surgery were similar. I was planning on a quick recovery.

The doctor explained that this surgery to donate part of my liver was completely different than anything I'd ever experienced before. I would be sick, weak, and in bed for a long time after the surgery—perhaps months, or even a year. I told the doctor if it came to that, we would hire a nurse to take care of me.

The doctor asked about the history of David's liver disease. When I recounted the details of David's illness, the doctor shook his head and said I knew a lot. I couldn't tell if he thought this was an advantage or a disadvantage for a living donor, but I suddenly wished I hadn't told him quite so much. The more we got into the questions and answers, the more I felt I was hurting rather than helping David's chances for living donor surgery. Although I was answering honestly, I didn't feel prepared for the questions and the probing. I'd been expecting a simple physical exam and this conversation was catching me completely off guard.

When the doctor was done asking questions, he asked if I had any questions of my own and told me he would answer as honestly as he could.

"What happens if David and I both end up with partially functioning livers after the surgery and both need a liver transplant? Will you be able to put us at the top of the waiting list and give us a new liver right away, or will we have to start all over at the bottom of the waiting list?" I asked.

"You know we cannot do that," he said.

His answer was clear. Legally, they would not be able to give us special treatment and move us up on the waiting list. If this risky surgery was unsuccessful, they would have to treat us the same way they treated all of their other living donors and patients awaiting liver transplants. We might both be sick and on the waiting list for years.

I was expecting a little more encouragement and support. When people buy a toaster or a television, they get a performance warranty and sometimes a satisfaction guarantee. How could these doctors ask us to put our lives on the line for an experimental surgery and then leave us alone to face the consequences? Ideally, I was hoping he would say, "Our job as doctors is to heal people. We went to medical school to save lives and if this surgery doesn't go the way we hope it will, we will do everything we can to save you and your son." But he didn't say that and I was disappointed. Was it possible that the doctor was trying to change my mind?

Half-jokingly I said, "But what about the rights of the guinea pig? Even guinea pigs have rights!" (I didn't know whether guinea pigs had rights or not.) The doctor didn't answer and it was obvious that our meeting was over. I got the feeling that I had probably failed the test and ruined David's chance for living donor surgery. I just wasn't good at hiding my thoughts and feelings. To do that, I needed practice, preparation, and lots of prayers.

I was worried that David would be devastated if he found out that I failed the tests so I asked the doctor, if I had failed the test, not to tell David. I asked him to wait at least until David had a chance to recover from his infections before delivering any bad news.

After the exam, I went back to David's room and took Rachael for our usual ride in the elevator and visited the hospital gift shop and cafeteria. Rachael and I left the hospital before dark and Sara stayed with David. Even though Rachael had missed her afternoon nap, she still wasn't sleepy. In the car on the way home, we talked and she sang along with the cassette tape. We played "The Bear Went over the Mountain" again and again. When Sara returned late in the evening, we enjoyed the dinner that Laura had cooked and brought over earlier.

I tried not to think about what the doctor had said about the difficult recovery for the living donor. I was pinning my hopes on David receiving a cadaver liver while he was in the ICU. David had transferred over all of the "points" he'd earned from being on the waiting list for 17 months in Pittsburgh. This improved his position on the waiting list at Northwestern, but put him back down to the bottom of the waiting list in Pittsburgh. That was the sad reality. I wished David had put his name on the waiting lists at all the transplant centers in Chicago at the very beginning, but he hadn't been interested in considering other centers then. Now he was desperate and knew that the end was near, but his choices were limited by his earlier decisions.

The antibiotics were making David feel better and we started a routine. Sara spent days at the hospital with David and I brought Rachael to visit in the afternoons as often as I could. The rest of the family visited in the evenings and on weekends. I did not encounter any of the doctors and surgeons on my visits and no more tests were ordered for me.

One afternoon, when I walked into David's room, he said, "Have you heard? Walter Payton died!" This was shocking news for all of us. A man with the fame, strength, energy of Walter Payton died on the waiting list. Later, we learned that a cancerous tumor of the bile duct had metastasized and spread out of the liver. We were devastated! If Walter Payton had died, how would David survive? It was a sad day for all of us. The one thing David had going for him was that he didn't have cancer. Maybe he would be able to survive the waiting list.

Another day, when I was alone with David in the hospital room, he got up to go to the bathroom and I saw his skeletal body through the back of his open hospital gown. His tailbone was sticking out and I thought he looked much like he did before his first transplant in September 1981. That made me shiver, but I tried to keep my hopes up. I wondered what kept David going. Where did he find the energy to even get out of bed to go to the bathroom? In 1981, by the time he was this sick, he could barely even move his limbs. When David got back into his bed, he told me that he had good news: Sara was two months pregnant! David had a plan. He felt that he had seven months to have his transplant and recover so that he would be ready when the time came to help Sara through labor and childbirth. After the shock of his skeletal body, news of Sara's pregnancy was uplifting and all the more reason for David to fight to survive! My mother had just passed away and now God was sending us a new life!

I got up and kissed and congratulated David. I wish I had known sooner, I told him. My mother would have been happy to know. During David's illness, she had been asking me if he was able to fulfill his responsibilities as a good husband. I had told her that I didn't know. When it came to the subject of sex, my mother was way ahead of her time. She had given all of us sex education at a time when most parents of her generation considered sex a taboo subject. When I was young, my girlfriends would all come over to our house to ask my mom their questions about sex. We lived in a culture that expected girls to stay virgin and untouched until their wedding night and my mother felt that knowledge and understanding would keep us safe. From an early age, she taught us the difference between a "good touch" and a "bad touch," and instructed us how to run away and tell if anyone approached us to molest or take advantage of us. She also educated us about the role of a good wife, what to expect from a good husband, how to practice birth control, and what pregnancy and childbirth would be like. She wanted us to enter the marriage relationship with a good understanding of love, sex, and marriage. When my mother, sisters, and I were together, we talked about these things.

To my mom, the fact that Sara was pregnant in spite of David's illness would have meant that Sara and David had a good, loving relationship. Now she was gone, and there was no way I could let her know. I knew that with Sara pregnant and David so ill, the transplant and recovery process would be even harder on the rest of us. At the same time, the joy of anticipating a new baby would give us more hope and more reason to encourage David to fight for his survival. Rachael was already a source of joy and inspiration for us; she always entertained us with her singing, her love of life, and her energy and made us smile. With another baby, we would have even more reason to smile! Although I had been thinking about the doctor's words, I didn't really believe that any surgery could make me weak or tired, as long as David was alive and Rachael was happy.

David had been in the hospital for ten days when the surgeons finally told us that living donor surgery was a dangerous surgery for both the donor and the recipient, and neither David nor I were good candidates. David's surgery would be extremely difficult because it was a retransplant and there was 17 years of scar tissue built-up around his failing liver. He would have the best chance for survival with a whole cadaver liver.

During his hospital stay, David's health had improved rather than declined as the doctors had predicted. He was up and around, so there was no reason to transfer him to the ICU. In fact, it was time for us to leave the hospital. David needed to finish his course of intravenous antibiotics, so the hospital made arrangements for him to receive home care from a visiting nurse. Once again, David was being released without being cured. It was a bittersweet occasion. We were happy to have him coming home, but we knew he would be hospitalized again once the next crisis arrived.

Once again, the hope that David was on the verge of receiving a liver transplant was lost. The minimum wait for a liver transplant in Pittsburgh or Omaha was two years for someone in David's situation. David had been on the list for sixteen months, and none of us felt that he had another eight months to live. If he did manage to survive the waiting list, by the time his turn rolled around, he would probably be too sick to be considered a good candidate. David had been down this road before and the picture looked bleak, but he wasn't planning to give up.

Once again, Ben brought us the information we needed. From the Internet, he printed out complete 1998 and 1999 transplant center statistics for four centers: the University of Pittsburgh, University of Nebraska (Omaha), Northwestern University, and the University of Miami. We were surprised by what we learned. The University of Miami had performed more transplants than any of the other three centers!

Now, almost a year after my first call to Dr. Tzakis, I again called his office. This time, I was calling with David's approval. I was grateful that Dr. Tzakis' secretary Jennie remembered us. I explained what was happening with David and Jennie left a message for him. The next morning, Dr. Tzakis called David and invited him to come to Miami to be evaluated for the waiting list. David decided to go, but we had to wait until he was finished with his course of intravenous antibiotics. There were only a few days left but the visiting nurse was on a mission to teach either Sara or me to administer the antibiotics. Even though David only needed a few days of home treatment, this is what the insurance company required. Sara was unable to do it because her morning sickness made her too nauseous, and I was in no condition to learn to treat David. I knew that in his condition, a small mistake could kill him. That's why the Jewish religion forbids a parent to administer medical treatment to their own child. Parents can get emotional and make a mistake. Each day, we had to go over this with the visiting nurse.

On the weekend, Sara took Rachael home to Grand Rapids to pack for the trip to Miami. While they were there, Sara visited her mom at the University of Michigan Hospital where Johnie was waiting for a bone marrow transplant to treat her non-Hodgkin's lymphoma. My heart went out to Sara. Here she was, torn between her husband in one state and her mother in another, both gravely ill, and both awaiting a transplant to cure their terminal illness. Now, if we traveled to Miami, the distance between Sara and her mom would be even greater and Sara wouldn't be able to see her as often. It reminded me of what I had just gone through with my mother, except that Johnie's prognosis was better. If the bone marrow transplant was successful, it wouldn't be long before she was home. She also had her husband John, her mother Cora, and her other daughter Christy, by her side.

Appendix 8A

CHOOSING A TRANSPLANT CENTER

I n the past 20 years, the number of transplant centers in the country has grown from two or three to over 200. Now that transplant surgery has become routine, there are new transplant centers opening all the time as hospitals find the resources to purchase transplant equipment and hire an experienced transplant team. This is very helpful for transplant patients, who no longer have to travel long distances to receive a transplant.

Visit More Than One Center

However, all transplant centers are not created equal. Each center is unique because it is based upon the mission, philosophy, and working practices of the institution of which it is a part. That is why getting a second, and even a third opinion is so important for patients with a life-threatening condition, such as liver failure.

Most centers will accept biopsy results, x-rays, and other test results from another center. However, if additional tests are required at a new center, you will only gain more information to bolster (or refute) your diagnosis. Each time you seek another opinion, you should meet with several members of the transplant team. It is especially important to talk with the head of the transplant team personally to discuss your diagnosis, and to learn as much as you can about the center.

Research Centers in Different Geographical Regions

It is important to remember that each U.S. geographical region maintains its own waiting list. You may wish to get on the waiting list at several different centers, since different regions may have longer or shorter waiting lists. The length of the region's waiting list may depend on how many organs are donated in the region, how many transplant centers exist in the region, and how many transplants each center is able to perform in a given period of time. The Internet can be an invaluable tool for research about transplant centers and the regional waiting lists.

Keep Centers Up-To-Date on Your Condition

After you get on the waiting list at one or more centers, it is important to schedule appointments and visit each center frequently, so they will be aware of your condition and the degree of liver failure you are experiencing. Be sure to notify each of the centers when you experience changes in your symptoms or general health. Symptoms to report include, but are not limited to, changes in blood chemistry, fever, cold, flu, nausea, vomiting blood, bloody stools, and abdominal pain. You should also notify the transplant centers immediately if you are hospitalized for any reason.

Make Your Choice

At some point, as your symptoms progress, your local doctor may feel that your medical needs will be best served by hospitalization at a transplant center. At this time, you will have to choose which transplant center is best for you. The transplant center will most likely provide you with a folder or booklet of information to guide you through your waiting list and transplant experience. Study the information as you would study the "Rules of the Road" for your Drivers' License Test. *This is important information that will help to guide you through the days ahead!*

Find Housing

Most large transplant centers have reasonably priced housing facilities for transplant patients arriving from out of town. For example:

- University House – University of Pittsburgh, Pittsburgh, PA
- Potter's Family House – University of Nebraska, Omaha, NE
- Transplant House – University of Miami, Miami, FL

These houses were established by nonprofit organizations, and they are generally run by volunteers. They provide out-of-town patients and their families with a rented room and kitchen facilities in a friendly, clean environment. Each resident is expected to clean up after himself/herself, and often chores are assigned equitably to keep the group home running smoothly. These homes are so popular for their affordability and the companionship they provide that there is often a waiting list to get in.

The transplant team social worker will usually be able to provide you with housing information and a list of rentals available for out-of-town patients.

Transplant Center Contact List

Name	Location	Phone	Region
University of South Alabama Medical Center	Mobile, AL	(334) 471-7000	3
University of Alabama Hospital	Birmingham, AL	(205) 934-3411	3
Baptist Medical Center	Little Rock, AR	(501) 202-2000	3
Arkansas Children's Hospital	Little Rock, AR	(501) 364-1100	3
The University Hospital of Arkansas	Little Rock, AR	(501) 686-7000	3
Banner Good Samaritan Medical Center	Phoenix, AZ	(602) 239-2000	5
Mayo Clinic Hospital	Phoenix, AZ	(480) 515-6296	5
University Medical Center, Univ. of Arizona	Tucson, AZ	(520) 694-6000	5
St. Bernardine Medical Center	San Bernardino, CA	(909) 883-8711	5
Children's Hospital and Health Center	San Diego, CA	N/A	5
Children's Hospital Los Angeles	Los Angeles, CA	(323) 660-2450	5
Cedars Sinai Medical Center	Los Angeles, CA	(310) 423-5000	5
Scripps Green Hospital	La Jolla, CA	(858) 455-9100	5
University of California Irvine Medical Center	Orange, CA	(714) 456-6011	5
Harbor UCLA Medical Center	Torrance, CA	(310) 222-2345	5
St. Mary Medical Center	Long Beach, CA	(562) 491-9000	5
Loma Linda University Medical Center	Loma Linda, CA	(909) 824-0800	5
Santa Rosa Memorial Hospital	Santa Rosa, CA	(707) 546-3210	5
Lucile Salter Packard Children's Hospital at Stanford	Palo Alto, CA	(650) 497-8000	5
California Pacific Medical Center	San Francisco, CA	(415) 600-1000	5
Riverside Community Hospital	Riverside, CA	(909) 788-3000	5
Arrowhead Regional Medical Center	Colton, CA	(909) 580-1000	5
University of California San Diego Medical Center	San Diego, CA	(619) 543-6222	5
University of California San Francisco Medical Center	San Francisco, CA	(415) 476-1000	5
Sutter Memorial Hospital	Sacramento, CA	(916) 733-8133	5
Sharp Memorial Hospital	San Diego, CA	(858) 541-3400	5

Name	Location	Phone	Region
St. Joseph Hospital	Orange, CA	(714) 633-9111	5
University of California Davis Medical Center	Sacramento, CA	(916) 734-2111	5
Stanford University Medical Center	Stanford, CA	(650) 723-4000	5
St. Vincent Medical Center	Los Angeles, CA	(213) 484-7111	5
University of California at Los Angeles Medical Center	Los Angeles, CA	(310) 825-6301	5
University of Southern California University Hospital	Los Angeles, CA	(323) 442-8500	5
Western Medical Center	Santa Ana, CA	(714) 835-3555	5
The Children's Hospital	Denver, CO	(303) 861-8888	8
Centura Porter Adventist Hospital	Denver, CO	(303) 778-1955	8
Presbyterian/St. Luke's Medical Center	Denver, CO	(303) 839-6000	8
University Hospital-University of Colorado Health Science Center	Denver, CO	(303) 372-0000	8
Hartford Hospital	Hartford, CT	(860) 545-5000	1
Yale New Haven Hospital	New Haven, CT	(203) 785-2565	1
Children's National Medical Center	Washington, DC	(202) 884-5000	2
Georgetown University Medical Center	Washington, DC	(202) 687-1000	2
Howard University Hospital	Washington, DC	(202) 865-6100	2
Washington Hospital Center	Washington, DC	(202) 877-7000	2
Walter Reed Army Medical Center	Washington, DC	(202) 782-1000	2
Alfred I. DuPont Hospital for Children	Wilmington, DE	(302) 651-4000	2
All Children's Hospital	St. Petersburg, FL	(813) 898-7451	3
Broward General Medical Center	Fort Lauderdale, FL	(954) 355-4400	3
Bert Fish Medical Center	New Smyrna Beach, FL	(386) 428-5000	3
Cleveland Clinic Hospital-Florida	Weston, FL	(954) 659-5600	3
Florida Hospital Medical Center	Orlando, FL	(407) 896-6611	3
Southwest Florida Regional Medical Center	Ft Myers, FL	(239) 939-1147	3
Jackson Memorial Hospital-University of Miami School of Medicine	Miami, FL	(305) 585-1281	3
Shands Jacksonville	Jacksonville, FL	(904) 244-9800	3

Name	Location	Phone	Region
St. Luke's Hospital (Mayo Clinic)	Jacksonville, FL	(904) 296-9074	3
Tampa General Hospital	Tampa, FL	(813) 844-7000	3
Shands Hospital at The University of Florida	Gainesville, FL	(352) 265-0111	3
Children's Healthcare of Atlanta at Egleston	Atlanta, GA	(404) 325-6000	3
Emory University Hospital	Atlanta, GA	(404) 712-2000	3
Medical College of Georgia	Augusta, GA	(706) 721-0211	3
Piedmont Hospital	Atlanta, GA	(404) 605-5000	3
St. Joseph's Hospital of Atlanta	Atlanta, GA	(404) 851-7001	3
St. Francis Medical Center	Honolulu, HI	(808) 547-6011	6
Iowa Methodist Medical Center	Des Moines, IA	(515) 241-6212	8
Iowa City VA Medical Center	Iowa City, IA	(319) 338-0581	8
University of Iowa Hospitals and Clinics and VA Medical Center of Iowa	Iowa City, IA	(319) 356-1616	8
Mercy Medical Center-Des Moines	Des Moines, IA	(515) 247-3121	8
Children's Memorial Hospital	Chicago, IL	(773) 880-4000	7
Loyola University Medical Center and Hines VA Hospital	Maywood, IL	(708) 216-9000	7
Memorial Medical Center	Springfield, IL	(217) 788-3000	7
Northwestern Memorial Hospital	Chicago, IL	(312) 926-2000	7
Rush-Presbyterian/ St. Luke's Medical Center	Chicago, IL	(312) 942-5000	7
OSF St. Francis Medical Center	Peoria, IL	(309) 655-2000	7
University of Chicago Medical Center	Chicago, IL	(773) 702-3000	7
Univ. of Illinois Hospital and Clinics	Chicago, IL	(312) 996-7000	7
Clarian Health- Methodist/IU/Riley	Indianapolis, IN	(317) 962-2000	10
Lutheran Hospital of Fort Wayne	Ft Wayne, IN	(260) 435-7001	10
St. Vincent Hospital and Health Care Center	Indianapolis, IN	(317) 338-2345	10
Via Christi Regional Medical Center, St. Francis Campus	Wichita, KS	(316) 268-7000	8
University of Kansas Medical Center	Kansas City, KS	(913) 588-5000	8

Name	Location	Phone	Region
Jewish Hospital	Louisville, KY	(502) 587-4011	11
Kosair Children's Hospital	Louisville, KY	(502) 629-6000	11
University of Kentucky Medical Center	Lexington, KY	(859) 323-1692	11
Children's Hospital	New Orleans, LA	(504) 899-9511	3
Ochsner Foundation Hospital	New Orleans, LA	(504) 842-3925	3
Memorial Medical Center	New Orleans, LA	(504) 483-5000	3
Louisiana State University Medical Center Shreveport	Shreveport, LA	(318) 675-5000	3
Tulane University Medical Center	New Orleans, LA	(504) 588-5263	3
Willis Knighton Medical Center	Shreveport, LA	(318) 212-4000	3
Beth Israel Deaconess Medical Center	Boston, MA	(617) 667-7000	1
Baystate Medical Center	Springfield, MA	(413) 787-5300	1
Boston Medical Center	Boston, MA	(617) 638-8000	1
Children's Hospital	Boston, MA	(617) 355-6000	1
Lahey Clinic Medical Center	Burlington, MA	(781) 744-5100	1
Massachusetts General Hospital	Boston, MA	(617) 726-2000	1
New England Medical Center	Boston, MA	(617) 636-5000	1
Brigham and Women's Hospital	Boston, MA	(617) 732-5500	1
University of Massachusetts Memorial Medical Center	Worcester, MA	(508) 334-1000	1
Johns Hopkins Hospital	Baltimore, MD	(410) 955-5000	2
Warren Grant Magnuson Clinical Center/National Institutes of Health	Bethesda, MD	(301) 496-1211	2
University of Maryland Medical System	Baltimore, MD	(410) 328-6363	2
Maine Medical Center	Portland, ME	(207) 871-0111	1
William Beaumont Hospital	Royal Oak, MI	(248) 898-5000	10
Children's Hospital of Michigan	Detroit, MI	(313) 745-0073	10
Henry Ford Hospital	Detroit, MI	(313) 916-2600	10
Harper Hospital Detroit Medical Center	Detroit, MI	(313) 745-8040	10
Hurley Medical Center	Flint, MI	(810) 257-9572	10

Name	Location	Phone	Region
St. John Hospital and Medical Center	Detroit, MI	(313) 343-4000	10
St. Mary's Mercy Medical Center	Grand Rapids, MI	(616) 752-6090	10
University of Michigan Medical Center	Ann Arbor, MI	(734) 936-4000	10
Abbott Northwestern Hospital	Minneapolis, MN	(612) 863-4000	7
Hennepin County Medical Center	Minneapolis, MN	(612) 347-2121	7
Rochester Methodist Hospital (Mayo Clinic)	Rochester, MN	(507) 266-7890	7
St. Mary's Hospital (Mayo Clinic)	Rochester, MN	(507) 284-2511	7
Fairview University Medical Center	Minneapolis, MN	(612) 273-3000	7
Barnes-Jewish Hospital	St. Louis, MO	(314) 747-3000	8
Cardinal Glennon Children's Hospital	St. Louis, MO	(314) 577-5600	8
St. Louis Children's Hospital at Washington University Medical Center	St. Louis, MO	(314) 454-6000	8
The Children's Mercy Hospital	Kansas City, MO	(816) 234-3000	8
St. Luke's Hospital of Kansas City	Kansas City, MO	(816) 932-2000	8
Research Medical Center	Kansas City, MO	(816) 276-4000	8
St. Louis University Hospital	St. Louis, MO	(314) 577-8000	8
University of Missouri Hospital and Clinics	Columbia, MO	(573) 882-4141	8
University of Mississippi Medical Center	Jackson, MS	(601) 984-1000	3
North Carolina Baptist Hospital	Winston Salem, NC	(336) 716-2011	11
Carolinas Medical Center	Charlotte, NC	(704) 355-2000	11
Duke University Medical Center and Durham VA Medical Center	Durham, NC	(919) 684-8111	11
Pitt County Memorial Hospital, East Carolina University School of Medicine	Greenville, NC	(252) 816-4100	11
University of North Carolina Hospitals	Chapel Hill, NC	(919) 966-4131	11
Medcenter One Health Systems	Bismarck, ND	(701) 323-6000	7
MeritCare Hospital	Fargo, ND	(701) 234-6000	7
BryanLGH Medical Center East	Lincoln, NE	(402) 489-0200	8
Nebraska Medical Center	Omaha, NE	(402) 559-4000	8

Name	Location	Phone	Region
Mary Hitchcock Memorial Hospital	Lebanon, NH	(603) 650-5000	1
Newark Beth Israel Medical Center	Newark, NJ	(973) 926-7000	2
Hackensack University Medical Center	Hackensack, NJ	(201) 996-2000	2
Our Lady of Lourdes Medical Center	Camden, NJ	(609) 757-3500	2
Robert Wood Johnson University Hospital	New Brunswick, NJ	(732) 828-3000	2
St. Barnabas Medical Center	Livingston, NJ	(973) 322-5000	2
University Hospital	Newark, NJ	(973) 972-6000	2
University Hospital, University of New Mexico Health Sciences Center	Albuquerque, NM	(505) 272-2111	5
Presbyterian Hospital	Albuquerque, NM	(505) 841-1234	5
Sunrise Hospital and Medical Center	Las Vegas, NV	(702) 731-8000	5
University Medical Center of Southern Nevada	Las Vegas, NV	(702) 383-2000	5
Albany Medical Center Hospital	Albany, NY	(518) 262-3125	9
Buffalo General Hospital, Children's Hospital, and Buffalo VA Medical Center	Buffalo, NY	(716) 859-5600	9
The Presbyterian Hospital in New York City/ Columbia Presbyterian Medical Center	New York, NY	(212) 305-2323	9
State University of New York Health Science Center at Brooklyn	Brooklyn, NY	(718) 270-1000	9
Erie County Medical Center	Buffalo, NY	(716) 898-3000	9
Strong Memorial Hospital, University of Rochester Medical Center	Rochester, NY	(585) 275-2121	9
Montefiore Medical Center	Bronx, NY	(718) 920-4321	9
Mount Sinai Medical Center	New York, NY	(212) 241-6500	9
The New York Hospital	New York, NY	(212) 746-5000	9
University Hospital of State University of New York at Stony Brook	Stony Brook, NY	(631) 689-8333	9
St. Luke's Roosevelt Hospital Center	New York, NY	(212) 523-4000	9
New York University Medical Center	New York, NY	(212) 263-7300	9
State University of New York Upstate Medical University	Syracuse, NY	(315) 464-5540	9

Name	Location	Phone	Region
Westchester Medical Center	Valhalla, NY	(914) 493-7000	9
Akron City Hospital	Akron, OH	(330) 375-3000	10
The Cleveland Clinic Foundation	Cleveland, OH	(216) 444-2200	10
Children's Hospital	Columbus, OH	(614) 722-2000	10
Children's Hospital Medical Center	Cincinnati, OH	(513) 636-4200	10
Medical College Hospitals	Toledo, OH	(419) 383-4000	10
Miami Valley Hospital	Dayton, OH	(937) 208-8000	10
Ohio State University Hospital	Columbus, OH	(614) 293-8000	10
St. Elizabeth Health Center	Youngstown, OH	(330) 746-7211	10
The Christ Hospital	Cincinnati, OH	(513) 585-2000	10
University of Cincinnati Medical Center/ University Hospital	Cincinnati, OH	(513) 584-1000	10
University Hospitals of Cleveland	Cleveland, OH	(216) 844-1000	10
Integris Baptist Medical Center	Oklahoma City, OK	(405) 949-3011	4
Children's Hospital of Oklahoma	Oklahoma City, OK	(405) 271-5437	4
Hillcrest Medical Center	Tulsa, OK	(918) 579-1000	4
OU Medical Center	Oklahoma City, OK	(405) 271-5656	4
St. Anthony Hospital	Oklahoma City, OK	(405) 272-7000	4
St. Francis Hospital	Tulsa, OK	(918) 494-2200	4
St. John Medical Center	Tulsa, OK	(918) 744-2345	4
Legacy Good Samaritan Hospital and Medical Center	Portland, OR	(503) 229-7711	6
Providence Portland Medical Center	Portland, OR	(503) 215-1111	6
Oregon Health Sciences University Hospital and Portland VA Medical Center	Portland, OR	(503) 494-8311	6
Albert Einstein Medical Center	Philadelphia, PA	(215) 456-7890	2
Allegheny General Hospital	Pittsburgh, PA	(412) 359-3131	2
Children's Hospital of Pittsburgh	Pittsburgh, PA	(412) 648-3200	2
Children's Hospital of Philadelphia	Philadelphia, PA	(215) 590-1000	2

Name	Location	Phone	Region
Geisinger Medical Center	Danville, PA	(570) 271-6211	2
Penn State Milton S. Hershey Medical Center	Hershey, PA	(717) 531-8521	2
Pinnacle Health System at Harrisburg Hospital	Harrisburg, PA	(717) 782-3131	2
Hahnemann University Hospital Tenet	Philadelphia, PA	(215) 762-7000	2
The Lankenau Hospital	Wynnewood, PA	(610) 645-2000	2
Lehigh Valley Hospital	Allentown, PA	(610) 402-8000	2
University of Pittsburgh Medical Center and Oakland VA Medical Center	Pittsburgh, PA	(412) 647-2345	2
St. Christopher's Hospital for Children	Philadelphia, PA	(215) 427-5000	2
Thomas Jefferson University Hospital	Philadelphia, PA	(215) 955-6000	2
Temple University Hospital	Philadelphia, PA	(215) 707-2000	2
Hospital of the University of Pennsylvania	Philadelphia, PA	(215) 662-4000	2
Cardiovascular Center of Puerto Rico and the Caribbean	San Juan, PR	(787) 754-8500	3
Auxilio Mutuo Hospital	Hato Rey, PR	(787) 758-2000	3
Rhode Island Hospital	Providence, RI	(401) 444-4000	1
Medical University of South Carolina	Charleston, SC	(843) 792-2300	11
Avera McKennan Hospital	Sioux Falls, SD	(605) 322-7350	7
Baptist Memorial Hospital	Memphis, TN	(901) 226-2000	11
Erlanger Medical Center	Chattanooga, TN	(423) 778-7000	11
Johnson City Medical Center Hospital	Johnson City, TN	(423) 431-6164	11
Le Bonheur Children's Medical Center	Memphis, TN	(901) 572-3000	11
Centennial Medical Center	Nashville, TN	(615) 342-1000	11
St. Thomas Hospital	Nashville, TN	(615) 222-2111	11
University of Tennessee Medical Center at Knoxville	Knoxville, TN	(865) 544-9000	11
William F. Bowld Hospital University of Tennessee Medical Center	Memphis, TN	(901) 448-4000	11
Vanderbilt University Medical Center and Nashville VA Medical Center	Nashville, TN	(615) 322-5000	11

Name	Location	Phone	Region
Brackenridge Hospital	Austin, TX	(512) 324-7000	4
Baylor All Saints Medical Center	Fort Worth, TX	(817) 922-4650	4
University Hospital University of Texas Health Science Center	San Antonio, TX	(210) 567-5777	4
Cook Children's Medical Center	Fort Worth, TX	(682) 885-4000	4
Methodist Children's Hospital of South Texas	San Antonio, TX	N/A	4
Children's Medical Center of Dallas	Dallas, TX	(214) 456-7000	4
Seton Medical Center	Austin, TX	(512) 324-1000	4
North Austin Medical Center	Austin, TX	(512) 901-1000	4
Harris Methodist Fort Worth	Fort Worth, TX	(817) 882-2000	4
Columbia Hospital at Medical City Dallas	Dallas, TX	(972) 566-7000	4
Hermann Hospital University of Texas at Houston	Houston, TX	(713) 704-4000	4
St. Luke's Episcopal Hospital	Houston, TX	(713) 785-8537	4
Methodist Specialty & Transplant Hospital	San Antonio, TX	(210) 575-8110	4
University of Texas Medical Branch at Galveston	Galveston, TX	(409) 772-1101	4
University Medical Center	Lubbock, TX	(806) 743-3111	4
Covenant Medical Center	Lubbock, TX	(806) 725-1011	4
Methodist Medical Center Dallas	Dallas, TX	(214) 947-1800	4
The Methodist Hospital Baylor College of Medicine	Houston, TX	(713) 790-3333	4
Parkland Memorial Hospital	Dallas, TX	(214) 590-8000	4
Christus Santa Rosa Medical Center	San Antonio, TX	(210) 705-6700	4
Sierra Medical Center	El Paso, TX	(915) 747-4000	4
St. Paul University Hospital	Dallas, TX	(214) 879-1000	4
Scott and White Memorial Hospital	Temple, TX	(254) 724-2111	4
Texas Children's Hospital	Houston, TX	(832) 824-1000	4
Baylor University Medical Center	Dallas, TX	(214) 820-0111	4
East Texas Medical Center	Tyler, TX	(903) 597-0351	4
LDS Hospital	Salt Lake City, UT	(801) 408-1100	5

Name	Location	Phone	Region
University of Utah Medical Center & Salt Lake City VA Medical Center	Salt Lake City, UT	(801) 581-2121	5
Primary Children's Medical Center	Salt Lake City, UT	(801) 588-2000	5
Children's Hospital of the Kings Daughters	Norfolk, VA	(757) 668-7000	11
Inova Fairfax Hospital	Falls Church, VA	(703) 698-1110	2
Henrico Doctors' Hospital	Richmond, VA	(804) 289-4500	11
Medical College of Virginia Hospitals	Richmond, VA	(804) 828-9000	11
Hunter Holmes McGuire Veterans Administration Medical Center	Richmond, VA	(804) 675-5000	11
Sentara Norfolk General Hospital	Norfolk, VA	(757) 668-3934	11
University of Virginia Health Sciences Center	Charlottesville, VA	(434) 924-0211	11
Fletcher Allen Health Care	Burlington, VT	(802) 656-2345	9
Children's Hospital Medical Center	Seattle, WA	(206) 987-2000	6
Sacred Heart Medical Center	Spokane, WA	(509) 474-3131	6
Swedish Medical Center	Seattle, WA	(206) 386-6000	6
University of Washington Medical Center	Seattle, WA	(206) 598-3300	6
Virginia Mason Medical Center	Seattle, WA	(206) 223-6600	6
Children's Hospital of Wisconsin	Milwaukee, WI	(414) 266-2000	7
Froedtert Memorial Lutheran Hospital	Milwaukee, WI	(414) 259-3000	7
St. Luke's Medical Center	Milwaukee, WI	(414) 649-6000	7
University of Wisconsin Hospital and Clinics	Madison, WI	(608) 263-6400	7
Charleston Area Medical Center	Charleston, WV	(304) 388-5432	2
West Virginia University Hospital	Morgantown, WV	(304) 598-4000	2

Appendix 8B

THE ROLES AND REACTIONS OF FAMILY AND FRIENDS

Reactions of Family and Friends

When one member of a close-knit family becomes ill with a life-threatening disease, the whole family dynamic is thrown into turmoil. If the family lives in a small community, their misfortune may also affect the entire community as well. These types of life-changing events often have the effect of showing who your real friends are. Some friends are lost and new ones are made.

Some people don't know how to respond to the misfortune of others. When a friend or neighbor becomes ill, they do nothing. They are afraid of interfering with the family's privacy and/or making things worse, so they act as if nothing unusual has happened and avoid the topics of illness and hardship. Other people, when they hear of a friend's illness or misfortune, their natural instinct is to offer help. These people may already know what it's like to experience hardship themselves and may have been helped in the past by the goodwill of others. Still other people think that the safest place to be, in relation to a sick person, is as far away as possible in case the illness is contagious!

If these are people we care about, it helps if we accept each of them on their own terms, and realize that people have different ways of reacting to and coping with misfortune. We should continue to communicate with them, but not let the ones who react negatively bring us down. Our experience was that for every friend we lost, we gained two new ones!

Support Network

Whether a new friend or an old one, there is much that a good friend can do! Letters, emails, cards, and prayers are great spirit-lifters. Most of all, a good friend will listen when you need to talk about things.

If the transplant center is far from home, and we find ourselves living in a new town, it is helpful to find a place of worship nearby. This is an excellent place to make new friends and find support.

Advocate for the Patient

Hopefully, all of the important decisions have been made before the patient becomes too ill to handle his/her own affairs: choosing the transplant center, writing a will, getting finances in order, deciding whether to execute a living will. These are all decisions the patient should make while still relatively healthy. The primary role of family and friends is providing love, understanding, and emotional support, and keeping their own spirits up so they can be a source of strength for the patient!

However, there is one important role that a trusted friend or family member can fill. This is the role of advocate for the patient. Most doctors and hospitals encourage this relationship. An advocate should be someone who knows the patient well and is willing to stay with him/her throughout their illness. The role of the advocate is to:

- learn as much as possible about the patient's illness;
- get to know the doctors and nurses;
- sit in on meetings between patient and doctors;
- learn about and be present for medical procedures performed on the patient;
- learn about and monitor medications administered to the patient;
- stay in the hospital room with the patient day and night, if necessary; and
- assist the nurses with nontechnical patient care.

Most doctors and nurses will welcome such an advocate. An advocate can be a big help to doctors and nurses, especially for patients that are hospitalized for long periods of time.

Advocacy is also discussed in Appendix 2B, "Care and Coverage Considerations."

Cooperative Caregiver

Some hospitals have a special unit called "Cooperative Care" for patients that are not critical, but still require hospitalization. If the patient has a family member or friend willing to accept the responsibility, the hospital will train the person to care for the patient and provide room and board for both patient and caregiver in the Cooperative Care Unit. A nurses' station is situated on site to answer caregiver questions and come to the aid of caregivers when necessary. This type of arrangement costs much less than traditional hospitalization and, in general, helps to ease the shortage of nurses. Additionally, patients may recover faster having a loved one caring for them.

9

SECOND LIVER TRANSPLANT SURGERY

Fourth Transplant Center
University of Miami School of Medicine
November, 1999

The night before we left for Miami, we had a nice family gathering. We didn't know when we would all be together next. Rebecca and Dave, and Ben, Laura, Josh, and Jacob all came by to visit. The next morning, Joe took David, Sara, Rachael, and me to the airport. He told us he would be joining us soon in Miami.

Back in 1981, when we went to Pittsburgh, David was so weak he could hardly walk. Joe and I had to stand up during the airplane flight so David could lie down on the seats. This time, we used a wheelchair in the airport, but David walked onto the plane. He was slow and using a cane, but he was walking.

Rachael was very excited. She was fascinated with the airplane. I wondered if she understood the difference between flying and driving. We gave Rachael the window seat, and she fixed her attention on the hustle and bustle outside the window, ignoring the coloring book and crayons Sara offered her. As soon as the plane took off, she took her eyes off the window and shouted, "We are flying! We are flying! Is Dad coming? Is Mom coming?" She looked around to make sure that we were all flying with her. When we were up in the air above the clouds, Rachael opened her coloring book and kept one eye on the coloring book and the other one out the window.

David's medical records, x-rays, and test results had been prepared for us by Northwestern on short notice. They filled my carry-on bag. We hadn't packed them in the luggage because we couldn't take the chance that they would be lost or arrive late. We had an appointment at the clinic the next day and we had to have those records with us.

The captain's voice came over the speaker. He was talking about the mountains we were flying over and I was reminded of Rachael's favorite song, "The Bear Went over the Mountain," and how all he saw was the other side of the mountain. I wondered if that was going to happen to us in Miami.

"Will we just be seeing another transplant center and getting on another waiting list? Will David once again be released without being cured? What if the doctors tell us David is too sick to survive a liver transplant and they can't risk wasting an organ on him?" If he wasn't already too sick, I felt that he would be soon. When that happened, where would we go next?

David spoke very slowly now and his speech patterns reminded me of the way he talked two weeks before he fell into the coma in 1981. But now, because he was hopeful that he would receive a transplant in Miami, he was holding on. He was trying to be strong, to be the man that was taking care of his pregnant wife and 2-year-old daughter. I felt the responsibility of caring for a dying man, pregnant woman, and little girl weighing heavily on my shoulders. Rachael's song continued to play in my head as I pondered these sobering thoughts.

The plane landed and when we went to get our luggage, Rachael's car seat and stroller weren't there. The airline promised to deliver them to our hotel the next day. It was early evening, but it felt like midnight because it was November and the days were shorter. David tried to help with the luggage, and called the shuttle to pick us up. The shuttle took us to the hotel where we had reserved a room. The hotel was nearly full and we ended up in two rooms with windows facing the stairwell, but at least the rooms were next to each other.

The next day, before our 10:00 a.m. appointment at the clinic, we were to attend an orientation for new patients. When we got out of the elevator, we were surprised to see Sara's Uncle Ray and Aunt Connie waiting for us. Sara's mom Johnie had called them to give them our schedule, and they were here from Boca Raton to baby-sit for Rachael during our appointment at the clinic. It was a good surprise and it meant a lot to us. It gave us the feeling that we weren't alone, even though we were hundreds of miles away from home. Rachael recognized them and was happy to go with them.

Victoria Cosley, a social worker and member of the transplant team, was teaching the orientation class. We introduced ourselves to everyone in the room. Like David, they were all patients in varying stages of liver failure. They were inspired by David's 17 years of healthy, normal life after his first liver transplant. The social worker covered various topics related to liver transplant, including the waiting list, the transplant surgery, expenses, insurance considerations, fundraising for patients without insurance, and where out-of-town patients should look for housing. David also received a handbook that had more detailed information.

In the clinic, we met with Dr. Tzakis and the transplant team. I could see the concern in their faces and knew that they considered David to be very ill. My heart was pounding so hard, I was afraid they would hear it. I was consumed with fear: fear that they would decide David was too sick for a transplant; fear that they would tell us that we should have come last year when they first invited us, because now it was too late; fear that they would blame David for participating in the experimental program to stop taking antirejection drugs. My thoughts were racing as fast as my heart.

Dr. Tzakis asked for David's x-rays and records. He wanted to take them back to the x-ray room to go over them with Dr. Antonio Pinna, another Pittsburgh-trained doctor. I asked to accompany them. I had been trying to look at the x-rays at home, but didn't have the proper light and didn't know how to read them. I was hoping that by looking at the x-rays, I would be able to understand the mystery of David's liver failure after 17 healthy years. I believed that a buildup of scar tissue was probably the major cause.

In the x-ray room, I stood back as Dr. Tzakis and Dr. Pinna examined the x-rays. Dr. Tzakis started explaining Dr. Starzl's transplant techniques to Dr. Pinna. That didn't interest me as much as the respect and admiration that I could see both men had for Dr. Starzl. I thought to myself, "With that much respect for Dr. Starzl, Dr. Tzakis won't refuse David." Dr. Tzakis had learned to be a transplant surgeon from Dr. Starzl and I hoped that he had learned more than just technique from Dr. Starzl; I hoped that he had also learned not to give up. David might be very sick, but I prayed that Dr. Tzakis would follow Dr. Starzl's example, and that meant not being afraid of big challenges.

When Dr. Tzakis and I had spoken on the phone a year earlier, he told me that David's surgery would be very difficult. He had operated on other patients who'd returned for a retransplant after ten or more years, and the buildup of scar tissue made it a challenge just to get the old liver out. Then I remembered what Dr. Starzl wrote about Dr. Tzakis in his memoir, *The Puzzle People*:

> Tzakis *could* do liver transplantation and did. One night at 4 a.m., I was awakened by an anesthesiologist who asked me to come to the operating room and order Andy Tzakis to pronounce dead a recipient whose heart had quit beating while the liver was being sewn in. Against the advice of the more senior surgeon assisting him and the anesthesiologist, Andy had refused to give up trying to restart the

heart. When I arrived, I told the person who called that I would not give the order she wanted. I went upstairs to the observation dome and watched the activities below. It was a scene in pantomime because those on neither side of the glass could hear the others.

Using their hands as a makeshift pump, members of the surgical team performed heart massage and propelled the life-giving blood through the inert heart to the waiting body. Periodically, the heart was shocked and would jump, only to fall motionless once again. Finally, it shuddered like a dog awakening from a long slumber, and began to beat. The patient lived. Every Christmas since then, he has written to me, always giving the date of his transplant as the anniversary of his second life. It was also the day when Tzakis completed his training.

Dr. Tzakis was not the type to give up easily.

We spent the rest of the morning in the clinic while other surgeons and doctors examined David and spoke with him. David was becoming more hopeful with each new doctor that he saw. During his first transplant in Pittsburgh in 1981, David was the center of attention. Now, here in Miami, David was the center of attention once again. Most of the doctors knew of him through Dr. Starzl's book or had heard his story at transplant conferences.

After examining David physically, the doctors examined David's Pittsburgh liver biopsy slides and his Northwestern CT scan and ultrasound. They then drew blood for a blood chemistry profile. They assigned a transplant coordinator to David and requested that he transfer his waiting list points from Northwestern to Miami. We were instructed to return in a week to find out where David was on the waiting list.

I was relieved and David was as happy as he could be, given his condition. We had lunch with Sara's Uncle Ray and Aunt Connie. They invited us to come to their house and stay with them while we were in Miami, but as sick as David was, we preferred to stay near the hospital.

After lunch, we returned to the hotel. Rachael loved the hotel room! Sara put a rail on the double bed and Rachael loved it because she had plenty of room for all of her toys, books, and stuffed animals. She set out all of her toy cars, put people in them, and played for a long time. She would be able to fall asleep with her blankie surrounded by the things that she loved. But I found the hotel room dark and depressing and I couldn't wait to get out. When David fell asleep, I returned to my room and began looking for a new place for us to live.

From the list of housing that we'd been given, we chose to rent a furnished apartment in Brickell Key. As we drove over the bridge between Miami and Brickell Key, we found ourselves in a quiet and peaceful place. Our apartment faced the bay, and Rachael could stand on the sofa and watch the boats sailing below.

The next morning, I woke up to find Rachael standing over me with a big smile on her face. That will be a great reason to wake up every morning, I thought to myself. David was making breakfast and I could tell he was excited about the prospect of receiving a liver transplant soon. He was sick and tired of being sick.

A few days later, David woke me up at 2:00 a.m. "I don't feel good," he said. "Can you take me to the hospital?" What could be wrong with him right now, at this moment? It was hard to guess.

He asked me to drive, but I still didn't know my way around. Just getting out of the apartment building parking lot was a challenge at that time of night. David felt that I should learn my way to the hospital in case a liver came in the middle of the night. With Sara pregnant, he didn't feel right waking her up in the middle of the night to drive him to the hospital. David had a good sense of direction and was able to learn his way around new places quickly. I knew if he could direct me to the hospital correctly, I could be sure this midnight trip wasn't just another case of encephalopathy.

With David's help, we made our way to the Jackson Memorial Hospital emergency room. When David saw all the people in the waiting room, he decided that he didn't have the energy to wait, that he just wanted to lie down. So that I would take him home, he said he was feeling better. We returned home and went back to bed, but it was hard to get back to sleep.

I still remembered the many sleepless nights we spent waiting for a liver in Pittsburgh in 1981. In those days, he was just 12 years old and I could distract him from his worry or discomfort just by talking about his Bar Mitzvah or plans for the future. Now the future was here. The Bar Mitzvah was over and the flying lessons were behind us, yet once again he was back on the waiting list. It just didn't seem fair, but he knew that life wasn't fair and there was nothing that I or anyone else could do about it. David was too old to distract from his physical and emotional pain. All I could do was to wait and see what he wanted me to do.

Joe drove down from Chicago and arrived on Monday. He brought my car so we would have our own car in Miami. We all went to David's one-week appointment with Dr. Tzakis. Dr. Tzakis' office was not very big, but the walls were covered with pictures of his wife, daughter, and patients. We sat quietly and waited for him to talk. He spoke with compassion and told David that he was at the top of the waiting list. I stopped holding my breath and inhaled deeply. David wiped a tear from his eye. It was a big relief to know that Dr. Tzakis was willing to take the chance and operate on David! I wondered if David had been sharing my worries about him being too sick to be considered for a transplant. I thought it was possible, given the way that he was fighting sleep to avoid falling into a coma.

Joe asked if we should return to Chicago and wait to be called.

Dr. Tzakis recommended that we stay in Miami, but not as a patient. "Pretend you're on vacation," he told us. "Michigan is cold this time of year and Florida is beautiful. Go outside and enjoy the sun and warm weather."

"When will it be my turn?" David asked.

"Soon," Dr. Tzakis answered.

It sounded too good to be true and I reminded myself that one of the jobs of a transplant surgeon is to keep their patients hopeful. We had been hearing "soon" for 17 months. The transplant team couldn't predict exactly when a liver would be available, but the important thing was that they were willing to operate on David.

In a few days, the Thanksgiving holiday would be upon us. We decided we should rent a bigger apartment and plan to spend the winter in Miami. We rented a two-bedroom apartment in the same building. On Thanksgiving Day, we moved into the new place. Joe and David were in a hurry to get us settled; they were both optimistic that the liver that David needed so badly would be coming any day now. On past Thanksgivings, Joe would cook a large turkey overnight and the house would be filled with good smells all day. There wouldn't be time for that tradition this year, but we could buy everything already cooked from the food store on the island and warm it up in the oven. When we opened the oven, we found that the previous occupants had sprayed the inside with oven cleaner and neglected to clean it out. By the time we cleaned out the oven, it was too late for turkey so we ordered a pizza. On Friday, we warmed up the turkey and the fixings and celebrated Thanksgiving a day late. We missed the rest of our family.

That night, David woke us up and told us he had called 911 and an ambulance was on its way. He was not feeling well at all. The paramedics arrived and examined David. They told us he was a very sick man, but it was not an emergency. They recommended that David visit his doctor and/or go to the emergency room the next day since we were there to drive him.

As we were going back to bed, David reminded us that his bed was a water bed (something that we hadn't noticed when we rented the apartment) and was very difficult to sleep on. He felt he would be more comfortable on a hard mattress. It was too late at night to switch rooms, so Joe and I offered him our bed and we slept on the sofas in the living room.

In the morning, the sun was shining and the crystals on the living room lamp reflected rainbows of light all around the room. The rainbows reminded me of "God's Signature" and the rainbow in Niagara Falls. I remembered how that sign gave me hope that David would be all right. We decided to take Dr. Tzakis' vacation advice and made plans to visit Miami Beach to see what all the hoopla was about.

When we were all dressed and ready to go, the telephone rang. It was Saturday morning and we thought it might be Ben, Rebecca, or Sara's sister Christy. David picked up the phone. Joe, Sara, and I all watched David, secretly wondering if this could be the call we'd been waiting for the last 17 months. David smiled, and for the first time in the last 17 months, I saw the light of joy in his eyes. He gave us the thumbs-up, hung up the phone and told us that, instead of Miami Beach, we would be going to the hospital.

When we told Rachael that instead of going to the beach, we would be taking her dad to the hospital for a transplant, she didn't miss a beat. She just said, "Again?" Then, she exchanged her enthusiasm for a trip to the beach with enthusiasm for a visit to the hospital.

After David registered, we went up to the 15th floor. As David was being prepped for surgery, I opened my purse and retrieved three pages that I had been carrying with me for the last 17 months. It was a special prayer[1] published by the Union of American Hebrew Congregations Committee on Bioethics (UAHC) for people who are receiving an organ, tissue, or bone marrow transplant. Rabbi Steven Mason, our rabbi at North Shore Congregation Israel, had sent the prayer to us when he learned that David was on the waiting list. We all read our parts from the prayer, then David was put on a stretcher and we rode in the elevator with him to the third floor. In the room adjacent to the operating room, we hung around David's bed

---

[1] See Appendix 11

waiting for the moment we'd been anticipating for 17 months—the moment when they wheeled David into surgery. I was already planning ahead. Six weeks was the average recovery time for a liver transplant patient. In six short weeks, David would be well on the road to recovery and life would get back to normal. We handed David's x-rays, CT scans, and test results over to the doctors and kissed David before he was wheeled into the operating room.

A nurse was assigned to keep us updated on David's condition in the operating room. We could call her every two hours and she would answer our questions. We were told that it would be a long wait and we would be better off waiting in the comfort of our apartment since we were only a short drive from the hospital.

In the apartment, we tried to keep busy. We called all the people who were following David's condition and waiting for David's transplant with us. Ben arrived on the next plane out of Chicago and joined our group. After the phone calls, Sara and I kept ourselves busy with laundry, ironing, and unpacking in the apartment we'd just moved into a few days ago while Rachael played with her toys.

We ate lunch and at the two-hour mark, we called the liaison nurse. The report was good; everything was going as planned. When Rachael awoke from her afternoon nap, we called again. According to the nurse, progress was still good. After supper, there was nothing left to do and we were getting fidgety. We gave Rachael a bath, read her a bedtime story, put her to bed, and called the liaison nurse for the third time. This time, she told us it was a very bloody surgery. I had seen some transplant slides and knew that a lot of blood was both lost and transfused during transplant surgery, so this didn't worry us too much. Throughout the night, we continued to call every two hours and each time, the news was the same: "It's a bloody surgery, but David is doing fine." Sometime after midnight, Dr. Tzakis called us. He told us that the liver was in David, but the incision wasn't closed yet and it would take a while. He recommended that we go to bed for the night and return to the hospital in the morning to see David.

Appendix 9

LIVER TRANSPLANT SURGERY
AND MEDICATIONS

Liver Transplant Surgery: What to Expect

(Parts reprinted with permission from UNOS and from the Patient and Family Guide to Liver
Transplantation, developed by the pretransplant and posttransplant coordinators at the University
of Miami Department of Surgery, Division of Transplantation)

The Phone Call

For the patient that is still living outside the hospital, the most important
phone call of his life is the call from the pretransplant coordinator telling him
that an organ is available for him. For the patient's sake, the transplant team
is hoping that the phone line is open and monitored day and night. Patients
must be especially vigilant about answering those nighttime phone calls
because most organs become available during the night. If the patient miss-
es that all-important call, the organ will go to someone else.

Organ Preservation Time

Vital organs are often transported hundreds of miles in order to reach the
patient. This is possible, in part, because of advances in medical technology
and improved organ preservation techniques. However, each organ has a
limited "preservation time," after which the organ is less likely to be viable:

ORGAN	PRESERVATION TIME
Heart	4 – 6 hours
Liver	12 – 24 hours
Kidney	48 – 72 hours
Heart-Lung	4 – 6 hours
Lung	4 – 6 hours

Travel Arrangements

The out-of-town patient should have a list of commercial flights with him at all times, and the in-town patient should rehearse the route ahead of time if he is driving himself to the hospital. Advance planning is required so that precious time is not wasted while the organ is waiting. When the coordinator reaches the patient by telephone, and the patient accepts the organ, the patient should immediately make travel plans and transport himself to the hospital.

Evaluation of the Organ

The patient's transplant center will have the donor's health history and a record of medications used for attempted resuscitation. When the donated organ arrives at the transplant center, it is evaluated by the transplant team. Sometimes an organ classified as normal, healthy, and suitable for transplantation doesn't pass this final evaluation. Under these circumstances, the surgery may be cancelled after the arrival of the patient at the center. This is called a "dry run." Disappointingly, the patient is discharged and sent home to await another donor.

Consent Forms

If everything goes well with the donor organ evaluation, the recipient will go through patient registration and then proceed to a designated area in the transplant center to meet with the anesthesiologist and the transplant team. After meeting with the team, the patient will be asked to sign consent forms for anesthesia and transplant surgery. In signing the consent forms, it may be helpful for patients to know that liver transplant is now considered to be a routine, although major, surgery with a success rate of about 85%.

After the patient is prepped for surgery and taken to the operating room, family members who've accompanied the patient may choose to wait either at home or in the hospital waiting room, depending on their distance from the hospital. The surgery generally takes between 8 and 12 hours.

The Surgery

In the operating room, the patient is moved from the gurney to the operating room table. A team of professionals will care for the patient throughout the transplant. The anesthesiologist begins by connecting a heart monitor to the patient's chest so he can monitor the patient's heart rate and rhythm. An IV is inserted to administer fluids and medications. The anesthesiologist then sedates the patient. Once the patient is asleep, he inserts a breathing tube, an IV into the patient's neck or shoulder area (a very large IV through which a catheter is threaded to monitor pressures in the heart), a nasogastric tube to keep the patient's stomach empty, a Foley catheter to monitor the patient's urine output, and an arterial line to monitor blood pressure (usually a small IV catheter in the artery of the wrist).

After all lines are in place, the surgeons work quickly to remove the damaged organ. This process usually takes about three hours but can take longer if there are adhesions (scar tissue) from any previous abdominal surgery. Once the diseased liver is removed, the new liver is put in place and the surgeons connect the arteries, veins, and bile duct. The process of transplanting the new organ takes about three hours, but can take longer to make sure the vessels and bile duct are properly connected.

Closing the surgical wound takes approximately two hours. All in all, it is not uncommon for a transplant to take ten to fourteen hours.

The nursing staff in the operating room will contact the family at intervals throughout the surgery to give progress reports. At the completion of the transplant, the surgeon will contact the family either in person or by telephone. He will provide an overview of the operative procedure and provide guidance on what to expect in the next 24 hours.

Post-Surgery

After the transplant, recipients are placed in the Intensive Care Unit (ICU) for around-the-clock care. Many hospitals allow family members to visit transplant patients as soon as they are settled in the ICU. Transplant patients without serious complications usually remain in the ICU for one to three days.

Ideally, transplant patients and their families will visit the ICU beforehand to become familiar with the environment and experience the sights and sounds of the life-saving machines and caregivers as they go about their work of providing 24-hour-a-day care for critical patients. Familiarity with the ICU before surgery may help transplant patients to orient themselves more quickly after transplant.

Unlike many other postsurgical patients, liver transplant recipients are usually attached to several IV lines and often life-support equipment as well. Family members and visitors will notice immediately that the patient looks different, but this is nothing to worry about. Some of the things that might be observed are:

Swelling

The patient may look like he/she has suddenly gained weight due to a swelling of the face, upper extremities, and legs. The swelling is due to the massive amounts of fluids administered during the surgery. The swelling is only temporary and will subside as the patient recovers.

Breathing Tube

The breathing tube is inserted in the patient's mouth, passes between the two vocal cords, and rests in the trachea (windpipe) just before the lungs. While the breathing tube is in place, the patient is unable to speak. When the doctors determine that the patient is able to breathe independently, the respirator tube is removed. In some cases, when the patient is strong and healthy before surgery, the breathing tube may be removed before the patient comes out of the anesthesia. In any case, patients with breathing tubes should be encouraged to communicate by writing or using signals.

Pulse-Oximeter

A pulse-oximeter is a small monitor that helps the doctors and nurses to care for the patients by measuring the amount of oxygen in their blood. It tells if the patients are receiving enough oxygen from the ventilator and it helps the doctors determine if the patients are ready to have the breathing tube removed. This machine works by attaching a small "Band-Aid"-like adhesive to the patient's finger, toe, or ear lobe. When the machine is turned on, a small red light appears at the tip of the adhesive. This light is actually measuring the amount of oxygen a patient has in his/her blood stream.

Intravenous Lines

One of the intravenous lines that the patient has had placed in the operating room is called a Swan-Ganz, or pulmonary artery catheter. This specialized catheter is placed through a vein in the neck or upper chest and directed through the chambers of the patient's heart into the pulmonary artery. It helps the doctor measure the pressures in the patient's heart, the amount of blood the patient's heart pumps, and how much oxygen the patient's body uses. This is a very important tool for the surgeons and anesthesiologists during the transplant, and for the staff caring for the patient in the ICU, but it will be removed before the patient leaves the ICU.

Arterial Line

An arterial line is a catheter that is inserted into an artery, usually into the wrist while the patient was in the operating room. The doctors use it to measure the blood pressure, to draw blood, and to avoid sticking the patient too many times. Since this catheter is in an artery, much care must be taken not to dislodge it. If it does become dislodged, bleeding occurs quickly. There may also be a special board on the back of the patient's hand to keep the catheter in proper position. When it is removed, someone will hold pressure over the site for several minutes so that it doesn't bleed. This too will be removed before the patient leaves the ICU.

Nasogastric Tube

A nasogastric or NG tube is a soft, flexible plastic tube that is inserted through the patient's nose and down into their stomach. The other end is connected to a suction container. The purpose of this tube is to keep the patient's stomach empty. If the patient should vomit, there is a danger of that liquid going into their lungs. Even though the patient is not eating, the stomach still secretes fluid. Anesthesia causes the normal movement of the bowel to slow. Once things start moving along (usually two to three days) and bowel sounds return, it will be safe to remove the tube. Until that time, the NG tube may be used to give medication. When the patients are ready to eat again, they will start slowly with sips of clear liquids (apple juice, broth, Jell-O), advance to full liquids (milk, pudding, ice cream), and then progress to a regular diet.

Foley Catheter

A Foley catheter will be used to drain the patient's urine. While the patient is in the operating room and for the immediate post-operative period, urine output is monitored hourly. The catheter allows this to be done.

Wrist Restraints

Wrist restraints are commonly used in the ICU because it is a normal instinct for patients just waking up after surgery to try to pull out the breathing tube, which is a foreign body in their mouth. The restraints prevent patients from putting their life in jeopardy and/or injuring themselves as come out of the anesthesia.

Frequently Asked Questions

What does the incision look like?

The abdominal incision is made in such a way as to have access to the entire abdominal cavity. It looks like a Mercedes Benz emblem, hence the name "Mercedes" incision. The wound is as big as the exterior abdomen. It is closed with staples and stitches. The staples and stitches remain in place for about 30 days. They will be removed during a visit to the outpatient clinic. Usually the patient is allowed to shower within 7 to 10 days. As time goes by, the scar may fade to a thin white line (depending on the patient's own healing process).

What are the rest of the tubes?

At the end of the operation, a Jackson Pratt drain is usually placed in the abdomen to drain any fluid that might collect after the operation. Jackson Pratt drains are grenade-shaped collection devices that work by compressing the air out of them and closing the cap. This creates a suction, which helps remove the fluid that is collecting inside the abdominal cavity. These drains are usually removed two to four days after surgery. If the patient had ascites before surgery, the drain may be left in longer because this fluid continues to accumulate after the transplant and sometimes takes up to a week to control. Once the drain is removed, diuretics or water pills are used to control any additional fluid accumulation and eventually the fluid subsides. If fluid continues to leak from the drain site after the drain is removed, doctors may numb the area and put in a stitch or two to close the hole tighter and prevent leakage.

Depending on the type of procedure used to connect the patient's new bile duct, the patient may require another drainage tube called a T-tube. If the patient's bile duct is connected directly to the donor liver's bile duct (duct to duct), the patient may have a T-tube. The long part of the T-tube is brought out through the skin to allow for drainage of the bile into a bag connected at the end of the tube. The color, amount, and consistency of the bile tell the doctors how the new liver is functioning. The bile should have the color of a gold ring. Usually before the patient leaves the hospital, the bile bag is removed and the tube clamped. (However, there are times when the surgeons discharge the patient from the hospital with the bag and tube intact. In this case, the assembly is removed by the patient's doctor during a posttransplant follow-up visit.) By clamping the tube, the doctors are allowing the bile to drain into the small intestine. Even though the tube is clamped and not draining anything, it still needs to remain in place to allow the area to heal and to act as a stent to help the suture line from scarring and causing a complete or partial obstruction. It will stay in place for 3 to 6 months, clamped and covered with a dry dressing. The patient should not go swimming while the T-tube is in place.

Many times, when a duct to duct bile duct anastomosis is done, the doctors place a small stent (rubber tube) in the bile duct and sew the two ducts together over this stent. If this type of connection is made, there is no drainage tube after the transplant.

Another type of connection is called a Roux-en-y, where the bile duct is connected directly to the small bowel. When this type of surgical connection is made, no additional drainage tubes are necessary. The bile drains directly into the small bowel.

Is there very much pain?

Pain management is always a big concern of anyone undergoing a surgical procedure. The steroids the patient will receive as immunosuppressive therapy will ease their postsurgical pain. Surprisingly, many patients state that they had no pain, but were "uncomfortable." Some untoward effects of pain medications are that they may decrease normal motility of the bowel and/or mask symptoms of possible complications. During the first few days following surgery, pain medication will be available to the patient. While in the ICU, medication is given through the IV. A patient-controlled anesthesia pump (PCA) may be used during the first few days after the surgery. Once the patient is eating, medication will be given in pill form.

What should the Patient expect after the ICU?

Patients without major complications may expect to spend about three days in the ICU before being transferred to a regular floor. Many patients are able to go home within seven to ten days, some sooner, some later. To minimize the postsurgical hospital stay, patients must keep themselves in the best possible condition prior to the transplant. Eating well, not smoking, and getting as much exercise as possible will keep the patient in good condition. Still, there are no formulas for how long the patient will remain in the hospital.

Ambulation is key. The patient will probably be out of bed the first day after the transplant. Spending as much time as possible in a chair rather than in bed will facilitate a speedy recovery. Physical therapy may also useful for the patient after the transplant to help strengthen the patient's muscles during the postoperative period. Patients who are extremely debilitated prior to transplant may need to be transferred to a rehabilitation facility rather than being discharged directly to home.

Posttransplant Medications

In the early days after the transplant, the patient may require many different medications, such as medication to control blood pressure or diabetes, antibiotics to prevent or fight infection, antacids to neutralize stomach acids, and/or diuretics to combat edema (swelling). However, the most important medication for the posttransplant patient is anti-rejection medication, or immunosuppressants. While many of the other medications will eventually be eliminated from the patient's regimen, antirejection medication is required for the rest of the patient's life.

It is important for the patient to take control of his own treatment and medications as soon as possible after the surgery. As soon as the patient is out of the ICU, he should be educated about his medications, dosages, possible side effects, etc. If the patient is not yet conscious, it is helpful for a family member to assume this role until the patient is able to do it himself. Having the patient and family members observe the patient's reactions to medications and watch for possible side effects will be helpful to the doctors who are trying to determine the best medications and dosage levels for the patient.

Anti-Rejection Drugs
Generic Names followed by Brand Names and Manufacturers

Transplant patients take medications each day to prevent organ rejection. Because the patient's immune system recognizes the new organ as a foreign tissue, it's normal for the immune system to try to reject the organ. Drugs called immunosuppressants help suppress the immune system to prevent or reverse rejection. At the same time, these drugs may have side effects. The patient's risk of rejection and susceptibility to side effects are both considered when prescribing drugs and their dosage.

Although researchers continue to study new drugs, these are the most common drugs used to prevent organ rejection:

- Alemtuzumab (Campath)
  Campath, manufactured by ILEX

- Azathioprine (Imuran)
  Imuran, manufactured by Prometheus Laboratories, Inc

- Basiliximab (Simulect)
  Simulect, manufactured by Novartis Pharmaceuticals Corporation

- Cyclophosphamide (Cytoxan)
  Cytoxan, manufactured by Baxter Oncology

- Cyclosporine (Sandimmune, Neoral)
  Sandimmune, manufactured by Novartis Pharmaceuticals Corporation
  Neoral, manufactured by Novartis Pharmaceuticals Corporation

- Daclizumab (Zenapax)
  Zenapax, manufactured by Roche Laboratories Inc

- Everolimus (Certican)
  Certican, manufactured by Novartis Pharmaceuticals Corporation

- Muromonab-CD3 (Orthoclone OKT3)
  Orthoclone OKT3, manufactured by Ortho Biotech

- Mycophenolate Mofetil (CellCept)
  CellCept, manufactured by Roche Laboratories Inc.

- Prednisone (Deltasone, Meticorten, Orasone)
  Deltasone, manufactured by Upjohn
  Meticorten, manufactured by Schering
  Orasone, manufactured by Solvay

- Tacrolimus/FK-506 (Prograf)
  Prograf, manufactured by Fujisawa Healthcare Inc.

- Sirolimus/Rapamycin (Rapamune)
  Rapamune, manufactured by Wyeth

10

THE INFECTIONS

December, 1999

On Sunday morning, we found David unconscious and on a respirator in the ICU. He had retained a lot of fluid and looked like he'd gained 50 pounds. Dr. David Levi was sitting on a stool at the end of David's bed. He looked tired and we knew he hadn't gotten any sleep. "What a surgery!" he said. "It took hours just to get the sick liver out." He admired Dr. Tzakis for his patience and perseverance throughout the night, saying if there was only one surgeon who could perform this surgery successfully, it was Dr. Tzakis.

Dr. Tzakis arrived and told us that, in spite of the long surgery, David's prognosis was good. During the surgery, he'd repaired David's portal vein, the major blood supply to the liver. Apparently, David's portal vein hadn't grown much in the years since his first transplant. I wondered if that might have contributed to his liver failure.

I knew from David's first liver transplant that a recipient could suffer from any of a number of postsurgical complications, especially if they were as sick as David was at the time of the surgery. I tried to be optimistic and I hoped for a fast recovery, but in the back of my mind, I had doubt. I later learned that my doubts were well-founded when one of David's surgeons told us how difficult David's surgery was. He said that their hospital had so many transplant surgeons that they could staff three transplant teams and were able to perform two transplants simultaneously in two different operating rooms. Anticipating a long and difficult surgery, possibly 20 hours or more, all 30 surgeons were called to scrub in for David's transplant. David lost much more blood than usual during his surgery and required transfusions of 120 units of blood.

By the end of the Thanksgiving weekend, David's recovery was progressing normally, and Joe and Ben returned to Chicago to go back to work. The first morning after they left, I awoke to find Rachael crawling into my room. She told me there was a mouse in the house, and she was pretending to be the mouse.

Sara and I planned our day. After breakfast, we went to the hospital to visit David in the Surgical ICU (SICU). One of us watched Rachael, while the other was with David. After lunch, Sara stayed at the apartment with Rachael while she napped, and I sat with David at the hospital. After Rachael's nap, we were all together again at the hospital. Rachael wasn't allowed in the SICU, so we rode the elevator with her, took her to the gift shop and cafeteria, and played outside. She was interested in new places and experiences. With her imagination, she could amuse herself in an empty waiting room. She was shy in front of others, but if the waiting room was empty she would say, "Here comes a train! Grandma, get in!" She would pretend the empty rows of chairs were train seats. She sat in the first one and was the engineer. I was invited to be the passenger.

After David got off the respirator, he became friendly with Dr. Akin Tekin, a member of the transplant team responsible for patient care in the SICU. Dr. Akin looked like he was about David's age. When Dr. Akin learned of David's computer expertise, he nicknamed him "Professor." Soon David was able to sit in a chair and was encouraged to walk. Sitting in his chair, David could see Dr. Akin behind the computer and whenever Dr. Akin looked up, David gave him the thumbs-up.

Every morning, we looked with interest at Dr. Akin's printout that showed David's blood test results. After 17 months of discouraging results, we were happy to be seeing good liver function numbers. I also checked David's urine bag, just as I had after his surgery in 1981, and could see that his urine color was normal again instead of the dark urine produced by people with end-stage liver disease.

By Thursday, just five days after the transplant, David was off the respirator and ready to be moved from the SICU to the 15th floor postsurgical unit. Now, we could spend more time with David, but Rachael was still only allowed into the waiting room on this floor. The rules said that when David was able to sit in a wheelchair, he could come into the waiting room to visit with Rachael.

In the bed next to David was Robert Bank, a young man from Michigan who'd received a multiple organ transplant. He didn't have a large family, but his fiancé Elisha visited as often as she could. He seemed to be doing well.

When we arrived at the hospital on Friday afternoon, the nurse told me that David was uncooperative when he'd tried to wash and shave David that day. That didn't sound like David to me and I had the feeling that something must be wrong with him. David had lost the fluid buildup from the surgery and looked skinny again, but he didn't seem as upbeat as he'd been in the SICU after his surgery. He seemed depressed and was having trouble sleeping. I noticed that when he did manage to nap, his eyes were only half-closed.

I knew that this major surgery could be causing depression. We'd been through that after his surgery in 1981. The doctors had explained that his body was preparing to die when David received his first transplant. The messages from the new liver were trying to turn around a dying body and that was a lot of change! Last time he'd been unable to speak, but this time he was talking and it wasn't very encouraging.

He told me, "You know, Mom, I'm dying."

I told him those days were over and he was on his way to recovery. His bed was next to the window and I urged him to look out at the sky and pretend he was flying an airplane. I told him we wouldn't let him die.

"It's not in your hands," he replied, and then he was quiet.

Dr. Roberto Verzaro entered. He was a pleasant and friendly doctor who talked to us like we were old friends, explaining his role in David's transplant surgery. He told us that after David's operation, he'd looked at the name and remembered David from Dr. Starzl's book, *The Puzzle People*. He seemed happy with David's progress.

After Dr. Verzaro left, David dozed for a while with his eyes half open. In that half-awake, half-asleep state, he was talking to Rachael and looking for her around the bed, calling "Where are you, Rachael? Where are you, Rachael?"

I reminded David that Rachael was not in the room, but he would get to see her soon. David had been able to see Rachael other times when he'd been hospitalized and it was hard for him to understand why he couldn't see her now. It had been a whole week since David had last seen Rachael!

When the transplant surgeons arrived for afternoon rounds, Dr. Pinna was leading the team. David was in a chair, dozing off and on, his body jerking frequently. The doctors were unable to communicate with him and Dr. Pinna prescribed some additional medication for him. I asked for permission to have Rachael visit for a short time and Dr. Pinna wrote in David's chart that Rachael was allowed in. I was hoping that a visit with Rachael would lift David's spirits and bring him some joy, and I knew Rachael would be excited to see David, too.

I took the written permission to the nurses' station by David's room. To my surprise, Ruth, the assistant head nurse on the floor, refused to honor Dr. Pinna's written permission. "These are hospital rules that neither we nor the doctors can change," she said. We were disappointed and I realized that in a large hospital like this, the rules aren't easily changed.

On Saturday, Joe arrived. David's emotional state was unchanged. Now, as he dozed, he was ordering a pizza in his dreams and talking to Ben, Josh, and Jacob. His eyes still half-closed, he began looking for the pizza in the bed sheets. Months later, David told us in detail about another one of the bizarre hallucinations he'd experienced while in this altered state. The story involved Robert Bank, the man in the bed next to his. David imagined one of Robert's visitors brought him a pet mouse, which Robert kept in his bedpan. When the nurse found the mouse in the bedpan, it ran away. As it fled, one of its legs became caught and separated from its body. The surgeons took the mouse to the operating room and sewed its leg back on.

To David, these events were real; they didn't seem like a dream. That's why he acted on them, looking for Rachael around his bed and talking to Josh and Jacob about bowling and pizza even though they weren't even in the room. Joe and I hoped this was just a temporary state, perhaps a side effect of David's medication or the result of stress from the surgery.

That night at midnight, the telephone in the apartment rang. It was David asking for Dr. Malatack's phone number. Dr. Malatack was David's pediatrician in Pittsburgh during his liver transplant in 1981. I reminded David that we were in Miami, Dr. Malatack was no longer his doctor, and it was the middle of the night. We asked David to give the phone to the nurse. The nurse told us that David had pulled out his feeding tube and was not falling asleep despite the late hour, so Joe went to the hospital and spent the rest of the night at David's bedside. David explained his actions, saying that he'd pulled out his feeding tube to eat the pizza that he'd ordered and wanted Dr. Malatack's phone number so he could call him to put the feeding tube back in.

On Sunday, Dr. Pinna told us that he would perform a liver biopsy the next day to check the condition of David's liver. On Monday, the results showed that David was suffering from an infection and that the liver had some preservation damage because the surgery took so long. The doctor told us that David might need another liver so they were putting him back on the waiting list. In the meantime, they would do everything they could to help this liver survive.

It was not good news, especially the prospect of being on the waiting list again and David having to live with a partially-functioning liver. I'd seen the numbers and they didn't look good. I rationalized that since I wasn't a doctor, I might not be reading them right, but the biopsy had confirmed that the liver wasn't working as it should. It was disappointing, but not totally unexpected. Most centers alert patients to the possibility that a second transplant may be needed shortly after the first, explaining that failure sometimes occurs for unknown reasons even when the operation is performed flawlessly. Since 1981, we'd met many patients who had gone in for a transplant and ended up receiving two or three transplants in the course of their hospital stay. All of these patients eventually recovered and returned to normal lives. We were lucky that David's first transplant had worked perfectly and lasted for 17 years. Now, looking on the bright side, we could be thankful that David was at least in the hospital receiving the medical care he needed. But how were we going to break the news that David needed another liver to him and to everyone else? That was a problem.

David's incision was not completely closed. The doctors took David back to the operating room and irrigated his abdominal cavity with antibiotic to combat the infection. After that, David needed to stay in the SICU until he could be removed from the respirator. The SICU nurses were very good to David and devoted most of their time and attention to him. Dr. Akin talked to David as if they were old friends.

Now, Hannukkah was here. Hannukkah is the Jewish holiday of the Festival of Lights. It is a time when the Jews celebrate the miracle that occurred 2,200 years ago when they fought to free their temple from enemy occupation. After driving the enemies from Jerusalem, the Jews wanted to rededicate the temple, but found only enough oil to light the menorah for one day. The miracle was that the oil lasted for 8 days! The holiday is celebrated by lighting the candles for eight days, exchanging gifts, and eating potato latkes.

I wished I could postpone the holiday until David was better, but I knew that life had to go on. The big hanukkahie (menorah) in the lobby of the hospital was a constant reminder of the holiday and the SICU nurses invited me to say the prayers and put up a fabric menorah with David. It was impossible to have a real menorah with lighted candles in the SICU because the oxygen used there is extremely combustible. I appreciated the staff's support in helping us to celebrate the holiday.

Jackson Memorial Hospital is part of the University of Miami. It is one of the largest hospitals I have ever seen with such a diverse and international atmosphere. Among the patients, doctors, nurses, and other hospital staff, you will find people from all over the world working together in harmony. We felt welcome there.

I took Rachael to the toy store to pick her Hannukkah gift. She chose a large mother monkey holding a baby monkey. The monkey pair was bigger than she was, but she managed to carry it through the store. Once she'd made her decision, she wasn't interested in any of the other toys.

Back in the apartment, we lit Hannukkah candles and made potato latkes. It was my responsibility to communicate changes in David's condition to the rest of the family when they weren't here. Ben and Laura were having our yearly Hannukkah gathering at their house, and I thought after dinner would be a good time to call and tell Joe about David's problems with the new liver. The family would be together and they would be able to comfort one other.

On the phone, I confided to Rebecca that I didn't know how to tell David the bad news that he might need yet another liver transplant. Rebecca said she was pretty sure David already knew. She told me that when she'd asked David what he wanted for Hannukkah, he said, "Another liver." He knew the liver wasn't working the way it should by the way he was feeling.

We told David that his name was back on the waiting list in case his condition didn't improve. From that day forward, we no longer asked for the sheet with David's daily liver function test results. We didn't need to see it; we just needed to see David. Every day, the surgeons changed the dressing on David's incision. The drainage from David's wound was increasing and now even his bed was getting wet from the drainage.

After just one day in the SICU, David was removed from the respirator and moved back to the 15th floor, to the room in front of the nurses' station. Only three of the four beds in the room were occupied. At least one assistant nurse was present at all times; the first week, we had two nurses. One of them was Elizabeth, a beautiful young black woman nicknamed "Chocolate Elizabeth," to distinguish her from other nurses with the same name. She had been working on the 15th floor for a long time and we could see that she had a lot of experience. In addition to having an assistant, she was also training Bessie, a student nurse.

Elizabeth quickly became familiar with David's condition and got to know him well. She had a lot of compassion for David and the two of them had a rapport that made David feel comfortable with Elizabeth and her assistant nurse. The assistant nurse, Clyde, was a young man who was well-dressed in his nurse's uniform. He was so confident as he went about his work that if he hadn't told us he was an assistant nurse, we'd have thought he was the doctor.

On Wednesday night, 11 days after the transplant, I was in David's room when Dr. Tzakis came to check on him. Like Dr. Starzl, he tended to drop in on his patients at different times of the day and night. I was helping Clyde change David's sheets for the second time that day. I could see that the nurses were overworked and if I was in the room, I helped them with David's care. Changing the sheets was something I could help with, especially since David wasn't getting out of bed much anymore.

Dr. Tzakis changed the dressing on David's incision and showed me the green color on the white bandage that indicated that the liver was still making and releasing bile. "Maybe there's still hope for the liver," he said. He would do a biopsy the next day to check its condition.

Apparently the biopsy results weren't too bad, because the nurse in charge of caring for the wound arrived to measure the opening of the incision. It was a 1x1x1 inch triangle. She pasted a drainage bag over the incision. Now, we would just have to empty the bag instead of changing the sheets several times a day. David's mental state seemed better, too. He didn't talk much and he didn't complain.

David was still unable to sit in a wheelchair and visit Rachael in the waiting room, and they hadn't seen each other in two weeks. So one night I decided to bring her into the unit to see him. I took Rachael in my arms and carried her into the room and we stood at the end of David's bed while David talked to her. Before long, the nurse arrived and "invited" me to take Rachael out of the room. I had achieved my goal: the father and daughter had seen each other, so we left the room. As we left, all the nurses at the station looked at us as if we'd committed a crime but I still felt like I'd done the right thing. David and Rachael needed to see each other. I felt those rules were probably designed for the average transplant patient who stays in the hospital for one week after their surgery. It seemed to me that the hospital should have a different set of rules for patients who had to stay longer than a week.

I understood why they had the rules they did. If they allowed children in a large hospital like Jackson Memorial, it would be impossible for patients to rest. In addition, the children might contract infections from the patients or patients might contract infections from the children. Regardless, I didn't think there was any harm in Rachael's visit. I knew she was healthy and she hadn't even touched David, so she wouldn't be able to catch his infection. The bed next to David was empty.

Rebecca took a few days off and came to visit David. Their cousin Danny Banayan also came to visit from California. It was always nice to have visitors to keep us busy and distract us from our worries about the waiting list.

David's condition had improved enough that he could be moved to a private room. That meant we could visit with him longer and even sleep in his room, since there was a recliner that opened out into a single bed. Saturday was David's first day in the private room and Joe was in town for the weekend. David couldn't get out of bed to use the private bathroom, so Elizabeth brought in a portable commode. Weak and not eating much, David asked me at the end of the day if I would stay overnight in the room with him. I went home, packed a small bag, and returned to stay over with David.

I wasn't sleepy, so I didn't bother to open the recliner. On the wall in front of me were a calendar and a clock. They were the only decorations in an otherwise bare room. The date on the calendar was December 18. Patty, the assistant nurse, arrived to empty the large drainage bag that was filled with the pink fluid from David's incision. David then got ready to settle down for the night.

The date was tugging at my memory. I knew there was something special about December 18, but I couldn't remember what it was. I knew it wasn't a birthday or an anniversary in our family. Then I remembered! December 18, 1981 was the day we returned from Pittsburgh after David's first transplant. What a wonderful day that was! I was glad that I didn't know then where I would be on that very same day 18 years later! The inability to know what the future holds is a double-edged sword. While it saves us from seeing the pain that is in store for us in the future, it also prevents us from knowing when our suffering will end.

December 18 was also the date I had dreamed about last March. It was the day I dreamed David would receive his second transplant. I thought about how little I'd known nine months ago when I'd had that dream and how much I'd disliked the date, thinking it was too far away. I resolved to keep my hopes up. Maybe this day would fulfill my dreams after all and David would receive a new transplant that worked perfectly, instead of only partially.

The doctors had decided to give David a feeding tube. They hoped that with proper nutrition, the liver would regenerate and repair its damaged areas. David had refused the feeding tube in the morning and he refused it again in the evening, telling the resident in charge that he felt full.

Now, once again, I found myself listening to the footsteps and voices outside the door just as I had back in September 1981. Maybe tonight will be the night, I told myself. Maybe tonight David will receive a new healthy liver. As David slept, I went on thinking and hoping, my eyes locked on the calendar. When the clock struck midnight and December 18 came to an end, I realized that this day was just one more dream that hadn't come true. It was time to move on. I would have to go to sleep and wake up with new hope for tomorrow. As long as there was life left in David, there was hope.

David's voice brought me back to reality. He had to go to the bathroom. Elizabeth had said that David should not walk the ten steps to the bathroom. Instead, he should use the portable commode next to his bed. David sat up on the bed and put his feet on the floor. With my support, he stood up, took a step, and immediately passed out in my arms. My first thought was that he had dozed off again and I tried to wake him. "Wake up, David, wake up! I can't hold you by myself!" I told him. The bed was two feet away from us and he was too heavy for me to carry back to the bed. I felt my knees starting to buckle and tried to steady myself. While supporting David with my left arm, I searched for the nurse's call button and pressed it. A moment or two passed with no sign of the nurse. His 100 lb. body was too heavy for me to support much longer and I began to fear that we would both fall. I knew that the fall wouldn't be good for either one of us, so I began to yell for help. It seemed like forever, but within moments, the room was full of nurses, assistant nurses, and the resident on call. Ruth, the assistant head nurse, and another nurse took David from me and put him back in bed. David opened his eyes, and the doctor checked his blood pressure, measured the amount of oxygen in his blood, and asked him how he was feeling.

David complained that he felt full and the doctor could feel the pressure in his belly. He inserted a suction to empty the contents of David's stomach, and the container at the other end filled up with fluid. Ruth asked the nurses to move David from his private room back to the unit in front of the nurses' station where he could be more closely monitored.

The nurses settled David in his new room, connected him to a blood pressure monitor, and Ruth checked everything. Before she left the room, she reminded me that family members were not allowed to spend the night in this unit. She told me I could return to David's private room and sleep on the recliner, or I could go home. David spoke up and said, "Are you sending my mother out into the street in the middle of the night?"

I told Ruth that I would sit with David until he fell asleep and then I would return to the other room and sleep on the recliner. She didn't answer, but she pulled the drapes that divided the beds around us, said goodnight, and left. "She has a heart after all," I thought! I had found out how religiously she enforced the hospital rules when she had refused Dr. Pinna's permission to let Rachael visit just weeks before.

I couldn't sleep. I knew David was sick. Apparently he wasn't digesting anything. That was why he felt full and felt the pressure in his stomach. Even his digestive juices were not passing through, because the container attached to the suction continued to fill even after the doctor emptied his stomach. In 1981, I could pick David up and put him in the wheelchair. Now I was no longer able to carry his adult body. I had to accept another reality. I could no longer take care of David, tending to his every need, as I had in the past. We would need a miracle to bring David back to health!

In 1981, the whole ordeal took eight months from the time we knew David was sick until he recovered from his transplant. Now, after 17 months waiting and one transplant, David was still dying! I did not for a minute believe that this liver would regenerate; David was too sick. This was worse than any nightmare I'd ever imagined! Never in my worst dreams had I imagined standing helplessly in the hospital next to my dying child's bedside, waiting for morning. If I had, I would have awakened in a cold sweat with a headache and I would have been thankful that it was just a dream!

I knew I had to be strong for David, Rachael, and the rest of the family. I couldn't fall apart. As a mother and a grandmother, I was supposed to be a source of strength and support. I was counting on my emotional energy to sustain David when he felt weak. I wasn't planning to give up because I felt as long as we didn't give up, David wouldn't give up either. We had first-hand experience with the positive outcome of successful liver transplant. What we knew about Dr. Tzakis and his transplant team made me believe that he shared our convictions. It would be much easier to let David die on the waiting list than take on another grueling 20 hour surgery, but that wasn't Dr. Tzakis' style. He wasn't the type to take the easy way. With all this, we knew we couldn't afford to give up.

The light streamed into the room from the window. I waited for the morning nurse to bring the results of David's tests. David's voice reminded me that he was alert and not in a coma.

"Mom, I don't feel good at all," he said. David wasn't normally a complainer, so I knew he must be very ill.

"I know," I said.

Ruth heard our voices and came in to check David's blood pressure and blood oxygen saturation. "The kidney machine will be here soon," she said.

"Then we'll move you to a private room."

Now David and I knew that his kidneys were no longer working and that the new liver was dying. We were familiar with the kidney machine. Before David's first transplant, we learned that when the liver stops working, perfectly healthy kidneys stop working soon after. And after the transplant, we learned that nonfunctioning kidneys start working again as soon as the new liver starts working.

Elizabeth and Bessie were on duty again, and I realized that Elizabeth had known before we did where David was headed. She was the one who'd brought the portable commode and discouraged him from getting out of bed at a time when most liver recipients on the way to recovery are encouraged to get out of bed, sit in a chair, and walk around. She'd known that David was more likely to pass out and fall than he was to recover. Even though we weren't in the SICU, Elizabeth set up David's room as if he was an ICU patient. She said that David would be transferred to the SICU as soon as possible but in the meantime, she and Bessie would make sure David got the care he needed.

That Sunday morning, the dialysis machine removed the waste products from David's blood. Dr. Tzakis arrived with Dr. Jose Nery, a member of the transplant team, and Dr. Adrian Cottorreal, who was on fellowship. For the first time, we were seeing Dr. Tzakis in a suit, and since it was Sunday, I thought he must be on his way to church. The doctors looked at David's test results, examined his incision, and checked the fluid that was being removed from his stomach by the suction machine. They observed a thin thread of blood in the tube draining David's stomach, but there wasn't much discussion among them. Dr. Tzakis asked if they were in agreement that David needed another liver and they concurred. I felt that the transplant committee would reach the same decision.

We spent the rest of the day trying to keep David cool as his body temperature rose. Someone was always with David, and Joe, Sara, and I took turns taking care of Rachael. Miami was pleasant in December, and we passed the time with Rachael walking around the hospital. There was a short wall surrounding the gardens dedicated to the memories of the organ donors. The wall had a flat top that Rachael loved to walk on and look at all the butterflies that the garden attracted. Living in the Midwest as we did, spring weather and flowers in the month of December were a gift! We tried to enjoy the outdoors as much as we could, and left riding the elevator and visiting the gift shop for rainy days.

One of the garden paths took us out to the street and we saw a restaurant called The Miami Grill across the street. Just inside, there was a vending machine with plastic Disney toys, and Rachael began collecting characters when our garden walks brought us near the restaurant. We all kept up a happy face, as though this was just another short trip to the hospital; I was grateful that Rachael was too young to comprehend how sick David really was.

Just before David was moved back to the SICU, I brought Rachael in to see him again. When the hallway was clear of the watchful eyes of the nurses, I brought Rachael to the end of his bed and David was able to talk to her for a few minutes. David seemed comfortable returning to the SICU; I think it gave him peace of mind to know that he would be monitored 24 hours a day and he wouldn't have to worry about slipping away when no one was paying attention.

Joe's school district was on winter break, so he would be staying with us for two weeks. He came to the hospital with us on Monday morning. To visit David in the SICU, we first had to stop in the waiting room and call David's nurse for her approval to enter David's room. The SICU[1] was a large room with about 15 beds. Each bed was surrounded by drapes which could be closed for privacy. The nurses' station was located in the center of the room and David's bed was just to the right. We pushed the button to open the double doors. As we entered, I noticed that David was once again on a respirator and the kidney machine was positioned at the end of his bed. He was awake and I could see that he wanted to talk. I told him that he was at the top of the waiting list and I handed him a pencil and paper. He wrote one word: "Omaha." I understood him well; he only needed to write that one word for me to know what he was thinking. He was trying to tell me that if things didn't improve here fast, maybe we should call Omaha and tell them that David was in the ICU in desperate condition. For the eight months we were in Omaha, they'd told David that the first available livers would go to patients in the ICU. Now he was in the ICU and he wanted the first available liver! I admired his fighting spirit and his courage. I knew that the respirator was extremely uncomfortable. As soon as most patients come out of the anesthetic they want the respirator out, but it's only removed when the doctors are sure the patient can breathe on their own. I didn't have the heart to tell David that he was too sick to travel, but I did remind him that he was getting the best possible care. Once again, I looked in my purse and found the three pages of prayer for organ recipients. I read the prayers to David to calm him and give him hope.

The important thing was that his brain was alive, his heart was pumping, and thanks to the respirator, he wouldn't stop breathing. The dialysis machine and the respirator were machines that helped to delay the process of dying until a donor liver could be found. But the fact that David wasn't

---

[1]The SICU at Jackson Memorial has since been moved into a newly constructed wing, next to the old one.

giving up, after all he'd been through in the past 18 months, was remarkable and probably the key to his survival! A lesser person might have given up and asked to be removed from the life-sustaining machines, but David still had hope for a normal life!

Visiting hours were soon over. It was time for us to go home, but we could return for the afternoon visiting hours. The late visiting hours were past Rachael's bedtime, so I stayed with her while Joe and Sara returned to visit David. They returned in an optimistic mood because David was off the respirator and in good spirits. We speculated that if things continued this way, David might be able to return to the 15th floor and wait for a liver there.

There are some moments in life that you always remember. At 3:30 a.m. on the morning of December 21, the phone rang. Joe answered and when he hung up, he said it was David's nurse calling. David was bleeding internally. How and where? He hadn't asked. It was unusual for the SICU nurses to make that type of phone call, especially in the middle of the night. The only thing that occurred to me was that maybe David was dying—or was dead already—and they thought we should be there with him. I had no idea what protocol the hospital followed when a patient dies or is near death in the SICU. We needed to get to the hospital to find out what was happening. Someone would have to stay with Rachael; I hated to wake Sara but she needed to be there with David. If David was dying, he would want her there, not me. And if the surgeons needed to operate and David was unable to give his consent, they would need Sara's signature for the paperwork, not mine.

Feeling that I didn't have much of a choice, I went to her bedroom. She awoke easily, or maybe she'd heard the phone ring and was already awake. I gave her a hug and told her what the nurse had related to Joe. As Sara and Joe left, I asked them to call me as soon as they had some information about David. I sat on the sofa and waited, my stomach was twisted with feelings that I'd never had before. For the first time, I feared that David was definitely dying. It was more acute than anything I'd felt during his first liver transplant in 1981 and I was unprepared for it.

When the phone rang 30 minutes later, I didn't want to pick it up—I was afraid it would be bad news. Joe told me that the surgeons were trying to find the source of David's bleeding; meanwhile, they were giving him transfusions. Sara and Joe were going to stay at the hospital, leaving me alone with thoughts that were not positive at all. I asked myself, "What will we do if David dies?" David hadn't left us with any plans and now I understood why. He wasn't planning to die. He'd never even read my book, *The Gift of*

Life, about his first transplant. He'd started to read it only once and found it too painful to continue. He'd returned it to me, saying, "I lived it. Why should I read it?" The only parts of the book he read were the ones that were reprinted in the newspaper reviews.

The Jackson Citizen Patriot, a newspaper from Jackson, Michigan, published a review of my book along with a large picture of David and me. The picture was taken during our celebration of David's eighteenth birthday and the fifth anniversary of his transplant. The caption underneath read, "How can I pray for me to live, when I know another child must die so I can live?" He'd asked me that question in Pittsburgh while we were waiting for his first transplant and I'd answered, "It's not in our hands who should die and who should live. It's in God's hands. All we have to do is pray that you stay healthy and strong until a liver becomes available."

When David read that newspaper article, he told me, "When I asked that, I knew I was dying."

I replied, "If you knew you were dying, why didn't you tell me what you wanted me to do with your toys and belongings after you died?"
He said, "I knew I was dying, but I wasn't planning on it!"

When David was twelve, Joe and I were pretty clear about our role as his parents. Now David was married. He had a wife, one child, and another on the way. But he didn't have a will. I could only surmise that it was for the same reason: he didn't plan on dying.

Back then, while he was in a coma, I'd thought about the possibility that he might die and how I would have to plan his funeral. But this time the thought of losing David had never even entered my mind. Now I could see that he was close to dying. If he was going to die now, I wondered why he'd had to suffer so much over the last 18 months. Most of us imagine that when our time comes, we will die suddenly of a heart attack, or pass away peacefully in our sleep. We don't imagine a chronic, terminal illness with months spent in the hospital before the end comes almost as an afterthought. David had suffered so much over the last 18 months, both emotionally and physically with all the IVs, feeding tubes, respirators, kidney machines, open wounds, and biopsies. Thinking about this overwhelmed me with negative thoughts and emotions and I found myself asking "why," even though I knew there was no answer to this question.

Just when I was beginning to feel that I would never find my way out of the darkness, Rachael woke up and I had to put on my happy face so she wouldn't worry. I knew that if Rachael saw me unhappy, she would be unhappy, too. After Rachael ate breakfast, I wanted to go to the hospital to be with Joe and Sara, but I was afraid that as soon as we arrived the doctors would come out and tell us that David was gone. What would we tell Rachael? We weren't prepared at all for this. She was a smart child and would ask a lot of questions. I hoped and prayed that Sara had considered this and would know how to explain it to her, but no one close to us had died since Rachael was born except my mother, and Rachael never met her.

I decided to stay home. At home, I would have time to call a rabbi and ask him how to explain all of this to a child. We were fortunate enough to have met many rabbis during the course of our lives and we'd kept close ties to all of them. Now that David was sick, they called us frequently, reminding us that they were keeping David and all of us in their prayers. They offered their help and support and were always there to talk to when we needed them.

I stayed in the apartment, but I just couldn't sit still—I ran around cleaning places that didn't need to be cleaned and vacuumed while Rachael vacuumed along with her toy vacuum. Joe called with an update every half-hour. There was no good news—David was still bleeding and the doctors were still trying to find the cause. We'd promised to call Ben and Rebecca if there was a major change in David's condition, so I called them. I got Ben, but couldn't reach Rebecca. Rebecca was a classroom teacher and didn't have immediate access to a phone. Speaking to Ben, I told him all that I knew about David's bleeding. A few minutes later, Laura called me and told me that Ben was on his way to Miami. I told Laura that I hadn't asked him to come, and she replied that Ben could tell from my voice that the situation wasn't good.

Friends and relatives called often to see how David was doing. Nearly every time we came home from the hospital, there were messages on the machine. It was a relief to know that so many people cared about David and about us, but I hoped and prayed that none of them called today because I wouldn't know what to tell them.

I made lunch for Rachael, but was unable to eat myself. After lunch, I put Rachael down for her nap and went to my own room to pretend that I would sleep as well. Soon it was clear that Rachael wanted to "escape" from her nap. She crawled into my bedroom saying, "There's a mouse in the house."

I was no longer questioning why this was happening to us because I realized that there just wasn't an answer. That type of thinking just made me feel down and depressed. As I had told David, "It's in God's hands who should live and who should die." The doctors were doing everything they could to keep David alive, and I was hoping and praying that this was not David's time to die.

Rachael, oblivious to the gravity of the situation, was as playful as always. She examined my travel sewing bag and had many questions. Through the clear plastic, she could see many spools of colored thread, and she pointed at them. "What are these?" she asked.

"Spools of thread," I answered.

"Can I have a piece of thread?"

"Sure. What color do you want?"

"One of each," she requested. "Blue, red, purple, yellow, white . . ."

"How long?" I asked, as I pulled thread from the spool.

She showed me how long by holding her hands about a foot and a half apart. I cut one length of thread from each spool and gave her the strings. As I reorganized the sewing bag, I could see that Rachael was deeply involved in her work. With her little fingers, she was arranging the threads in a half-moon shape on the bedspread. "Rachael, what are you making?" I asked.

As she turned her attention from the threads and looked up into my face, I saw David's eyes looking back at me. "I'm making a rainbow!" she answered.

Another rainbow. I remembered the rainbow in Niagara Falls that I interpreted as God's promise to me that David would be all right. Was God reminding me again with words from the mouth of David's 2-year-old daughter? I picked Rachael up and gave her a hug.

When Joe called, I asked him to come get us. It had been 12 hours since the first call from the SICU and David was still alive. And God had just showed me another rainbow! "David will live. David will be okay," I kept telling myself. While we waited for Joe, Rachael and I played tent. We draped a blanket over the suitcases, and crawled inside. It was Rachael's idea and showed how creative and adventurous she was.

A half-hour later, we were at the hospital. I asked Joe if he'd been able to see David. He said he had, but it wasn't a pretty picture. It was bloody. David was on the respirator, blood was coming out of his mouth, with the doctors working on him. I pushed the button to open the double doors of the SICU and saw the doctors around David's bed. I knew I would be denied if I called the nurse to ask permission to see David, so I just walked in. Before I got to David's bed, the nurse blocked me and said, "You can't come in here."

"I'm his mother," I said and pushed her aside gently. Joe was right. It wasn't a good scene. Dr. Tzakis, still in his surgical gown, had just arrived from the operating room, and the other doctors were consulting with him.

"What is wrong with David?" I asked Dr. Tzakis.

"Ulcers. David has three bleeding ulcers," he said.

I tried to comprehend the diagnosis, mentally running down the list of David's problems. David's kidneys were not functioning, his liver was dead and infected, and now his stomach was practically falling apart. "How did he get ulcers?" I asked.

"Patients who go through as much trauma as David has often develop ulcers," he answered.

"Can you do anything about it?" I had to ask the question even though I wasn't sure I wanted the answer.

"Yes," he answered with confidence. "If we had a suitable donor, we would do the liver transplant and then repair the ulcers. We were hoping for one, but unfortunately we don't have a donor, so we will just repair the ulcers. We have two possibilities for a donor liver tomorrow."

Once again, I felt the frustration of organ transplant. Waiting for a donor organ could make even the best surgeons feel helpless. Even though there was a cure for their patients, the doctors couldn't do a thing about it until they had a suitable donor organ.

I looked at David one more time. He was completely unconscious. The nurses were ready to take him to the operating room. Quickly, I touched his head and whispered to him, "Hang in there. God will be with you." Then I left so the nurses could prepare him for surgery.

In the waiting room, I saw Ben working quietly on his laptop. After seeing David in such poor condition, seeing Ben healthy was a joy! "How could any mother send two sons into the operating room for living donor surgery?" I asked myself. I was relieved that I was not facing that situation and that Ben was here to give support during this time of crisis.

We found Sara on the public phone in the hallway. She was talking to her mom who'd had her bone marrow transplant on November thirtieth. Now Johnie was on the road to recovery. Sara told us that her sister Christy was coming to Miami for her Christmas vacation and would be arriving in a couple days. I could hardly imagine what Sara had been going through for the last 12 hours. I had my husband Joe to share this crisis with, but Sara had no one from her immediate family, only us—her in-laws. I felt it would be good for Sara to have her only sister with her, to share her pain in these dark days.

It was two hours later, but seemed like forever, when Dr. Nery called to tell us that the surgery was successful. David was out of the operating room and the bleeding had stopped. After the transplant three weeks ago, we hadn't spent much time in the SICU waiting room because David was healthy enough to have visitors. Now that David was critical, we were there from early morning until late at night. We were spending hours waiting there because the SICU nurses would only let us in when it was a good time for David. In fact, we were spending more time in the waiting room than in the SICU with David who was unconscious much of the time.

We weren't the only ones spending a lot of time in the waiting room. We introduced ourselves to the other families who were spending as much time in the waiting room as we were, and we shared our stories. We met the wife, daughter, and sister of a man from Venezuela that we called Dr. Madrid. Dr. Madrid caught hepatitis from one of his patients and had received a liver transplant. We also met the family of patient Dolores Becerra. Her husband Juan was a pleasant, optimistic man who arrived every morning with a huge container of coffee and a box of donuts that he shared with everyone. We knew that whenever Juan was around, there was a box of donuts at the nurses' station. We also exchanged stories with the family of Edita Cuba. Edita had a teenage daughter, Cory, who amused Rachael when Joe, Sara, and I changed shifts at David's bedside. All of these patients were liver recipients. Mateo Mascoli, a man from Italy, also spent time in the waiting room with us. He'd brought his wife to the U.S. from Italy for an intestinal transplant. He hardly spoke any English, but we could tell from his body language whether his wife was having a good day or a bad day. Luckily, Dr. Roberto Verzaro spoke Italian and conversed often with Mr. Mascoli. Another person we got to know was Charlotte Smith, the mother of Kathryn Smith. Kathryn was a multiple-organ transplant recipient like Robert Bank.

Knowing that David had survived 17 years with his first transplanted liver was an inspiration for these families. Hoping to draw on our experience, they shared their concerns with us. Without planning to, we became a support group for each other, even though we didn't know the patients themselves. The SICU was a big place, and we didn't have occasion to see the other patients unless they happened to be in the bed next to David's.

We arrived early Wednesday morning hoping that it would be the day that David received a new liver, his third transplant in his young life. David was on a respirator and his bed had been moved to the back wall of the SICU, next to Kathryn Smith.

Kathryn was a 20-year-old college student who'd been diagnosed three years earlier with autoimmune hepatitis, a condition that caused her own body to attack her liver. In 1998, she received a liver transplant at Emory University Hospital in Atlanta, Georgia. Complications led to a second transplant, which also failed when blood clots developed in the vessels connected to her bowels. After the failure of her second liver transplant, Kathryn's intestines shut down and she almost died. But by what seemed a miracle, Kathryn pulled through and was referred to Jackson Memorial Hospital for a transplant of both liver and intestines. For months, Kathryn battled life-threatening infections. By the time the infections cleared enough to make the surgery possible, Kathryn also needed a new kidney, pancreas, and stomach. In August, 1999, Kathryn received a new liver, kidney, stomach, pancreas, and intestines—all from the same donor.

Now Kathryn could hardly move her arms and legs. She'd lost most of her hair from the massive doses of antibiotic and had a breathing tube in her trachea. Like David, she also had an open wound. What caught our attention was that her corner of the SICU was decorated like a college dorm room all decked out for the holidays. A large poster of a male tennis team hung on the wall, and a window allowed her a view of the outdoors. If we removed all of the life-saving and monitoring equipment from this corner of the SICU, it could be just another college student's room. With the help of the younger nurses, Kathryn's sister and her college friends had created this atmosphere for Kathryn so she would feel as at home as possible.

Kathryn hardly ever spoke, but I could see a lot of questions in her eyes. Kathryn's mother, Charlotte, and I related David's story to Kathryn. I could see that she shared our concern for David, and was waiting with us for David to receive a new liver.

Before lunch, we received an update on the two possible donors for David. One of the families did not grant the permission that would allow their brain-dead relative to become an organ donor. We were told that the other potential donor was not a "model citizen," but the surgeons would examine the liver and see if it was viable.

I wondered why we'd been told that the other donor wasn't a "model citizen." That didn't really matter to us. An unsavory past was inconsequential when we considered that someone else's donated organ might save David's life. I thought maybe the surgeons could sense how desperate we were and were trying to prepare us in case they decided that this other donor's liver wasn't right for David.

The surgeons were looking for a local donor for David because they wanted their own team to harvest the liver. We didn't know why, but we guessed that they needed to harvest certain ducts and blood vessels along with the liver, to give David a better chance at survival. Years of built up scar tissue in David's abdomen had changed his body in ways that made it different from the average liver recipient.

We went home for lunch. At 2:00 p.m., Dr. Levi called and told us that the potential donor was a prisoner whose liver had been damaged by years of drug and alcohol abuse. Now we knew what they meant by "not a model citizen." This would not be David's donor. Once again, our hearts sank. David would have to hang on for a few more days, or perhaps weeks, in the SICU until a suitable donor was found. Dr. Levi told us they would irrigate David's abdominal cavity daily until they found a donor. That gave us hope that they weren't giving up on David.

By Thursday, December 23, David was going on his fourth day in the SICU, still with no donor liver in sight. The requirement that it be a local liver made the possibility of finding one in time seem all the more remote. We knew that liver transplants were being given to other patients as we saw their families come to the SICU waiting room and then follow the recipients up to the postsurgical unit on the fifteenth floor. The average transplant patient didn't spend more than a few days in the SICU.

That day we also learned that Dr. Madrid's first transplant was failing and he would need a new liver. His family was devastated, but we comforted them and reminded them that this was not uncommon. Once he got the right liver, he would recover and be fine. Dr. Madrid's blood type was different than David's, so at least they wouldn't be competing for the same liver.

On Thursday morning, there was again no possibility of a donor liver. David's abdominal cavity was irrigated with antibiotics to help his body overcome the infection. Since his liver was not working, David was also developing ascites, a buildup of fluid in his belly. His body was so riddled with infection that this fluid in his belly was also infected. We knew that David would have the best chance of survival if his body was free of infection when the transplant was performed, but I didn't see how this would be possible. David's liver and kidneys weren't functioning and his body was becoming weaker, not stronger.

Now we were becoming desperate. I called all the newspapers and television stations, hoping that by publicizing David's story, I would encourage more people to become organ donors and, perhaps, find a liver for David. They found our story interesting, but were not willing to publish it or put it on the air. The news was filled with stories about Elian Gonzalez, the six-year-old Cuban boy plucked from the sea after his mother, stepfather and others died trying to flee Cuba in an overloaded boat. The media didn't have time to cover the miracles that were occurring daily at Jackson Memorial Hospital. Some didn't even know that one of the top transplant centers in the country was right here in Miami!

We were with David whenever he was awake. We noticed that Kathryn had a lot of visitors. Her young friends brought the joy and fun of their normal lives into the SICU. As they combed Kathryn's hair or manicured her fingernails and toenails, they spoke of a carefree college life and healthy, happy days outside the SICU. It was an atmosphere that fostered hope and optimism, and I could see that it was good for both Kathryn and David.

The next day, we all visited with David. Sara played some of Rachael's videos for him. When David was taken for antibiotic irrigation, we waited with Rachael in the hallway between the SICU and the elevator so David and Rachael could visit with each other for a few moments on his way to the operating room. Then we went back to the apartment.

After lunch, the phone rang. Sara and I each picked up an extension. It was Dr. Levi, who had been personally taking care of David for the past few days. Dr. Levi said that while irrigating David's abdominal cavity, he'd found an abscess under the liver. There was a possibility that the irrigation procedure had disturbed the abscess. In that case, the infection might spread to David's bloodstream and lead to toxic shock. If David developed toxic shock, Dr. Levi felt that he would have less than 24 hours to live. David's eligibility for a transplant would be suspended until tomorrow, when the doctors would know whether David was developing toxic shock or not.

I knew I needed to sit down, so I sat on the kitchen floor. I asked Dr. Levi if anyone had ever survived infections this severe. He said that there was one patient, Gloria, who'd won her battle with this type of infection. For us, this was a ray of hope. I hung up and told Joe about David's condition. Curiously, Sara, Joe, and I were not devastated. Over the past few days, we had developed a sense that David was going to survive all of this. We were in denial that David was dangerously ill and on the verge of death.

Later that afternoon, the phone rang again. My friend of 30 years, Naida Cohn, was calling for a weekly update on David. Each week, after she called me, she sent an e-mail to all of our friends who were concerned about David. She included David on her mailing list, and forwarded the replies she received from David's well-wishers.

I told Naida what Dr. Levi had related that afternoon. This time, when I said the phrase, "If he lives until tomorrow," its full impact sunk in and hit me hard. I realized that Joe, Sara, and I were so close to the situation that we were deluding ourselves in order to keep going. I asked Naida not to share that phrase in her e-mail. We might be denying how close David was to death, but our friends were not and I didn't want them to worry.

With Sara's sister Christy here, I felt a little less worried about Sara's emotional state. The sisters were close and Christy was strong enough to bear the burden of Sara's pain. Christy was an energetic, optimistic, joyful young woman, and she shared these gifts with all of us. She got Sara and Rachael out of the apartment, rousing them for a picnic lunch in the park, or an impromptu swim in the pool. She decorated the apartment, organized Rachael's toys, and made a videotape of Rachael singing and dancing. Rachael was much happier since her arrival and my nagging migraine headache that had started with David's transplant here in Miami slowly went away.

Now when we visited David in the SICU, we had to wash our hands and don gloves and gown. When we left his side of the room, we were to remove the protective coverings and wash our hands again. We were under strict orders from the nurses to follow these procedures to the letter to prevent the transmission of infection.

David was in and out of consciousness. When he wanted to talk, he resented the respirator. Sara made a sheet with the letters of the alphabet and some common words, and David communicated his thoughts by pointing to the words and letters. Dr. Akin was always nearby and the time he spent talking to David and Kathryn helped to keep their spirits up. Robert Bank was now in the bed on the other side of David. Apparently, he was having complications, too. Next to Robert Bank, there was another young transplant patient named Tulio. Kathryn's mom, Charlotte, jokingly referred to this part of the SICU as "the nursery," because David, Kathryn, Robert, and Tulio were all so young.

On Friday night, when we arrived to visit with David, we noticed that he was covered with a special air-filled comforter, and his head was wrapped with towels. We guessed that these measures were needed to help prevent toxic shock. David was unconscious and the respirator was helping him to breathe. He looked peaceful as we held his hand, talked to him about Rachael, and urged him to "hang in there."

That night, there was a death in the SICU. We didn't know the patient, but we met his wife in the waiting room. She was pale, shaken, and looked like the life had been drained out of her. We didn't know the cause of her husband's death. Not all of the patients in the SICU were transplant patients. There were also terminal patients transferred in from other local hospitals, hoping for a miracle cure that the first hospital had been unable to provide. All the woman told us was that her husband's heart suddenly stopped beating and he died. Then her friends and relatives arrived and took her home to plan the funeral. We tried not to think about dying, but her face and her words were hard to forget.

At home, I prayed into the night, finally falling into a fitful sleep. Each time I awoke, I prayed some more. Finally, Saturday, December 25 arrived. At the morning's first light, we were up; none of us had gotten much sleep. I prayed again this morning, as I did every morning, for strength for David and for all of us. I prayed that God would help the surgeons to make good decisions and give them the energy and wisdom to cure all of their patients, including David. Then we were on our way to the SICU to wait for news of David.

We knew David was alive simply because no one from the SICU had called to tell us otherwise during the night. In the SICU, only the patients slept. We wanted to be there when the night shift came off duty so the nurses and doctors who'd cared for David could tell us how he'd spent the night. We saw Dr. Levi and he told us that he was happy David had survived the night and that he said he would irrigate David's abdomen with antibiotics again today.

We waited and prayed in silence as another day passed with David hovering between life and death. Then came good news. Dr. Madrid had received his second liver transplant and was doing well. His group in the waiting room was larger, too. His mother had just arrived in Miami to be with the family. We were happy for them.

Appendix 10

PROBLEMS AFTER SURGERY

Postsurgical Complications

(Reprinted in part with permission from the Patient and Family Guide to Liver Transplantation, developed by the pretransplant and posttransplant coordinators at the University of Miami Department of Surgery, Division of Transplantation)

Primary Nonfunction

Occasionally when the liver is transplanted, it fails to work. This is referred to as primary nonfunction. The only recourse is to relist and retransplant the patient. Frequency of this happening is very low (two to three percent) but the patient must be aware that it can happen.

Hepatic Artery Thrombosis

The hepatic artery provides nourishment/oxygen to the liver tissue. If the hepatic artery occludes (gets blocked) soon after the transplant, the organ will usually not survive. This is another reason for retransplantation. To determine the blood flow into the new liver, a Doppler Ultrasound will be done at the patient's bedside to check the flow, just as was done prior to transplant. If the Doppler is inconclusive or further information is needed, the patient may need an arteriogram and/or a CT scan.

Rejection

Acute rejection means that the body's defense (immune) system is attacking the transplanted organ. This type of rejection episode, if caught early, is most often treatable. Rejection occurs in about 80% of all liver transplants. It may occur as early as five to six days after transplant, but is most common at two to twelve weeks after the transplant. Rejection can also occur at any time if the patient stops taking their medications or changes their medication dosage without approval of the transplant team. Rejection is identified by blood tests and confirmed by biopsy.

In the months to come, when blood tests are less frequent, the patient may identify rejection episodes when they experience one or more of the following signs and symptoms: fever, jaundice (yellowing eyes or skin), dark tea-colored urine, clay-colored stools, fatigue, or abdominal pain or tenderness. However, on occasion, rejection may occur with no outward signs or symptoms and for no apparent reason. That is why having blood tests as ordered by the transplant team is imperative.

Infection

By suppressing the immune system so the patient's body does not fight the new organ, the patient will be at a greater risk for viral, bacterial, and fungal infections. The patient must exercise great care to not expose him- or herself to any situation that puts the patient at risk. Avoiding crowds and individuals who are sick with the flu are recommended. Notify the doctor immediately if the patient has been exposed to any communicable diseases that they have not had before transplant. Report any spots that may develop on the back of the throat or a white coating on their tongue. Develop good hand washing habits. Avoid vaccines that consist of live viruses, such as oral polio, measles, mumps, German measles, yellow fever, smallpox, or flu vaccines. The live virus can cause infections; therefore, only attenuated (dead) vaccines are permitted.

Pets can also present an opportunity for infection through breaks in the skin caused by scratches, exposure to fungus in bird droppings, etc.

Thrush

Candida (yeast) is a fungus that can cause a variety of infections in transplant patients. It usually appears in the mouth and throat but may also occur in the surgical wound, eyes, or respiratory and urinary tracts. Candida is most severe in the bloodstream. If infection occurs in the mouth or throat, it is called thrush. Thrush produces white, patchy lesions (raw areas), pain or tenderness, a white film on the tongue, and difficulty swallowing. Candida can also infect the esophagus (the tube from the mouth to the stomach) or, in women, the vagina. Vaginal infections usually produce an abnormal discharge that may be yellow or white. The patient should notify their post-transplant coordinator if they think they have a Candida infection.

Recurrent Hepatitis C or Hepatitis B (HCV or HBV)

These viruses stay in the patient's body for the rest of their life even though they had a liver transplant. The immunosuppressive therapy necessary to prevent their body from rejecting the new liver may increase the opportunity for these viruses to become a problem again. The medical team will watch the viral load very carefully by testing the patient's hepatitis levels as deemed necessary. If the virus becomes active, the physicians will cut back on the patient's antirejection medication and/or start them on additional medications. This is another example of why doing the labs on a regular basis is vital!

Cytomegalovirus (CMV)

This virus is present in most adults and usually does not present a problem. However, when the patient is immunosuppressed, this virus can be a problem. The usual presentation is fatigue, high temperature, aching joints, headaches, and visual disturbances. This virus is treated with medications that are given initially through an IV and then continued in pill-form. Hospitalization is usually not required.

Herpes Zoster (shingles)

Shingles appear as a rash or small water blisters, usually on the chest, back, or hip. The rash may or may not be painful. The patient should contact his coordinator if they have such a rash.

Anxiety and Depression

A serious procedure such as liver transplant can create many personal and family stresses. It is common for transplant patients to experience anxiety and perhaps depression following their surgery, hospital confinement, and return home. To help the patient adjust to life at home and their eventual return to work or school, counseling is available through the social worker at all centers.

Diabetes

Some of the immunosuppressive medications that recipients take may cause diabetes. Diabetes is an increased level of sugar in the blood. Symptoms of diabetes include increased thirst, increased frequency of urination, blurred vision, and confusion. The recipient should notify the transplant team if they experience any of these symptoms. Blood sugar can be reduced through weight loss, careful diet, and exercise. An oral diabetic drug or insulin injection may be necessary to further help control the blood sugar. If the recipient develops diabetes, they will receive specialized teaching about how to deal with this problem.

High Blood Pressure

High blood pressure (hypertension) is a possible side effect of some of the medications the patient will be taking; therefore, they may need to take a medication to help control their blood pressure. There are many different types of drugs available to control high blood pressure. The patient may need to try several different medications and/or dosages. The transplant team and the recipient's local physician will select the one that works best for the patient. A diuretic (water pill) may also be prescribed to lower blood pressure, increase urine output, and remove extra fluid. Once the recipient is released from the outpatient clinic, their local physician should be responsible for monitoring and controlling the patient's blood pressure. The local physician should continue the medication for hypertension that was prescribed for the recipient at the outpatient clinic and any renewals should be directed to his office.

Graft vs. Host Disease (GVHD)

GVHD is a condition that can occur following transplantation that is most easily explained as the opposite of rejection. In rejection, the recipient's body attacks the transplanted organ. With GHVD, the transplanted organ attacks the recipient's body. Immune cells from the donor's transplanted organ make antibodies against the host's (transplant patient's) tissue and attack the patient's vital organs. This condition may be acute or chronic, severe or mild. Severe cases can be life threatening. Common symptoms include diarrhea, skin rash, bone marrow depression (low WBC, RBC, and platelets), lung problems, and abnormal liver function test results. In liver transplant patients, the liver functions will not be a problem because it is the liver itself that is causing the problem. GHVD is treated by increasing the immunosuppressant medication. Hospitalization is usually required for a short time with treatment continuing at home.

Infected Abdominal Wounds

Some times a decision is made in the operating room not to close the abdominal wound because of infection. After transplant surgery, these wounds will require local management in the ICU. The surgeon caring for the wound will scrub (wash hands and arms) and put on a sterile gown and mask as if in the operating room. The surrounding area of the abdominal cavity will be covered with sterile dressings. This will allow the area to remain as clean as possible. The old dressing will be removed and the cavity will be irrigated with large amounts of a sterile salt solution, which may or may not contain antibiotics or antifungal medications, depending on the cultures taken from the wound. The process is usually carried out once or twice a day until the infection is cleared and the tissues in the cavity begin to grow again to form a covering over the wound.

It is important that patients with these large wounds receive adequate protein and calories for wound healing. Sometimes these patients also require extra intravenous hydration because of the loss of fluid from these wounds. Many times patients with these large abdominal wounds are managed like burn patients in terms of protein and caloric needs and hydration. Burn patients require huge amounts of calories and proteins as well as hydration because of the large areas of skin loss.

ICU Psychosis

Information for Patient and Family

Not every patient experiences ICU psychosis, but for the ones that do, it is very important for family and friends to understand that the patient is not going insane. Patients with ICU psychosis are having dreams or nightmares that seem so incredibly real that they often act on them. Instead of arguing with these patients, it is helpful to remind them that they are in the hospital, have just received a successful transplant, and soon they will be alright.

In David's case, while he was in the throes of ICU Psychosis, he dreamed of the good days when family was gathered round and he went through the motions of ordering a pizza for everyone. He talked to family members as if they were in the room with him. As he tried to eat his imaginary slice of pizza, he would find his feeding tube and try to pull it out. Sometimes while he was "dreaming," he would try to get out of bed. The experienced nurses understood David's ICU psychosis and were able to calm him down. When he was on a regular floor, however, the nurses did not have time to sit with him and would restrain his wrists, which made David angry.

This is one area where friends and relatives can be very helpful. Familiar faces sitting with the patient, talking to him, and perhaps playing music that the patient likes may help block out the ICU noise and distractions and return the patient to reality for awhile. It is important to remember that eventually the patient will return to normal.

Friends and family may wonder whether the patient with ICU psychosis is experiencing physical or emotional pain. Although there are medications for pain and depression, many families watch their loved one suffer in silence with no outside help. The interesting part is that most patients, after they get well, don't remember the first few days or weeks after the transplant. Upon returning to the ICU for a visit, many patients cannot remember the details of their days in the ICU, nor can they recognize the doctors and nurses who cared for them during their days there. David remembers some of the dreams and nightmares he experienced with ICU psychosis; now he can laugh about it.

ICU Psychosis – Defined
(Reprinted with permission from the University of Miami School of Medicine website, www.med.miami.edu)

ICU psychosis is a disorder in which patients in an intensive care unit (ICU) or a similar hospital setting may experience anxiety, become paranoid, hear voices, see things that are not there, become severely disoriented in time and place and become very agitated, even violent. The condition has been formally defined as "acute brain syndrome involving impaired intellectual functioning which occurs in patients who are being treated within a critical care unit." ICU psychosis is a form of delirium or acute brain failure. Organic factors including dehydration, hypoxia (low blood oxygen), heart failure (inadequate cardiac output), infection, and drugs can cause or contribute to delirium.

The treatment of ICU psychosis depends on the cause(s). Family members, familiar objects, and calm words may help. Dehydration should call for fluids. Heart failure needs treatment with digitalis. Infections must be diagnosed and treated. Sedation with antipsychotic agents may help.

To prevent ICU psychosis, many critical care units now have instituted visiting hours, try to minimize shift changes in the nursing staff caring for a patient, and coordinate the lighting with the normal day-night cycle, among other strategies. ICU psychosis usually goes away when the patient leaves the ICU.

One patient out of every three who spends more than five days in an ICU experiences some form of psychotic reaction, according to current estimates. As the number of intensive care units and the number of people in them grow, ICU psychosis is increasing as a problem.

What causes ICU psychosis is not fully known. Something about the ICU causes some people who are already experiencing great debility, stress, and pain to "lose their minds." Among the factors believed to play into ICU psychosis are:

- Sensory deprivation (being put in a room often without windows, away from family, friends, and all that is familiar);

- Sensory overload (being tethered to noisy machines day and night);

- Pain (which may not be adequately controlled in an ICU);

- Sleep deprivation;

- Disruption of the normal day-night rhythm; or

- The loss of control over their lives that patients often feel in an ICU.

ICU psychosis often goes away with the coming of morning or sleep. Although it may linger through the day, severe agitation usually occurs only at night. (This phenomenon, called sundowning, is common in nursing homes).

Notifying the Family When a Patient in the ICU is Dying

Usually, a patient in the ICU doesn't just die abruptly. Most times, there is a continuing deterioration of their status. If something drastic happens, however, there is usually a drop in blood pressure and heart rate and the patient may fail to respond to treatment.

When a patient takes a turn for the worse and stops responding to treatment, an ICU nurse or the doctor covering the ICU contacts the family by telephone. They are informed that the patient has become unstable and is not responding to therapy. The family is asked to come to the unit as soon as possible.

If the patient dies before the family gets to the ICU, they are met in the waiting room and the circumstances are explained to them. They are told that the patient did not respond to all efforts made and has passed away. At that time, they are given the chance to see the patient and spend some time with them. Most family members want to do this, but occasionally they choose not to.

Many times, the family is asked for permission to perform an autopsy. The autopsy will make sure that nothing was overlooked in the care of the patient and may also reveal any unusual conditions that may help the transplant team to care for future patients.

Daily Herald

PADDOCK PUBLICATIONS — 127th Year, No. 44   Friday, November 27, 1998

Medical pioneer needs 3rd liver, 3rd chance at life

17 years later, son of Hawthorn schools boss seeks another donor

By MARK SPENCER
Daily Herald Staff Writer

Youssef Yomtoob immerses himself in work these days, trying temporarily to forget his family is reliving a nightmare.

The superintendent of the Hawthorn elementary schools in Vernon Hills — affectionately known as "Dr. Joe" — remains optimistic as his son waits miles away for a liver transplant. Again.

Liver transplants were highly experimental in 1981 when David Yomtoob, then 12, received the donor liver that brought him back from the verge of death.

His transplant at the University of Pittsburgh made front-page headlines in local papers, and doctors marveled at how the comatose, withered, 57-pound boy recovered.

David learned to walk again and went on to lead a normal life, graduating from college, marrying, becoming a father and working as a communications software designer in the aerospace industry.

After many years of success with his new liver, Yomtoob thought his son would never be back in this position again.

But after 17 good years, the liver that made his adult life possible has for reasons his doctors don't understand.

After his son's first transplant, Yomtoob began giving speeches advocating organ donation. His wife, Parichehr, wrote a book titled "The Gift of Life," chronicling their experience.

With his son on the waiting list again for what has now become a recognized procedure, Yomtoob is making a renewed appeal for organ donation for all those in need.

"We are not hoping that someone dies for David," Yomtoob said. "We are hoping that if somebody is going to die anyway, that they would give the gift of life."

David has Wilson's disease, a rare genetic disorder that causes damaging copper deposits to build up in the liver.

But this time copper does not appear to be the culprit. Doctors think an obstruction of his bile duct may have caused the liver to fail, although organ rejection or some late stage of Wilson's could also be a cause. Enlarged from cirrhosis, his first donor

See TRANSPLANT on Page 6

David Yomtoob, with his wife, Sara, in 1994, is waiting for a second transplant to replace the failing liver he received 17 years ago.

David's story whle he was waiting for his third liver transplant.

11

THIRD LIVER TRANSPLANT SURGERY

December, 1999

Monday, December 26, we were at the hospital early after another sleepless night. We were afraid the surgeons would decide to wait until the infections were gone before allowing David another transplant, but in my heart, I felt that the dead liver inside him might be the source of his infections. With no kidney function and a dead infected liver inside him, I didn't think it would be possible for the infections to clear up.

In less than a week, the year 2000 would be upon us. Dr. Tzakis was planning to take a few days vacation with his family. I was worried that David would die while Dr. Tzakis was gone. As soon as we arrived in the waiting room, Dr. Tzakis came looking for us.

"I'm worried about David," he said. "I even had a nightmare about him. I want you to know that I am not going anywhere until we give David a new liver."

I wondered if Dr. Tzakis could tell how relieved we were.

He continued, "There is a brain-dead patient in the hospital whose blood type matches David's. He is big and tall. His liver might be too big for David, but we can cut it down if we have to."

We were thrilled that Dr. Tzakis wasn't giving up on David. We had prayed that everything possible would be done to save David and that he wouldn't die on the waiting list. Clearly, some of my prayers had already been answered. Dr. Tzakis was doing everything in his power to save David and David hadn't died on the waiting list. He'd already received one transplant and was at the top of the list for a second. These were things for which to be thankful.

Dr. Tzakis left us and went back to the SICU. The hospital had several ICUs and we didn't know which one the donor was in. We hadn't seen any new faces in the waiting room, so I didn't think the donor was in the SICU with David. After the disappointment of the past few days, we wanted to be careful not to get our hopes up too high. After all, all Dr. Tzakis said was that the blood type matched and it would be a large liver.

We spent the rest of the day in the waiting room. We watched the surgeons come and go and visited with David when we could. By late afternoon, we learned that the donor liver was perfect and David's transplant surgery would begin in the early evening. We told David the good news and he was happy. We kissed him goodnight and left the hospital to wait in the apartment.

Ben arrived on the first airplane out of Chicago. This time the surgery didn't take as long. Seven-and-half hours later, Dr. Tzakis called to say the surgery was a success. The liver was beautiful, they hadn't needed to cut it down, and the donor had lived a healthy life. "It was easy this time," he said. "We just opened the old stitches and sewed in the new liver. David is doing fine." How amazing it was that Dr. Tzakis referred to seven hours of surgery as "easy"!

"Did David have a heart attack during the surgery?" I asked. Dr. Tzakis said no, he hadn't.

Tuesday morning, we picked up a daily newspaper and checked the obituary page for recent deaths close to the time of David's transplant. The closest was the death of a pastor of a nearby church. It fit with the fact that Dr. Tzakis had described a healthy lifestyle and a perfect liver. I would have liked to attend the pastor's memorial service and thank his family for their gift, but I wasn't sure that he was the one or if we would be violating hospital policy by attempting to contact the donor's family. We also didn't know the wishes of the donor's family; David's first donor in Pittsburgh had requested anonymity. If this donor's family didn't want us to know, then it wouldn't be right to contact them. We decided to send a donation in the pastor's memory to his church and try to get more information later.

That day, a new face appeared in the waiting room. Laura Obregon was a beautiful young woman who exuded a special glow. I thought maybe it was because her husband Patrick had finally received a liver transplant. When she told me that they'd only been married three weeks, I realized her glow was the radiance of a new bride. Laura was worried that the stress of the wedding and honeymoon had caused Patrick's sudden liver failure. We asked if he'd had liver disease before, and she said he had just been diagnosed with Hepatitis C. He was a little tired and jaundiced after the wedding, but she'd figured it was just the stress of the wedding festivities. In the three years they'd been dating, Patrick had never taken her to his doctor appointments so Laura didn't know much about liver disease. It was complete surprise to her when he was hospitalized and doctors performed a liver transplant. Fortunately, Laura had a large family and lots of friends who visited often, bringing flowers, stuffed animals, and their kind concern. We shared our story with her and she became part of our group, spending as much time in the waiting room and the SICU as the rest of us.

Now, once again, we were filled with hope for David. The transplant was a miracle, but the new liver would have a big job. It would have to turn around David's dying body. Surgeons who greeted us as they passed in and out of the SICU all said the same thing: David had received a beautiful liver. We believed them.

I saw Dr. Shinji Yamamoto in the hall and asked him about David's abscess. He said they'd washed and washed his abdomen with antibiotics before putting the new liver in and, hopefully, had washed away the infection. He added that David's wound was open, so any residual infection would ooze out instead of being trapped inside his body and seeping into his bloodstream.

Once again we started asking for the blood test results that would show whether David's new liver was functioning properly. Dr. Akin printed the results from the computer and answered our questions daily. The numbers were good. David's kidneys were working again. But with David's deteriorated physical condition and the damage caused by the infections, we knew his recovery would be long. However, we now had hope and the good feeling that everything possible had been done for David.

The year 2000 was upon us and the fear that Y2K would wreak havoc with computer systems worldwide was especially terrifying for David who was connected to a respirator and other computer-controlled ICU equipment. If the fears were to be believed, the consequences of Y2K had deadly potential for patients like David. The doctors and hospital staff reassured us and told us not to worry—all of the life support equipment and hospital computers had been modified and tested months ago. Ben suggested that we stay in the SICU waiting room until after midnight on New Year's Eve just to be sure, but the hospital announced that after the 9 p.m. visiting hour ended, no visitors would be permitted to remain in the hospital.

It was interesting to hear how other people were planning to spend New Year's Eve. We knew that for us, it would be pretty much business as usual. For the 9:00 p.m. visiting hour, we took nonalcoholic champagne to the SICU and celebrated the New Year with Kathryn's family and the SICU nurses. We were pleased to see that David was off the respirator and just on a little oxygen. He seemed to be aware of what was going on around him, but for us the whole thing was like a dream—celebrating the New Year in the hospital with David. Even though he had a new liver, he also had a long road to recovery ahead of him.

When we arrived home, Sara's sister Christy surprised us with a New Year's Eve spread, complete with food, party hats, and decorations. We rang in the New Year watching fireworks explode over the bay outside our apartment window. We said a prayer and asked that the New Year would be a healthy one for all of us. At the same time, my heart ached for the families that had lost a loved one in the last year, especially the families of organ donors. I prayed that they would know how much joy they'd brought to us and would overcome their grief so they could resume their lives with a happy heart.

David's recovery was off to a slow start. A week after the transplant, at the time when the average transplant patient leaves the hospital, David was battling acute rejection and trying to fight his way back from the damage of the infections. Surgeons took him back into the operating room to clean out his infected abdomen. David always had a rough time coming out of anesthesia, and this time was no different. He forgot how ill he was and tried to pull his breathing tube out. The nurses did everything they could to calm him down, but when nothing seemed to be working, they put him in wrist restraints. David didn't like that, but we tried to keep his mind off the restraints and remind him that soon the breathing tube would be removed and his hands would be free.

In the weeks after the transplant, we started our days early, arriving at the hospital as the night shift exited the SICU. The nurses took the time to fill us in on the details of how David spent the night, and afterward we settled into the SICU waiting room. As we saw surgeons going back and forth to the SICU, we flagged them down and asked them for news about David. Soon they got used to it and whenever they saw us in the waiting room, they stopped and gave us an update on David's condition and their plans for treating him in the upcoming days.

We knew it was difficult to treat infection in transplant patients because the antirejection medication that allowed the body to accept a donor organ also weakened the entire immune system to the point that it had a problem fighting off infection. It was a very fine line to create the balance that allowed the patient's body to fight off infection without rejecting the donor organ. We asked Dr. Akin if he should consult a world infectious diseases expert who had transplant patient experience. He reassured us that they had people with expertise in that area and they were doing all they could for David.

Well, that was true. Kathryn Smith was a perfect example of their expertise, as was Gloria, who was there in 1998.

Gloria had her first liver transplant in 1984 in Pittsburgh while Dr. Tzakis was on fellowship in Pittsburgh. After Dr. Starzl retired and Dr. Tzakis left Pittsburgh, Gloria followed Dr. Tzakis to Miami, and began coming to Jackson Memorial for her checkups. Like David, Gloria had lived a successful life after her first transplant. She married and had two children. When she needed a second transplant 14 years later, she wanted Dr. Tzakis to perform the operation. In 1998, with her kidneys failing due to liver failure, she came to Miami for the second transplant. Her second transplant operation was as long as difficult as David's, and she suffered from the same postoperative infections that David was now suffering from. After the operation, she spent five weeks in a coma in the SICU, but eventually recovered and returned home to live a normal life with her family. Knowing how Dr. Tzakis had witnessed Gloria's long, slow, painful recovery, we were amazed that he was still willing to take on patients like David and Gloria. But now they knew what to expect, they had had experience with difficult second transplants, and they weren't afraid of the challenge! I wondered if Gloria was as physically deteriorated and as sick as David before her second transplant.

Our group in the waiting room became quite close and the surgeons became accustomed to stopping in the waiting room and answering all of our questions. One week after David's third liver transplant, he and Kathryn were still in the SICU, fighting for every little milestone in their slow recovery. Dr. Madrid recovered sufficiently to be moved to the 15th floor postsurgical unit, his second transplant working perfectly. Dolores Becerra followed him a short time later. With Dolores' husband Juan gone, Joe began bringing the donuts to the SICU nurses' station. Patrick Obregon, having done very well the first week, began suffering from some complication, as did Mrs. Edita Cuba.

Now, new faces were appearing in the SICU waiting room and we were the old-timers, along with Robert Bank's fiancée Elisha. Elisha realized that Robert's recovery might be long and she applied for, and got, a job. After that, she came to visit in the early mornings dressed for work and returned in the late evenings. We met many interesting people, including one 75-year-old woman that we first met when we found her in tears in the SICU waiting room. Her 75-year-old husband had just received a liver transplant and she was worried. We comforted her, shared our story, and shared the many success stories that had unfolded while we were there. Laura Obregon and another woman took her to lunch to cheer her up, and before long her husband was wheeled out of the SICU and up to the 15th floor. Another member left our group.

Another interesting group was the large family of the man we referred to as "the prisoner." One day when we arrived, there was nowhere to sit in the waiting room; it was filled with new faces and they were all crying. One woman spoke up, "My son just received a liver transplant."

Joe said, "You should be happy. We waited a long time for our son's liver transplant. His first transplant lasted 18 years."

"We didn't have to wait. My son didn't have liver disease. There was a fight and my son got shot. A bullet destroyed his liver, and there was a lot of bleeding," she said through her tears. Joe reassured her that everything would be all right soon.

Later that day, Cary Cuba told us there was a new liver recipient in the bed next to her mother. He was a strong, healthy young man and he was chained to the bed. My first thought was about how weak David was. The prisoner was probably as weak, if not weaker, than David. "How far can he go in that condition?" I asked. I wondered why the chains were necessary, but then I realized that his large family was probably capable of carrying him right out of the hospital if they wanted to. The prisoner's family shared the SICU waiting room with us for a couple days, then followed their patient up to the 15th floor where he was guarded by a policeman until he recovered.

Patrick Obregon's condition seemed to be going downhill. Laura told us that the infection was spreading into his brain and he was not responding to treatment or medication. It was hard for us to believe since he was only 38 years old. We prayed for his recovery but on January 9, only 12 days after his transplant, he died. Patrick's death was shock for all of us, but Laura was a pillar of strength and I was amazed by her strength in the midst of grief and tragedy as she left with her relatives to plan his funeral.

Appendix 11

THE POWER OF PRAYERS

"Prayer invites God to let His presence suffuse our spirits, to let His will prevail in our lives. Prayer cannot bring water to parched fields, nor mend a broken bridge, nor rebuild a ruined city; but prayer can water an arid soul, mend a broken heart, and rebuild a weakened will." [1]

"Pray as if everything depended on God; act as if everything depended on you.

Who rise from prayer better persons, their prayer is answered." [2]

Other similar statements are attributed to Saint Augustine, Saint Ignatius, and Cardinal Francis J. Spellman as follows:

"We should pray as if everything depended on God and act as if everything depended on ourselves."

St. Augustine

"We must pray as if all depends on Divine Action, but labor as if all depended on our own effort."

St. Ignatius

"Pray as if everything depended on God and work as if everything depended upon man."

Cardinal Francis J. Spellman

---

[1] *Gates of Prayer: The New Union Prayerbook*, Central Conference of Ammerican Rabbis, (New York, 1975): page 152. Adapted from a statement by Rabbi Abrahamm Joshua Heschel; exact source unkown.

[2] *Gates of Prayer: The New Union Prayerbook*, page 157. Attributed to the late Rabbi Morris Adler by some, but appears to be a statement by the English novvelist George Meredith (1828-1909)

Most people don't want to be alone in times of major illness or crises. The best that loves ones, friends, and relatives can do is to let the patient and family know that they are praying for them and provide love and positive reinforcement. Praying not only provides positive reinforcement for the patient, it also gives him the feeling that others care for him and want to help ease his pain and suffering. This makes the patient feel special and worthy of the attention and care of others.

For me, as a mother and grandmother, I found peace and comfort praying both alone and in the company of family and friends. Whenever I woke up worried in the middle of the night during the time David was on the waiting list and in the ICU, I prayed for David, for all of us, and for his doctors and nurses. I asked for strength and wisdom for each person, and for help in finding our way through the days to come so that we would make the right decisions at the right time and for the right reasons.

I also used a small prayer book that my sister Sima sent from Israel. I kept it next to my bed and read from it whenever I felt the need for the comfort of prayer, especially late at night and early in the morning. During the day while I was with David, I hummed the *Mi Shebeirakh*, a Jewish prayer for healing.

While dealing with a health crisis of her own, Laura's aunt, Rose Forsthoefel, said something about the power of prayer that I found to be inspirational:

> "I am sure you can feel the love and prayers that go out to your family. Life can be pretty wonderful when you allow people to do what they can to help you through tough times."

Prayers for Healing

The Mi Shebeirakh, a Jewish Prayer

The Mi Shebeirakh may be a prayer for individuals as well as a prayer for congregations. It is most often recited during a worship service, usually around the time of the Torah reading. It asks God, who blessed our ancestors, to bless us as well: to remove sickness, provide healing of body and mind, forgive sins, and bless the work of our hands at all times. Prior to the recitation of the prayer, the service leader might read a list of names of those known to be ill and ask for others to speak names aloud or in their hearts.

A popular expression of this prayer is a song, "Mi Sh'beirach," written by Debbie Friedman and Drora Setel, based on liturgy; music by Debbie Friedman:

Mi she-bei-rach a-vo-tei-nu, (1)
m'kor ha-b'ra-cha l'i-mo-tei-nu (2)
May the source of strength who blessed the ones before us
Help us find the courage to make our lives a blessing
And let us say: Amen.
Mi she-bei-rach i-mo-tei-nu,
m'kor ha-b'ra-cha l'a-vo-tei-nu
Bless those in need of healing with
r'fu-a sh'lei-ma (3)
The renewal of body, the renewal of spirit
And let us say: Amen.
(1) May the one who blessed our Fathers, the Source of blessing for our Mothers.
(2) May the one who blessed our Mothers, the Source of blessing for our Fathers.
(3) A complete healing.

Here is another expression of the same prayer written by Naida Cohn, Temple Beth-El, South Bend, IN

May the One who blessed our ancestors, Sarah and Abraham, Rebecca and Isaac, Leah and Rachel and Jacob, bring courage and faith to those who are ill; may Your spirit rest among them and bring comfort to them. God, grant wisdom and insight to those who work to heal, that their curative powers may bring sustenance to the body and mind of those in their care.

By this expression of prayer, may all who are in need and all who care for those in need know that this community cares deeply for their health and well being. And let us say: Amen.

And another written by Dee Coplin, Temple Beth Shalom, Austin, TX:

Loving God, we thank You for the gift of life and the strength of faith. We ask that You bring blessing and healing to all our Temple members, their friends, and family who suffer illness of mind or body. Sustain them through these days of illness with the courage to endure weakness and pain.

We thank You for the healing powers at work within them. May they recover speedily from their afflictions and return to their family and friends in good health. May they gain a truer appreciation of life's gifts, a deeper awareness of life's blessings, and a fuller sympathy for all who are in pain. Blessed is Adonai, the Source of Healing.

Prayers For Strength and Renewal

God rest me. Rest that part of me which is tired. Awaken that part of me which is asleep. God awaken me and awake within me. Amen. (Author unknown)

■   ■   ■

Thank you, God, for the light that is breaking through the sky, the sun that shines upon my face, my mind that is still alert and functioning despite my limitations. Through the day You will join me on this journey, so that I will never be alone or frightened, for I know You will be there. I am thankful for what I am capable of enjoying this day.

(Author Unknown)

My mother's rabbi sent this prayer for David to read:

Psalm 91

Dwelling in the shelter of the Most High,

Abiding under the protection of the Almighty,

I say of the Lord: He is my refuge and my fortress,

My God, in whom I trust.

He will deliver you from the snare of the fowler,

And from the destructive pestilence.

He will cover you with His pinions,

And under His wings shall you take refuge;

His truth is a shield and armor.

You shall not be afraid of the terror by night,

Nor of the arrow that flies by day;

Of the pestilence that stalks in darkness,

Nor of the destruction that ravages at noonday.

A thousand may fall at your side,

And ten thousand at your right hand,

But it shall not come near you.

You shall behold only with your eyes,

And see the recompense of the wicked.

Because you have made the Lord your fortress,

And the Most High your refuge,

No evil shall befall you,

Neither shall any plague come near your tent.

For He will give His angels charge over you,

To guard you in all your ways.

They shall bear you upon their hands,

Lest you strike your foot against a stone.

You shall tread upon the lion and asp,

You shall trample on the young lion and serpent.

'Because he has set his love upon Me, I will deliver him

I will protect him because he has known My name.

He shall call upon Me, and I will answer him;

I will be with him in trouble;

I will rescue him and bring him to honor.

I will give him abundance of long life,

And he shall witness My salvation.'

The Bible
The Book of Psalms, 91:1 - 91:16

Figure 1: Another prayer my mother's rabbi sent for David

Rituals Surrounding Organ Donation and Transplantation

(Reprinted from Organ Donation and Transplantation, Congregation Study/Program Guide #9, Spring 1997, pages 75-79; with permission from Department of Jewish Family Concerns, Union for Reform Judaism, New York, NY)

Ritual Upon Signing Organ/Tissue Donation Card

Created by Rabbi Randi Musnitsky and Rabbi Deborah Pipe-Mazo

Present:

Person(s) signing the donor card and two witnesses (non-family); at least one witness should be a person familiar to and close with the donor's family.

Person Signing Card:

Our God and God of our ancestors, I am grateful for the gift of life and the blessings of good health and personal safety. I pray that you will continue to bestow upon me years of physical and mental strength and vitality. May I live all my days in accordance with Your teachings, striving to add meaning and purpose to my existence. Yet, should I come to physical harm, ending my presence on Earth, I offer my body's organs and tissues, that which I no longer need, so that another precious life might continue.

I recognize, *Adonai,* that my decision might prove difficult for my family. Be with them. Comfort them. Encourage them in their time of sorrow, grief, and loss.

I sign this organ donation card comforted by the knowledge that I am fulfilling Your Will: to sustain a single human soul is equivalent to sustaining an entire world. Thus may I bring pride to myself and my family, setting an example of care, compassion and generosity for others in death as in life.

Witness #1:

By my presence and with my signature, I lend my support and encouragement to _____. I wish him/her many more years of life filled with health, meaning, and purpose.

Witness #2:

May _____ live until 120. May his/her life be full. If, however, that is not Your will, may my signature represent a promise to both _____ and _____'s family that I will comfort and support them through the process of donation.

Together

Sign the card at the appropriate places, then recite: Praised are You, *Adonai* our God, Source of All Creation, Who has given us life, sustained us, and enabled us to reach this moment. Amen.

Ritual for Donating a Loved One's Organs/Tissues

Created by Rabbi Deborah Pipe-Mazo.
Opening Family Prayer: CCAR Rabbi's Manual

Present:
   Family members of the deceased, rabbi/chaplain procurement representative, physicians and nurses (optional).

Rabbi/Chaplain:
   The *mitzvah of pekuach nefesh* is valued in Jewish life above every other practice. Tradition teaches us that saving a single life is equal in measure to saving an entire world. Through the gift of_____'s organs/tissues (actual parts might be mentioned here, in full or in part) you are helping others to heal and live, whose lives, like _____'s life, impact an entire world. The reward for this deed is realized both in this world and in the world to come.
   Zecher Tzadik L 'ivracha. May the memory of_____ (English or Hebrew name) be for a blessing. May *Adonai* comfort and console you with all who mourn in Zion and Jerusalem.

Family:
   Adonai, you give us loved ones and make them the strength of our days, the light of our eyes. They depart and leave us bereft on a lonely way, but You are the living fountain from which our healing flows. To You we look for comfort and consolation.
   We thank You, *Adonai,* for the blessing of years shared with _____, although too few. We are grateful for the paths we walked together and the love in which we grew, delighted, and celebrated.
   Comfort and sustain us as we offer others the chance to live and heal, even as we grieve _____'s death. We pray that spirit of care and generosity will become embodied through the gifts of his/her organs/tissues and that his/her memory will thrive through the immortality of his/her deeds. Praised are You, *Adonai,* the True Judge.
   (Family signs the donation paper, Rabbi or Chaplain acts as witness, as does any medical staff present.)

Medical Staff:
   I/We am/are saddened that it was not possible to help _____ heal and resume the life he/she lived prior to becoming sick. I pray that those who receive these organs/tissues are sustained during their surgery and recover well to full strength and potential.

OPO Rep:
   On behalf of the patients and families who will benefit from your generous gifts, thank you for *Matan Chaiim,* thank you for the Gift of Life.
   Praised Are You, *Adonai* our God, Source of All Creation, Who has given us life, sustained us, and allowed us to reach this moment. Amen.

Ritual for Receiving an Organ/Tissue/Marrow Transplant

Created by Rabbi Deborah Pipe-Mazo and Mr. Arnold Meshkov (recipient) of Elkins Park, PA.

This ritual can be observed in the hospital, at home, or in the synagogue within the context of a service. If this ritual takes place within a public forum, the Rabbi might introduce the Organ Recipient and give a brief history of his/her illness.

Present:
  Organ recipient, family, medical staff.

Organ Recipient:
  Adonai, for release from the danger/grave illness through which I have recently passed, I thank You. Praised are You, *Adonai* our God, Who has been so good to me.

All:
  May God who spared you continue to grant you all that is good.

Organ Recipient:
  Blessed is the Eternal God who has helped me find the strength to endure my illness, and has instilled in the human spirit the ability to provide the gift of an organ so that my life might be restored and renewed. Truly, the lives of my donor and donor's family have been a blessing, for to save one life is to save the world. May I be worthy of this greatest of gifts by appreciating each new day, and by being a source of compassion, strength and righteousness to my family, friends, and community. Hear, O Israel! *Adonai*, is our God! *Adonai* is One!

All:
  Praised are You, *Adonai* our God, Source of All Creation, Who has given us life, sustained us, and enabled us to reach this day.

To Remember Me

By Robert N. Test

This poem expresses the sentiments of countless organ donors, past and present.

The day will come when my body will lie upon a white sheet neatly tucked under four corners of a mattress located in a hospital busily occupied with the living and the dying. At a certain moment a doctor will determine that my brain has ceased to function and that, for all intents and purposes, my life has stopped.

When that happens, do not attempt to instill artificial life into my body by the use of a machine. And don't call this my deathbed. Let it be called the Bed of Life, and let my body be taken from it to help others lead fuller lives.

Give my sight to the man who has never seen a sunrise, a baby's face, or love in the eyes of a woman.

Give my heart to a person whose own heart has caused nothing but endless days of pain.

Give my blood to the teenager who was pulled from the wreckage of his car, so that he might live to see his grandchildren play.

Give my kidneys to one who depends on a machine to exist from week to week.

Take my bones, every muscle, every fiber and nerve in my body and find a way to make a crippled child walk.

Explore every corner of my brain. Take my cells, if necessary, and let them grow so that, someday, a speechless boy will shout at the crack of a bat and a deaf girl will hear the sound of rain against her window.

Burn what is left of me and scatter the ashes to the winds to help the flowers grow.

If you must bury something, let it be my faults, my weaknesses, and all prejudice against my fellow man.

Give my sins to the devil.

Give my soul to God.

If, by chance, you wish to remember me, do it with a kind deed or word to someone who needs you.

If you do all I have asked, I will live forever.

Memorial Prayer: We Remember Them

(Written by Rabbi Sylvan D. Kamans and Rabbi Jack Reimer. Reprinted from the Gates of Repentance: The New Union Prayerbook for the Days of Awe, New York, 1984, page 490)

This prayer is a part of the Jewish memorial service for remembering family members and special people in our lives who have passed away. In our family, we also recite this prayer for all the organ donors who gave David the gift of new life.

In the rising of the sun and in its going down, we remember them.

In the blowing of the wind and in the chill of winter, we remember them.

In the opening buds and in the rebirth of spring, we remember them.

In the blueness of the sky and in the warmth of summer,

we remember them.

In the rustling of the leaves and in the beauty of autumn,

we remember them.

In the beginning of the year and when it ends, we remember them.

When we are weary and in need of strength, we remember them.

When we are lost and sick at heart, we remember them.

When we have joys we yearn to share, we remember them.

So long as we live, they too shall live,

for they are now a part of us, as we remember them.

12

SURVIVAL

January, 2000

D avid was still struggling in the SICU. He didn't understand why, even with his new liver, he still didn't feel good. We showed him his blood test results, which were good, and reassured him. He was on a lot of medication to control his infections and we felt the side effects were probably causing his feelings of ill health. David was quiet most of the time, as was Kathryn in the next bed. But every once in a while, something would happen to remind us how alert and aware of their surroundings they were.

Kathryn, a dancer with years of ballet training, was now unable to keep her balance when she was standing. Daily physical therapy sessions and her mom Charlotte practicing the movements with her over and over were not enough to keep her steady on her feet. It took two nurses and her mom to hold her up, encourage her to walk, and help her balance. On the day she struggled through 10 steps away from and back to her bed, David held out his hands out and slowly clapped for her. Everyone was surprised that David was alert enough to notice her progress.

On January 8, almost two weeks after David's third transplant, he no longer needed the respirator and he was moved up to the postsurgical unit on the 15th floor. We heaved a sigh of relief, feeling that soon David would be leaving the hospital. On the evening that David arrived on the 15th floor, Pedro was the assistant nurse in charge of David. David knew Pedro from his previous stay and liked him. In the middle of that night, the phone rang. We all jumped. It was the floor doctor telling us that David was having breathing problems and they would have to move him back to the SICU. In the morning, we found David back in the SICU on a respirator, in the same bed next to Kathryn. Now David's chart included a diagnosis of pneumonia.

Thinking about the difficulty of David's first recovery from liver transplant helped to put things into perspective for us. When David received his first liver transplant at the University of Pittsburgh, he was comatose and had both liver and kidney failure. After the transplant, it took five days for him just to come out of the coma. Afterwards, he couldn't digest food, talk, or even move. When he opened his eyes for the first time, I could see the question mark in them. "We waited for this liver transplant that I needed so badly; why, now that I have a new liver, can't I move or talk?" they seemed to ask. David had chronic diarrhea and on some days, a fever. Since he was paralyzed, we had to change his diapers, change his position in bed to prevent bedsores, and lift him to a sitting position to prevent fluid from collecting in his lungs. Doctors installed an IV in his neck to get nutrients into him and warned us that he might never be able to swallow normally again. With a mother's faith, I knew in my heart that he was just weak and that slowly he would return to normal. I never lost that faith. Slowly, David began to talk and learned to swallow specially-formulated milkshakes. Physical therapy helped him regain movement in his hands and the nurses gave him a rattle to shake when he needed something. The diarrhea cleared up, but after two months David still couldn't walk, so they sent him to the Rehabilitation Institute of Pittsburgh. With rehabilitation, David learned to crawl, and then to walk. After two weeks of intense rehabilitation, we returned home on a trial basis and never looked back. One month later, David went back to school a normal child. My faith was rewarded, but David's first recovery took three long months.

This time, after battling liver failure for two brave years and avoiding sleep at the end to prevent falling into a coma, David went into surgery in better condition. David went into the operating room conscious, talking, and able to move his limbs. However, we had no experience with pneumonia.

Pneumonia is every surgeon's nightmare. They could operate and perform a perfect surgery, but later the patient could die of pneumonia. That's why postsurgical patients are led through a series of breathing exercises as soon as they are capable of performing them. Sitting up in a chair and walking are also encouraged as soon as the patient is strong enough to manage them. These movements are very painful after major abdominal surgery, but necessary to prevent pneumonia and speed recovery. David, who wanted to be a model patient, had bravely endured these painful exercises after the second transplant surgery. Now, after his third transplant surgery, with a body ravaged by infections, David seemed much weaker. We weren't surprised that he was finding it much harder to perform the exercises, but we were disappointed that as soon as David seemed to be improving, there was a new crisis to worry about. It reminded me of the old saying, "One step forward, and two steps back."

David was back in the SICU, existing in a dreamlike state where his body was healthy, and the respirator and feeding tube were foreign objects that didn't belong. In his semiconscious state, David tried to pull out his respirator and feeding tubes and, once again, the nurses put David in wrist restraints. When he was alert and awake, he had no recollection of why they had placed him in restraints.

These things added to our agony. None of them had happened after David's first transplant. It was all new territory for us. Through our experiences with David's three liver transplants, we knew that some patients experienced postsurgical complications and others did not. Of the patients who experienced complications, some of them succumbed to them and died, while others fought them off and lived. They were all getting the same treatment from the same group of doctors, so we didn't know why some patients lived and others died. We relied on our faith to sustain us; we had to believe that God made the final decision of who should live and who should die.

I couldn't help thinking that David had been in the hospital for a whole month, undergone two liver transplant surgeries, and was still gravely ill. That afternoon, sitting on a bench in the hospital garden, I opened a book about liver transplantation, hoping to read about other patients like David who'd survived in spite of tremendous obstacles. I also hoped to find advice on how to speed David's recovery. I looked in the index for pages with information about infections. Just before delving in, I saw Dr. Tzakis exiting the hospital. He greeted me, and for the first time I didn't have any questions for him; I knew he was doing everything he could for David. He said, "We had a little setback with David, but don't worry. He'll be OK." I tried to smile, but I didn't say much. I watched him make his way to the parking lot. He'd spent most of the day in the operating room, and I knew he must be tired.

My heart ached for David and for Dr. Tzakis, too. He knew how hard it was for us to see David so sick. He'd spent many hours operating on David, trying to save his life, and David was still severely ill. His optimistic words, "just a setback," gave me hope and reminded me of my husband Joe. Joe never concentrated on deficiencies or defeat; he kept his hopes high and his efforts directed towards the goal. Like Joe, Dr. Tzakis had arrived in the United States as a foreign student. Both of them had had the same drive to succeed, rise to the top of their field, and assimilate into American culture. Neither was afraid of hard work and their optimism helped them overcome the obstacles associated with their lofty goals. Instead of dwelling on the negatives, they celebrated their successes. Joe had started in this country as a college student, and now he was a successful school superintendent. Dr.

Tzakis had started as a surgical resident, and now was the head of one of the country's top transplant centers. Through optimism and hard work, both had succeeded. I prayed Dr. Tzakis' optimism, hard work, and dedication would succeed in saving David.

I turned to the pages about infections and began to read about them and the medications used to treat them. One sentence jumped out at me, "With better selection of patients, a lot of these infections can be eliminated." It occurred to me that this book was probably written by doctors for doctors. The mother of a severely ill infection-weakened transplant patient was not the intended audience for this book. That sentence had only one meaning to me. It was telling doctors to stay away from high-risk patients like David! If doctors chose healthier patients as their transplant candidates, they would-n't have to worry about infections. I closed the book. I knew I wouldn't be needing it again. "Better selection of patients" pounded in my head as I got up to return to the SICU waiting room. If I didn't have a healthy respect for books, I would have dumped that one in the first garbage can I encountered.

I was grateful to Dr. Tzakis and his team for accepting David as a patient, knowing as they did that David's problems would greatly challenge their medical expertise and maybe even adversely affect their transplant center statistics. I admired them for accepting these challenges and whole-heartedly committing to overcoming them. These were the same qualities we'd seen in Dr. Starzl as he cared for severely ill transplant patients back in 1981. I resolved to follow their lead and look at this new development through Dr. Tzakis' eyes, as just a setback.

Throughout the ordeal of being on the waiting list, we had focused on the liver transplant as the miracle we needed to save David. We had over-looked the fact that it might take another miracle for him to be able to recover from the two years of damage to his body. That fact was hitting home now. Two weeks after his third transplant, his liver was working perfectly, but David was back on the respirator with a high fever, in wrist restraints, confused, and out-of-touch with reality. Doctors were running tests to make sure his blood wasn't infected and checking to see whether the fungus in his digestive tract was spreading to other parts of the body. They were espe-cially concerned about David's eyes. The specialist came to the SICU to check for fungus in David's eyes and gave us the good news that his eyes were fine, but we needed to make sure David didn't touch his eyes. While we were unprepared for all of this, we were able to take comfort in the fact that the doctors seemed to be on top of all the problems.

We spent as much time as we could with David in the SICU, but sometimes we were in the way. The SICU wasn't designed for family members to spend a great deal of time there and I hated being asked to leave David's side. It was hard for me to see him in restraints with bruises on his wrists. He wanted so badly to free his hands. I talked to him soothingly to help him calm down and fall asleep. David was out-of-touch with what was going on around him, but he seemed to be responding positively to our voices. He could tell when we were around; if he had a nightmare, our presence helped him to feel safe. The experienced nurses appreciated our presence at David's bedside and understood that we could be helpful, but there were a few inexperienced nurses who bristled at our offers to help and asked us to leave while they cared for David. A power struggle ensued when I told one of the newer nurses that I would wait in the corner while she bathed David. She insisted that I leave the room or she wouldn't clean David. I knew that the loser in this power struggle would be David, so I left the SICU. I reported the exchange to Dr. Akin on my way out, who then went to check on David.

Interestingly, as out-of-touch as David was, he was much calmer with experienced nurses like Beth, Scott, Liz, Sam, Jim, and Elizabeth. The experienced nurses seemed to bring out the best in him, while the newer ones brought out the worst in him and brought tears to my eyes. Joe and I decided to see if we could do something about it. We met with Dr. Pinna and asked about the possibility of getting only experienced nurses to care for David. We didn't think it was an outlandish request given the fact that there were over 30 nurses in the rotation. Dr. Pinna told us that many families of SICU patients made similar requests, but if those requests were accommodated and the nurses didn't rotate, some patients might get stuck with nurses they didn't like, and new nurses might never gain the experience they needed to care for critical patients like David. While Dr. Pinna was unable to accommodate our request, he did bring the head SICU nurse into the room to listen to our concerns. Joe and I understood Dr. Pinna's point of view and realized that these transplant surgeons not only needed good operating skills, they also needed good people skills!

A day later, there was both good news and bad news. David's blood was free of infection, but now there was a problem with his kidneys.

Life went on in the SICU. Charlotte was able to stay with Kathryn most of the time, so we saw a lot of each other. Charlotte took Kathryn through the paces, making her do all the exercises that her physical therapist recommended. It was difficult for Kathryn. While she cooperated, she didn't say much; she knew her mom wanted the best for her.

It wasn't always obvious, but Kathryn and David were looking out for each other. Charlotte related this incident that drove this point home. David was confused and started struggling to get out of bed. Kathryn knew instinctively that David needed help, so she grabbed the rails of her bed and started shaking it, making enough of a racket to get the attention of the nurse who was on the other side of the room.

I didn't know whether or not Kathryn had experienced days that were as confused and out-of-touch as David's were. They seemed to understand each other so well, I wondered if they'd ever spoken to each other when Charlotte and I weren't around. They had a lot in common. Both were highly intelligent, had a love for life that was infectious, had doctors that wouldn't give up on them, and had families that had promised not to let them die.

By now, Kathryn had won her fight with infection. Robert Bank, on the other hand, had taken a turn for the worse. He had developed a viral infection and was moved to another ICU that was more isolated.

On January 15, Rebecca arrived for another visit. After being away from home for two months, it was a joy to see Rebecca's face. I knew David felt the same way because Rebecca and David were close. She spent time with David and helped with Rachael as well.

Now David was off the respirator again, but an additional antibiotic had been added to his medication list. We tried to pretend that everything was okay. David joked with Dr. Akin that he was going to fix him up with one of the nurses. Dr. Akin was single, but we didn't know whether or not he had a girlfriend. He jokingly pointed to Kathryn's tennis team poster and asked how he could compete with that. Dr. Akin was tall, lean, and good-looking. We didn't think he had anything to worry about.

David missed Rachael terribly. We added an autographed picture of the Miami Dolphins' cheerleaders to Kathryn's collection on the wall. It was another distraction and a conversation piece, but all David wanted to see were pictures of Rachael. We put an eight-by-ten picture of Rachael on the wall and another smaller photo at the end of his bed. We also put a picture of Rachael on a T-shirt for David, but that didn't last long, apparently it got mixed in with the hospital laundry and was never returned.

Dr. Akin tried to keep David's spirits up. While he was changing David's dressing, he would talk to David about computers. Dr. Akin needed a new computer and he asked David's advice about how to go about choosing the best one. Dr. Akin said he would wait until David was well and then they would go out shopping for the computer together. He respected David and went out of his way to engage him, instead of looking at him as just another critically ill body. We appreciated that and knew that David did, too.

On the evening of January 16, David was breathing on his own and resting comfortably when Elisha, Robert Bank's fiancée, asked to have a word with me outside. In the hall, she told me that Robert had died. We cried together. I remembered that Robert had arrived in Miami just a week after us. He'd been a good-natured young man that everyone had liked. He'd gone through all the pain, trials, and tribulations that David and Kathryn had endured. He'd had good days and bad days, and the surgeons had done everything they could for him. Knowing that his recovery would be difficult, Elisha had moved to Miami and gotten a job there. Still, Robert lost his battle with the virus that had taken over his body. Now, Elisha's mom was there to help her pack and move back to Michigan. They told us that Robert was in heaven with his parents, who'd also both died young. We hugged Elisha and wished her the best. She said she would pray for a quick recovery for David and Kathryn and left with her mom.

Robert's death just added to our worries and uncertainty over David's recovery. I wiped my face and put on a normal expression before going back in to see David. As soon as he saw me David asked, "Robert Bank died, didn't he?" I nodded and reported that Elisha said he was in heaven with his parents. I was surprised that David was alert enough to pick up on how ill the patients around him were.

It was now three weeks since David's third liver transplant. Dr. Madrid and Mrs. Becerra had recovered and been released from the hospital. Mrs. Cuba's daughter, Cary, still kept us company in the waiting room. Mrs. Cuba now occupied Robert Bank's old bed in the SICU. Mrs. Cuba's son Henrique was also a familiar face in the waiting room, along with her sister and niece. When they weren't visiting with Mrs. Cuba, they enjoyed Rachael's company and kept her entertained.

David's newest setback was fluid in the lungs. We were familiar with that, since he'd had it in Pittsburgh after his first transplant. On the plus side, David was awake more often and able to sit up for short periods of time in the chair next to his bed. When David and Kathryn were both awake and sitting at the same time, they did better, silently encouraging each other to sit for as long as the nurses wanted. David had lost a lot of weight and his tailbone was protruding, making it painful to sit in the chair, so the nurses brought a donut-shaped pillow to ease his pain and encourage him to sit longer.

SICU beds were state-of-the-art beds designed to change forms with the push of a button. David learned the buttons fast and, in spite of doctors orders, would switch from sitting to reclining when he was in pain. By the end of the fourth week after David's transplant, the nasogastric tube was out and David was encouraged to drink some liquid. By the end of the week, he was able to push himself up in bed and walk the length of the SICU, using a wheelchair as a walker. It seemed like David's healthy liver was finally winning the battle to turn around his dying body, and his energy was slowly returning. However, his hair was falling like autumn leaves and the nurses put a surgical hat on him to protect his bed from the falling hair.

Scott, an experienced nurse, was on duty at night. He and David understood each other. When David was confused and talking about things that didn't exist, Scott laughingly suggested that David was joking, instead of telling him he was confused and talking nonsense. Scott had respect and compassion for David, Kathryn, and all of the sick patients and their families. Scott and Liz, another wonderful night nurse, both arrived for work freshly groomed and with a smile on their face. When we arrived for the 9:00 p.m. visiting hour, they explained what was going on with David and reassured us that he would have a restful night. I slept better on the nights that I knew one of the experienced nurses would be looking after David.

David's hair was getting long and he was still too ill to leave the hospital to go to the barber. One day, Scott solved the problem for us. Scott wore his hair very short, and he pointed that out to David. He asked David if it would be alright to cut his hair in a similar fashion. David asked Sara, and Sara said whatever David wanted would be okay with her, so Scott trimmed David's hair. The Sunday nurses liked David's new short hair so well, they suggested he might look better with a buzz cut. David agreed to that, too, and before we knew it, he was bald! Before long, David started complaining that his head was cold. Joe brought David a warm winter hat from Chicago. Many patients are cold in the ICU, so there is a special warming oven for patient blankets. When David felt that he was freezing, we bought a comforter to warm and comfort him. However, he was so weak that we had to support the comforter on the rails of his bed because the weight of the comforter was too much for him. The infectious disease expert and Dr. Akin both explained that even though David's comforter was in perfect condition, when we left the ICU, we would have to put it in one of the red garbage bags to be disposed of with the rest of the dirty materials from the ICU because the comforter was capable of absorbing and containing infection-causing germs that were not safe for the general population. We agreed to dispose of the comforter when we were done with it.

Now, David was sitting unaided in a chair, walking the length of the SICU, exercising with a physical therapist, and drinking juice and nutritional shakes. That's when the diarrhea started. We were familiar with this problem and felt confident that he would overcome it. We began to hope that David was ready to be moved out of the SICU to a regular floor.

Sara's mom Johnie, recovered from her bone marrow transplant, arrived with her husband John and mom, Cora Byrd, to visit with David. It was wonderful for all of us, especially Sara and Rachael, to see Johnie back on her feet looking healthy. Johnie insisted on visiting David personally in the SICU but I worried that her immune system might not yet be strong enough to fight off the germs in the SICU after the massive chemotherapy she'd needed to have the bone marrow transplant. The nurses gave permission for David to walk out of the SICU to the waiting room so he could visit Sara's family without bringing them into the SICU. On January 26, almost a month after David's third transplant, he walked out of the SICU supported by two nurses and a wheelchair. He was wearing a hat on his bald head, and as he approached the doorway of the waiting room, he sat down in the wheelchair. It was a moving moment. Rachael recognized David and began to cry with joy. Then we were all crying tears of joy, relief, and sadness; even the nurses had tears in their eyes. There was joy for the father and daughter reunited after almost a month of not seeing each other; relief that David finally seemed to be turning the corner and getting better rather than worse; and sadness because we knew the joyful visit would be very short. After ten minutes, David had to return to the SICU.

That evening, David's chest x-rays showed one of his lungs was partially collapsed. He was given a special mask to wear. The mask would help his lung reinflate to normal size. It was uncomfortable, but he kept it on all night per doctors' orders. After 24 hours, there was still no improvement in his collapsed lung, so they put him back on the respirator again. The doctors told us if they had to put him on the respirator one more time, they would do a tracheotomy.

On Saturday, January 29, David was removed from the respirator. I could see that he was stronger. He still had a feeding tube and needed a little oxygen, but he was able to sit in a chair for several hours and pull himself up out of bed. It was time to leave Kathryn and Mrs. Cuba and move to the 15th floor! I didn't think this was the last time we would all see each other. In my heart, I thought there was a good chance that David might have to return to the SICU, but I hoped that wouldn't happen. I hoped that Kathryn and Mrs. Cuba would be joining David on the 15th floor instead.

On January 31, over a month after the third transplant, David moved from the SICU to the 15th floor postsurgical unit. He had a good liver, but a dying body. He was able to breathe on his own, but he'd developed asthma and was receiving breathing treatments. He had tubes to drain the fluid out of his lungs and a feeding tube in his nose to deliver nutrition to his stomach. His weight had dropped to 100 pounds. He was alert and awake during visiting hours, but he was very weak. We took him to the Visitors' Room on the 15th floor so he could see Rachael.

Over the first couple days, doctors made changes to his medications and gave him a blood transfusion. David was on antibiotics, antifungal medications, antirejection medications, and breathing treatments for asthma. All of these medications had different side effects. David was physically able to eat, but had no appetite. He had a tremor, and his body jerked unexpectedly. When no one was talking to David, he sometimes talked as if he was at home, and other times as if he was at work, holding conversations with coworkers who weren't there. On Thursday, February 3, after five days on the 15th floor, we could see that David just not himself emotionally. He'd had this same problem on the 15th floor after the second transplant and off and on in the SICU, but this time it seemed like he was getting worse every day. We'd always felt that we could help David to overcome any physical problem or illness, but this emotional problem left us feeling helpless. It didn't seem like he was getting any sleep because his eyes were always open and he talked constantly, almost as if talking in his sleep. We knew he wasn't hallucinating due to liver failure because we checked his liver and kidney numbers daily, and they were both fine. This condition seemed entirely different from the encephalopathy that he'd experienced before the transplant.

I was hoping that his confusion might be a side effect of the medications, but I was also worried about his mental health. The nurses that didn't know David from his first stay on the 15th floor asked us if he was always like that. When the doctors arrived to talk with David, he listened to them. After they left, he returned in his imaginary world. The same thing happened with the physical therapist. He was quiet and cooperative for the physical therapist, but once he was back in bed he went back to his surreal conversations.

On that Thursday, thinking he was completely healthy, David tried to get out of bed. He was oblivious to the IV pole, drainage bag, and feeding tube. Now the nurses were talking about putting him back in wrist restraints. All day, David lay in bed with his eyes open, not even closing them to take a nap. I knew that wrist restraints would not help his condition.

I decided to see what I could do. I found that when we touched David's shoulder to get his attention, he would return to reality with a jerk, as if awakened, and take his medication, drink what the nurses gave him to drink, and cooperate as asked. So, I sat next to his bed and when I could see him returning to a dreamlike state and trying to pull out his feeding tube, I talked to him to remind him that he was in the hospital.

At 11:30 p.m., the nurses asked me to leave. I told them I would leave when David fell asleep for the night and there was no longer any need to restrain him. David didn't close his eyes all night. The way he was talking and moving, I could see that he thought he was sitting in front of a computer using the mouse. Then the focus shifted, and he seemed to be holding a meeting at work, addressing each of his coworkers by name. Suddenly, his hand brushed the feeding tube and he tried to pull it out. I touched his shoulder gently and reminded him that he was in the hospital. He jerked as if I was waking him up and let go of the feeding tube. The night nurse was having a busy night with two other patients in the unit. When the assistant nurse arrived, she saw me sitting with David and brought me a cup of tea, then disappeared.

David carried on all night. In one of his attempts to remove the feeding tube, he managed to pull it out a centimeter. Then, the nurse arrived and removed it completely, telling me it was no longer useful. I blamed myself for that. I knew that until another feeding tube was inserted, perhaps the next day, David would be without food. Whenever the tube was in, David received constant nutrition from the bag on his IV pole. David was only hostile toward the feeding tube because it was in the way when he was dreaming that he was back in the office or at home living a normal life. He left his IV's, drainage tubes, and drainage bags alone.

Morning arrived without David ever closing his eyes. I had spent the night at David's bedside. Having observed David's behavior all night, I would be able to explain it to the doctors when they arrived and, hopefully, we would be able to find a solution that didn't involve wrist restraints.

Just before the shift change, the assistant nurse returned to David's room. This time, she was rude and angry that I had stayed the night. She asked me to leave and I could see that she was preparing to restrain David's wrists. I was exhausted from lack of sleep and worried about David's state of mind. I told her that I wasn't leaving until I talked to the doctors. The assistant nurse went and got the floor nurse, Hossein. Like Ruth, Hossein followed the hospital rules religiously. I reiterated my point and told Hossein that I would not be leaving until I spoke with the doctors. Hossein called the resident and fellows who were responsible for the 15th floor and they came to David's bedside. I thanked them for coming, but told Hossein that I couldn't leave until someone explained the reason for David's confused mental state and told us what they could do to reverse it. I had spoken with these young doctors the day before and their care had done nothing to change David's condition.

Through his confusion, David was following my struggle to stay by his side. Each time that I was asked to leave, David spoke up and, with tears in his eyes, implored me to stay and make sure they didn't put him in wrist restraints.

The morning nurses came on duty. David and I liked both Elizabeth, and her assistant Julie. Elizabeth suggested nicely that I needed a break from David's hospital room and she and Julie both assured me that they wouldn't place David in restraints. David accepted their promise, so I told David I was just going out into the hall to talk to the doctors to find a solution to this problem.

The nurses who didn't know David just assumed he was just an uncooperative patient, made worse by the transplant trauma or medication side effects. Elizabeth knew better. She knew that David was cooperative and eager to get well. She also knew how much he'd been through.

Soon Dr. José Nery arrived. He was apologetic about my rough night in the hospital and he was able to put a name on David's condition. He said David was suffering from ICU psychosis. Instead of wrist restraints, he said David would be transferred to a private room with a dedicated assistant nurse who would sit next to him day and night to remind him of his condition, so he wouldn't pull out his feeding tube or try to get out of bed alone. I would be permitted to sleep in the room, as well, if I wished. This was a big relief for all of us! Finally someone understood why David was suffering and offered a solution that made sense! The only sad thing was that Sara's 93-year-old grandmother had traveled all the way from Michigan to visit with David. She sat in the hall all day on Thursday, but because of David's confusion, was never able to visit with him.

The next day, a new feeding tube was inserted and David was finally able to sleep. However, like the day before, David talked with his eyes closed, held imaginary meetings, worked on a computer that wasn't there, and held and kissed his daughter Rachael in his imagination. He tried several times to pull the feeding tube out, but with the help of the 24-hour assistant nurse at night, and Sara and Joe helping during the day, David was unsuccessful in his attempts and didn't get out of bed. On Friday night, Joe came to take my place on the sofa bed in David's room and I went back to the apartment for the night to get some sleep.

After five days and several changes in David's medication, David was finally able to sleep peacefully with his eyes closed. By the second week on the 15th floor, David was cooperating with his treatment. He walked with a physical therapist, sat in a chair for as long as he was asked, and had a complete CT scan. The test showed that he had some fluid in his lungs and the fungus was still in his body. During his waking hours, David now showed interest in talking on the phone and using Joe's laptop computer. He was also able to move his body from the bed to the stretcher when he was going for an ultrasound scan. To us, those were all small signs of strength and improvement. Amazingly, behind the computer, David remembered everything. He remembered his passwords, checked e-mail, and sent e-mail to his friends and coworkers. To us, that was a sign that his mind was as sharp as it ever was.

Dr. José Nery and Dr. Roberto Verzaro were in charge of David on the 15th floor that second week. Dr. Verzaro had participated in both of David's transplant surgeries. Now, he treated David like a younger brother. He was very confident in his work. Once I observed him doing a liver biopsy on David. He numbed the location and told David to let him know if something hurt and he would stop. When David said, "Stop," Dr. Verzaro ended the procedure and showed us the sample. It was the least complicated and most painless biopsy David has ever experienced.

David was out of the SICU, but he wasn't necessarily out of the minds of the surgeons that operated on him and took care of him in the SICU. The young doctors on the pediatric team, like Dr. Joe Tector and Dr. Michael Angelis, stopped in for social visits with David. They were only a few years older than David and treated him like a friend or a brother, and were willing to help David with his daily problems. Dr. Akin came up from the SICU to visit with David frequently and sometimes called him on the telephone. David was no longer under Dr. Akin's watchful care 24 hours a day, but Dr. Akin told David he could page him anytime and that made David feel comfortable.

We have always been thankful for the doctors who care for their patients by getting to know them as a whole person. We understand that it takes more effort to become invested emotionally. We observed the sadness these doctors felt when their patients weren't doing well, and we saw their joy when their patients were on the road to recovery. I wondered if Dr. Tzakis had been looking for these qualities when he put together his team since most of his doctors were like this.

We saw Dr. Nery and Dr. Verzaro every day and they made sure that everything went well for David. Even though David was not bleeding internally, his hemoglobin was low. Each time his red blood count dropped below eight, doctors gave him a transfusion. The low RBC was not the worst of David's problems. At this stage, David's biggest problem was with food. He had no appetite, so it was difficult for him to eat. The doctors told us that he needed to consume 2,000 calories per day, and he could eat as much as he wanted. They encouraged him to eat whatever he craved while he was awake, and have formula through the feeding tube during his nap and at night. Every day, we kept a log of the food David ate and the nurses recorded how much formula David received through his feeding tube. It was difficult for David to eat as much as they asked because his body was in no condition to receive food. For the past two years on the waiting list, David hadn't been able to eat or hold down much food. Sara tried to help him by making a high-calorie milkshake similar to ones David drank in Pittsburgh after his first transplant, but no matter how much he tried to eat, he always ended up vomiting once or twice a day. Even toothpaste could make him gag. Sometimes he vomited so hard that the feeding tube came up from his stomach and out his mouth. To keep his spirits up, David sat in the chair and we played cards or, if he was feeling especially good, we walked the halls. He was like a newborn baby, needing naps in between his bursts of activity. He also woke up every few hours at night, not for food, but bathed in sweat, shaking with chills, or needing to use the bedpan.

When it was time to replace the central line used for blood transfusions, the surgeons considered putting in a long-term Hickman Line. This was very upsetting for David, not just because he wanted to get rid of all the attachments to his body, but because it implied that his recovery would be long. He didn't like to see the surgeons planning for a long and difficult recovery. He was sick and tired of being sick and tired, and he'd felt that way since last November. Now four months and two transplants later, he was still attached to IV's, tubes, and bags!

The doctors had a long talk with David and explained that the central line would prevent them from having to poke him with needles every time he needed blood. As soon as his body no longer needed transfusions, they would take the line out. David accepted this explanation and the line was replaced.

The nurses gave us a Teaching Transplant Journal. In this folder, all the medications and their side effects were described. Pages were included for the patient and his family to record medication doses. The purpose of the journal was to help the patient understand his medications and take charge of his treatment.

On Sunday, February 9, David visited with Sara's parents and Sara's best friend Rachael. Rachael had come from her home in Utah to spend some time with Sara and David. Finally things were beginning to seem normal and we felt that David was on the road to a slow recovery.

One morning during David's third week on the 15th floor, he woke up and, with a little help, got himself into the chair by his bed. He took his pills with chocolate milk and immediately choked, vomiting the feeding tube right out of his stomach. With the feeding tube out, we hoped that David would finally begin eating on his own and vomiting less. But the vomiting continued and could happen without warning. Once, while visiting with little Rachael in the Visitors' Room, he began to vomit. There were other people in the room and we were unprepared; we didn't have a basin with us. Sara and I kept Rachael and the others away while we cleaned things up as best we could and got David back to his room. This incident was embarrassing for all of us and taught us a valuable lesson: David's vomiting was unpredictable. We would be more prepared next time.

My heart went out to Rachael and David, who'd both looked forward to the visit. I thought how much better things would be if Rachael were allowed to visit with David in his private room, but the rules were the rule; they weren't about to be changed on David's account. The rules didn't distinguish between patients who spent a few days or a week on the 15th floor and those patients who spent weeks or months there. Besides, Ruth and Hossein were determined to make sure that no one violated the rule. I understood the reasoning behind the rules. It was a transplant floor and the patients were on medications that suppressed their immune systems. They couldn't risk being exposed to the germs children carried. Something as innocuous as the common cold could be life-threatening to a transplant patient on immunosuppressants. Conversely, the transplant patient could be harboring hospital-borne infections that would be dangerous to children. Each patient was a member of a family, and if each patient's family had several children in it and all were allowed into the hospital rooms, chaos would ensue.

In the hospitals in Grand Rapids, Omaha, and Chicago, we were always able to take Rachael right into David's room each time he had a private room. As far as we could tell, Rachael was no danger to him and he was no danger to her.

We felt that Rachael's visits were essential to David's recovery, and that Rachael also needed to see her dad in each stage of his recovery. David had been hospitalized for over two months now and, as much as we could, we kept Rachael involved in his progress. At 2 years old, she was smart and sensitive. We didn't want Rachael to think that hospitals were bad places where people got sick and died, so we tried to make things fun. We rode the elevators, visited with David, bought things in the gift shop and cafeteria, and walked in the gardens, searching for flowers and butterflies. To Rachael, these were the experiences of everyday life. If we were happy, she was happy, too.

I thought we might try playing a little game to sneak Rachael into David's room. I explained the new game to Rachael, stressing how important it was to be quiet. The Visitors' Room was on the right and David's room was down the hallway to the left. Since the nurses' station was past his room, my plan was to peak down the hallway to see if anyone was around. If the hallway was empty, I would push Rachael's stroller rapidly and quietly down the hall into David's room. If there were people in the hallway, I would wait with Rachael in the visitors' room until the coast was clear. We targeted midday and early evening, since those were the times of day when things were generally quiet and doctors were no longer making their rounds. My plan worked! When we got into David's room, Rachael knew that she had to stay in her stroller and if a nurse came in I would have to take her out.

Sneaking to David's room for a little while became part of our everyday activities. In the room, she talked with David and asked about different items in the room. She was the type of child who was interested in everything and wanted to learn about it. She really got a kick out of this game that we called "Sneaking into David's Room."

David finally came off the breathing treatments for asthma. His mental status was normal, but we noticed that as his awareness and understanding of his condition increased, he was becoming depressed. The source of his depression was waking up after his surgery and finding himself trapped in a body that was not as strong and as healthy as normal person's body. He reviewed his liver function tests daily. He understood that his liver was working normally, but it was hard to accept that he couldn't get up and go home and get on with his life. He was unable to eat and hold food down and a drop in his hemoglobin made matters worse. Because he needed nutrition, a feeding tube was put in after a day or two and the doctor added a new medication to prevent vomiting.

On February 12, Ben took a couple of days off work and came to visit David and to spend some time with him. The last three times that Ben came to Miami to see him, David was in the SICU and unconscious and David hadn't remembered. This time, Ben brought David a laptop computer that he could use while he was in Miami and the two brothers had fun talking about computer games.

David needed a battery for his cell phone and the doctors gave permission for David to leave the hospital for a short time. Ben packed a wheelchair in the car. With Ben there, he had forgotten about his weak body. When David tried to get into the car like a healthy person, he lost his balance and collapsed on the front seat of the car. Fortunately, Ben was able to pick him up and help him get situated in the front seat of the car.

We drove to downtown Miami and parked. Ben took the wheelchair out and helped David into it. We went a couple of blocks until we found the battery David was seeking. It was a nice, sunny afternoon and for a little while David had fun visiting his favorite stores. Although he sweated a lot, that night was the first night that David slept through the night. Joe was not able to come in that weekend and it was nice to have Ben around. One Monday, David's depression returned, but at noon he showed interest when I mentioned leaving the hospital for lunch.

David in the wheelchair, holding Rachael's hand, must have created a beautiful scene. There were people in the hospital lobby videotaping a documentary and they asked permission to videotape the father and daughter holding hands as they left the hospital. David agreed.

McDonald's was a block away from the hospital. David tolerated the wheelchair ride and all the bumps in the road without complaining. We ordered lunch and ate outside on the benches. Being used to living in a cold climate, it was nice to enjoy the weather which was warm and comfortable. This would be another activity that we could add to David's schedule— going out and about at lunchtime and dinnertime to enjoy the warm Florida winter in the hospital garden, and spending time with Rachael. Sometimes we saw Kathryn, who'd been moved up to 15th floor, out in a wheelchair with her mom and we'd say hello and have a short conversation.

At the end of the third week on a regular floor, the vomiting continued and the doctors continued adjusting David's medication. Even on his "healthy days," David wasn't eating that well. All of our trips to restaurants and stores outside the hospital to find David's favorite foods weren't helping much. He still wasn't able to eat all the calories he needed to recover. We knew from experience that it might take a long time for him to eat normally again. After his first transplant in 1981, it took several years for him to get his appetite back. This time would be no different. Eventually, David would eat normally again. However, every day he showed improvement in his body movement.

David was getting daily sponge baths. When his wound was covered with scar tissue, but there was still no skin on it, Doctor Tzakis suggested that David was ready for a shower. For David, the 15th floor was as cold as the ICU, so he was not showing any interest in taking a shower. Julie, an assistant nurse that David liked, was able to talk him into it. Julie loved her job and arrived each morning with a big smile. After David's first shower, she settled him in the warmest spot in his room where the sun streamed in the window. This was another step toward David's recovery.

On the weekend of February 19th, Joe came for a long weekend. David wanted to come home to the apartment with us and he enjoyed his visit immensely. When we returned to the hospital that evening, the nurse notified us that David's hemoglobin was below 8 and he needed a blood transfusion again.

The next day, David needed another transfusion. Again, we brought David for a short visit at the apartment and took a ride to Miami Beach. David ate 2000 calories that day and didn't vomit. In spite of the transfusion, it was a hopeful day!

It seemed every day Rachael said something that reminded us how quickly she absorbed things and how fast she was growing. On the return trip from Miami Beach, Sara read a sign on the road that referred to "Stars' Houses." Rachael's responded quickly, "Where is the moon's house?" Another interesting time, I noticed Rachael wearing a latex glove in the car on our return from the hospital. Earlier she had seen Sara and me wearing gloves while helping David, so she had asked for one. When I asked her why she still had her glove on, her answer was, "When we get home, I want to take the baby out." I have no idea how she figured that out! We had to remind her that when it was time for the baby to come out the doctors would do it, and that it was not yet time for the baby to come out.

Sara had her first prenatal checkup in Chicago right before we left. As soon as we arrived in Miami, she found a doctor and had regular checkups. Her mom accompanied her to her ultrasound, and then brought us the baby's first video. Thankfully, she was having a normal pregnancy and David was becoming healthier day by day. David's love for Sara, Rachael, and his unborn baby were keeping him going. He was filled with the joy of his second child on the way.

When David had an active day, he slept better at night. But whether he was sleeping deeply or not, he still had to be weighed. The night assistant nurses had to weigh all their patients before they went home in the morning. They arrived with the scale at 4:00 a.m. in the morning, turned on the light, and wanted David to stand on a scale. For a transplant patient, monitoring the weight after surgery is very important. The doctor needs to know if the patient is suffering from a buildup of fluid or beginning to dehydrate. For David, who was just starting to sleep normally, this 4:00 a.m. ritual was very uncomfortable. So with his doctors' permission, we made a sign that said "Do Not Disturb from 11 p.m. to 7 a.m." and posted it on his door.

Still, he had good days and bad days. Eating food and holding it down remained his biggest problems. He could go one day without vomiting and the next day he might vomit twice. We weren't seeing much change in either his weight or his appetite. The surgeon suggested installing a feeding tube on his abdomen, so it wouldn't cause gagging and vomiting like the nasogastric tube sometimes did. David agreed to that since this was not as uncomfortable as regular tube, and it was not on his face. Even so, it had to be put in by specialists.

We tried to keep David busy. We went out once, sometimes twice a day. When he came to the apartment, David played computer games with Rachael who truly enjoyed having him around. It seemed that each day held a "first" for all the normal activities like walking unaided, using the bathroom unaided, or shaving himself.

In the beginning of March, Debbie Weppler, the head of the transplant coordinators told us that Dr. Starzl's office in Pittsburgh called wanting to know how David was doing. She also gave us good news—David could leave the hospital, stay in the apartment, and return to the clinic weekly for checkups. David's day-to-day care would be handled by a home-care nurse.

On March 13, we brought David home from the hospital. Every day he needed to flush the Hickman line, change the dressing on his wound, and get a shot. Sara could not look at the wound, so a caring and wonderful home-care nurse showed me how to put the dressing on it each day after David showered. David volunteered to learn to give himself the shot. Rachael was not afraid of any of this. She wanted to help, too, so when I was putting the dressing on David's wound, Rachael would put her gloves on, stand on the opposite side of the bed and, resting her elbows on the bed, watch every move that I made. Even though the shower made David's wound bleed, I could see that the skin was slowly coming together and the wound was healing.

As soon as I pulled the mesh tank top (that held the dressing in place) over David's head, Rachael would remind me to pull the head of the feeding tube out of the mesh by saying, "Don't forget to take that thingy out."

Jokingly, I replied, "Thank you, Dr. Rachael Yomtoob," and this made Rachael laugh.

Five days after David came to the apartment, he had to be rehospitalized for two days for an overall checkup and to repair a bleeding hematoma that had developed on his belly button. Two weeks later, David and Sara went to the clinic for David's next checkup. Aside from the constipation, David had been feeling fine. He asked the doctor what he should use to relieve his constipation, since he'd been constipated all weekend. Surprisingly, the doctor told him he would need to be admitted to the hospital that evening. I didn't even know why. We were planning to go to Miami Beach, so David wasn't interested in returning to the hospital after dinner. However, the hospital called and said that the surgeons were waiting for David and we should page them when we got to admissions, so we went. When we got to admissions, we paged the doctors as instructed; then David went to the bathroom. I was surprised to see three surgeons waiting for him in the lobby—Dr. David Levi, Dr. Roberto Verzaro, and Dr. Michalino Scarlotta.

Dr. Levi asked, "Where is David?" All three of them looked worried.

"In the bathroom," I answered.

"Is he vomiting?" they asked.

"No, he's having a bowel movement," I replied. What a relief. Apparently, the doctor who'd examined David in the clinic that morning was concerned that David's constipation might be a sign of intestinal blockage. The surgeons were relieved that David was having a bowel movement, but insisted that he be admitted for another checkup to rule out the possibility of intestinal problems. I felt good knowing that they were as worried about David as we were. They were as concerned as if he were a member of their own family. It's no wonder why two months later, when a reporter asked, "How did you survive all of this?" David simply answered, "I always felt that my doctors wouldn't let me die. They made me feel like a very special person."

It turned out to be the last time that David was hospitalized. He had a complete checkup and an ultrasound scan of his intestines, and the hematoma on his belly button was drained. Tests showed that there was no blockage of his intestines. Elizabeth and her assistant, Patty, were David's nurses. As always, they were both wonderful. Patty treated her patients with motherly affection. Not a single one of her patients disliked her. Elizabeth, as serious as ever, couldn't understand why we were so grateful to her. As far as she was concerned, she was only doing her job.

By April 9th, David was back in the apartment again. We were trying to live a normal life until David got the OK to return home to Michigan. Sara's due date was June 6th, and her doctor didn't think she should take any airplane trips in the month before her due date. We hoped and prayed that David would be able to return home by then.

Wednesday, April 19th was the Eve of Passover. Laura, Ben, Josh, and Jacob hosted Passover in their home in Chicago. Joe, Rebecca, and Dave were with them. David, Sara, Rachael, and I celebrated Passover in Miami. David led the service for us. It was the smallest group with which I had ever celebrated Passover, but with David's condition, we just didn't feel comfortable accepting any of the invitations we'd received from the kind people in Miami. Our group was small, but we had joy in our hearts. After all, David had a new, healthy liver and was on the road to recovery.

A week later, during Josh and Jacob's spring break, Laura, Ben, and the boys drove with Joe to Miami for the week. Once again, we were all together. Ben and Laura rented an apartment in our building for a week, and I saw Josh and Jacob for the first time in five months. Josh and Jacob swam with Rachael in the pool, and Ben and Laura took Rachael sightseeing with their family. On one beautiful day, we all spent the early afternoon sightseeing. For dinner, we picked a restaurant on the water. Although we missed Rebecca and Dave (who had a different spring vacation), everything had gone well all day. Sitting at the lovely terrace table, it seemed the only problem for each of us was what to order. Josh had struggled with food allergies since birth. He was especially allergic to milk, so Laura and Ben consulted with the waiter over what would be safe to order for him.

We ordered soft drinks, and I liked the lemonade that I ordered. It was tasty and smooth. Josh also ordered lemonade, but after drinking a little, Josh ran to the restroom. Laura and Ben followed him. It didn't take long for Ben and Laura to figure out that there were dairy products in the lemonade. Since the restaurant didn't usually serve lemonade, they made our lemonade with carbonated water and sweet and sour mix from the bar. The sweet and sour mix had milk in it.

To Josh, dairy products were pure poison. He was having a severe allergic reaction, so Ben and Laura loaded him into the car and rushed him to the emergency room. Naturally, the rest of us lost our appetites and we returned to the apartment and ordered pizza later. After several hours of treatment at the hospital, Josh was released and the three of them returned to the apartment.

With David feeling better every day, we began getting ready to return home. David still needed a wheelchair for long walks, but by now, most of

David's tubes were out. There was only the feeding tube in his belly. At this point, we were only using it to get more calories into him at night while he was sleeping. Dr. Tzakis convinced David that it would be all right to return home with it. His local doctor would be able to remove it when David was eating normally again.

As we made our preparations to go, we thought of all the people we wanted to thank before we left. On Friday, April 29, we went to Friday night services at Temple Israel of Greater Miami. Rabbi Jeffrey Kahn introduced David to the congregation and David thanked them for their prayers and support.

We also wanted to thank the staff at Jackson Memorial Hospital, so we distributed flyers and invited everyone to come to the 15th floor meeting room on Monday, May 1 for cake and punch. We didn't ask for RSVP's since we knew how busy they all were, but we expected that the nurses and assistant nurses would come to our get-together. To our delight, most of the surgeons who were not in the operating room also joined us! It was a wonderful surprise. If we'd known that so many surgeons were going to come, Joe or David would have prepared a speech. As it was, all we had was a cake with "THANK YOU" written on it in big letters. Of course, if the surgeons were needed in the operating room, we had no doubt that's where they would be, but their presence there made us feel that they had become as attached to David as we were to them. They had spent hours in the operating room to replace David's failed liver with a healthy one, and then spent days and weeks nurturing him back to life. How could we ever thank them properly? Especially Dr. Tzakis, this man who was doing God's work on earth by giving second and third chances at life to patients like David, who were dying slowly and miserably of organ failure. We had witnessed how tirelessly Dr. Tzakis worked and how he never wrote off any of his patients. He accepted all available viable organs from any part of the country at any time of the day or night, weekends or holidays, it didn't matter. If there was an organ, he called his teams and patient, and they went to the operating room. He expected the same level of dedication from his team members and staff that he displayed himself. Having seen him in action, we had no trouble understanding how they'd managed to perform over 150 transplants in the year 1998 alone.

Dr. Tzakis had a big smile on his face, and we watched as he talked with David and Kathryn, who was now a recovering outpatient like David. The three of them were not discussing medication, IVs, respirators, or feeding tubes. These things were all in the past now that David and Kathryn were healthy and strong. It reminded me of a parent when it comes time for their child to move out of the house. Dr. Tzakis was letting them go and letting them know that he would always be there for them.

Back in April, after David was out of danger, I had written to Dr. Starzl and told him how Dr. Tzakis had brought his ideologies, teachings, tireless effort, and dedication to the transplant program at the University of Miami. I described the wonderful things that Dr. Tzakis was doing for his patients, and asked Dr. Starzl to autograph several copies of his book for the members of Dr. Tzakis' team, in honor of David's second and third liver transplants. Not only did Dr. Starzl autograph the books, he wrote a beautiful inscription in each, and I knew it would be special for the surgeons who so admired Dr. Starzl.

We presented the books to the surgeons as a small token of our appreciation in honor of David's return to a normal life. We gave a copy of our first book, The Gift of Life, to each of the fellows and residents. We also left copies of the books for the ICU nurses and the 15th floor nurses in their libraries.

Nurses and assistant nurses stopped by on their breaks for our celebration. Ruth, our assistant nurse from the 15th floor, also came by. We took pictures, offered them cake and punch, and said our goodbyes. It was a wonderful afternoon!

Many of the surgeons who were in Miami training under Dr. Tzakis would leave Miami and become associate surgeons or create their own transplant centers in other parts of the country or the world. We were glad that we'd had the good fortune to meet each of them during David's transplant and recovery. We will always remember them and they will have a special place in our hearts.

Now that David was healthy again, we had some final visits to make. With pleasure, we accepted a standing invitation from Sara's Uncle Ray and Aunt Connie to come to their lovely home for lunch. They'd come to visit David in the hospital often and had been waiting for the day when we could visit them in their home. We also accepted an invitation from Tom and Patty Sams in Naples. Our friendship had started in Pittsburgh in 1981, when their son Bobby had had his first, second, and third transplants around the same time David was there. Unfortunately, Bobby did not survive, but we had stayed in touch for the past 19 years and visited with them several times over the years. We had promised to visit them again as soon as David was able to travel, so we went to their house for lunch on the last Saturday that we were in Florida.

Before we left Miami, Sara invited me to return home with them and stay until they got settled back into their house again and I agreed. On May 3, we packed our bags and left Miami. Sara's parents picked us up from the Grand Rapids airport and took us to David and Sara's home in Lowell. While living in the apartment in Miami, Rachael had forgotten all about their house in Lowell. Even after we arrived home, she kept asking, "When are we going home?"

When David and Sara were settled in and it was time for me to return to Chicago, Rachael asked me why I wouldn't be living with them anymore. She didn't understand why I could live with them in Miami, but not in their house in Lowell. For a long time after that, whenever Joe and I would come from Chicago for a visit, when it was time to go, Rachael would say, "Please stay with us," or "Grandma, please don't go." She didn't know that I was as attached to her as she was to me. During the dark days when we weren't sure whether David would live or die, she was the one that showed me the rainbow and made me laugh. She was the one that talked and asked questions all the time to prevent me from having sad thoughts. She entertained me in the car by singing songs, and if she didn't know the words, she made up her own songs and lyrics. Her imagination turned the hospital waiting room into a train station. She was full of energy and life, and she gave me energy and kept me going. She wasn't afraid of anything. She even tried to help me find my way through the streets of Miami when I made a wrong turn by saying, "Turn around, turn around!" I didn't even know how she figured these things out! She was a little girl with a big heart, great understanding, and a big mission. She didn't know that she was the angel that guided David through his ordeal, and gave him will to live when he couldn't even breathe on his own and his dying body wouldn't accept food. David knew that Rachael and his unborn baby needed their father around to raise them. Rachael was a strong girl and I knew that she would adjust well. I hoped Rachael and I would always be as close in heart as we were in Miami.

Sara and David had a month to prepare for the birth of their son Nathan. Sara's parents, John and Johnie, lived only an hour away and were a great help to them. David and Sara took a Lamaze refresher course. On Tuesday, June 6th, David drove a car for the first time since his transplant, and we all gathered in the hospital for the birth of David's and Sara's son. Nathan was born healthy and perfect. David was a proud father, and the joyful look in his eyes for the first time since all of his troubles began told all of us that he was grateful to be alive and well to witness the birth of his son.

It was a time to be born. Nathan came into the world healthy and whole, and David had a new lease on life. In the hanging basket on David and

Sara's front door, birds built a nest and laid eggs. When we visited, David asked us not to use the front door so as not to disturb the nesting pair. From the living room window, we watched the birds taking turns sitting on the eggs, and before long we saw hatchlings in the nest waiting to be fed. For me, this was a hopeful sign from the world of nature. It was time for new lives and new beginnings in David's house!

The Grand Rapids Press

GES   © TUESDAY, MAY 23, 2000

David Yomtoob, finally home recovering after his third liver transplant, plays with his daughter Rachel, 2, as his wife, Sarah, looks on at the left.

PRESS PHOTOS/LANCE WYNN

ANOTHER CHANCE

After third liver transplant, David Yomtoob is home and ready to get on with life

HOW TO DONATE

The Grand Rapids Press

By Pat Shellenbarger
The Grand Rapids Press

David and Sara Yomtoob came home the other day to the house they had bought nearly two years ago but had barely occupied.

"We're still not completely unpacked," Sara said, in the living room of the tidy, new house.

That's because they've spent more time in hospitals and nearby apartments the past two years than in their home outside Lowell while David awaited a liver transplant. His new liver, which he received nearly five months ago, is functioning well, and he's slowly gaining strength.

He's been through this before. In 1981, when he was 12, David became one of the sickest patients ever to survive a liver transplant, helping prove its medical viability. He also was one of the first Michigan residents to receive a liver transplant.

In the years since then, liver transplants have become relatively common, though still very serious, last-ditch procedures. Today 30,000 Americans are living with transplanted livers.

Dr. Andreas Tzakis, a Miami surgeon, has performed hundreds of liver transplants the last several years, yet he recalls David Yomtoob's in minute detail.

"He's a special person," said Tzakis, calling from a convention of transplant surgeons in Chicago. "I knew of David

Rachel, 2, has adapted well to her father's illness and life on the move, her parents say.

before I met him."

That's because Dr. Thomas E. Starzl, a liver transplant trailblazer who performed David's first transplant, chronicled the case in his book, "The Puzzle People: Memoirs of a Transplant Surgeon." David's mother, Parichehr Yomtoob, also wrote about her son's first illness and recovery in her book, "The Gift of Life," which advocates organ donations.

"Anyone who knows about liver transplants knows David," she said, "because he was a pioneer."

As a boy, he made appearances at medical conventions to prove that liver transplants save lives. So by the time David entered a Miami hospital last year for a second liver transplant, his case was known to transplant surgeons

see TRANSPLANT, D2

Anyone can become an organ and tissue donor, regardless of age, although those younger than 18 must have a parent's or guardian's consent.

Since 1972, the Michigan Secretary of State has made organ donation stickers available at all branch offices. The sticker, expressing a person's desire to become an organ donor, must be signed by two witnesses and put on the back of the person's driver's license or Michigan personal identification card. Newer licenses already have a space to check off donation information.

A person also can carry an organ donor card, available from the Ann Arbor-based Transplantation Society of Michigan at (800) 482-4881 or through the nonprofit agency's Web site at www.tsm-giftoflife.com. Additional information on organ donation can be obtained at www.organdonor.gov.

It is essential that family members know your wishes, since they will be asked to sign a consent form in order for the donation to occur. All costs are paid by the recipient, usually through private insurance or Medicare.

Organs that can be transplanted include the heart, kidneys, pancreas, lungs, liver and intestines. Tissues include corneas, skin, bone marrow, heart valves and connective tissue.

David, with his wife Sarah and daughter Rachael, growing stronger after his third liver tranplant.

Appendix 12

The Importance of a Positive Attitude

The mind and body are not separate units. For years, scientists talked about this integrated system, exploring how the way we act, think, feel, and eat are related to our health and our ability to recover from illness and major surgery.

Having a reason to live is what inspires most people to get up in the morning and go on with their lives. Having a reason to live is also what can inspire an ill person to fight for their lives and continue the struggle for survival with each new crisis. Perhaps the ill person is determined to finish an important project or raise his children to adulthood. The ill child may want to graduate from high school or achieve a lifelong goal of becoming an actor, veterinarian, etc.

For twelve-year-old David, becoming well enough to celebrate his Bar Mitzvah and become a man in the eyes of his Jewish religion was reason enough to fight for survival after his first transplant. After David's second and third transplants, his will to live came from his desire to raise his two-year-old daughter and his anticipation of the birth of his second child. He also thought a lot about all the friends and family members who were praying for him. He didn't want to disappoint them.

So, what is the difference between the patient who wants to live and the one who doesn't? The patient who wants to live is aware of what is happening to his body. He will seek help for problems that he notices and will do all he can to cooperate with doctors and nurses while in the hospital. The patient who has given up will ignore what is happening to him, neglect to follow caregivers' instructions, and perhaps even refuse treatment.

Doctors and nurses have difficult work to do. They do not always have time to try to persuade patients who've already lost hope to take their medication or accept treatment. Many of these patients who've survived tell similar stories. They report that when they were first diagnosed with terminal cancer, liver disease, or other major illness, they decided to give up and die. Then, at some point, the love and concern of family and friends who were willing to hang around and help them through treatment and recovery got through to them. They changed their mind, began actively working for their recovery, and triumphed over major illness!

As Bernie Siegel said in *Love, Medicine, and Miracles*, "We must remove the word 'impossible' from our vocabulary." As David Ben Gurion once observed in another context, "Anyone who doesn't believe in miracles is not a realist." The miracle happens when people act for it. Although the recovery of transplant patients does not come easy, it is far from being impossible. It takes hard work. Everyone contributes—doctors, nurses, the patients, and their families. It is a team effort.

David survived his second and third liver transplants in spite of complications from infections that kill 99 percent of the transplant patients who contract them. We attribute that, in large part, to David's optimistic and hopeful character. He had great trust in his doctors, surgeons, and nurses. Many times David was put back on the painful, uncomfortable respirator, and many times returned to the operating room for an emergency procedure to treat complications. It was very painful for us to see David in such a debilitated condition and it seemed that he was being tortured each time they put him back in wrist restraints. Our hearts ached for him. When he got well, I asked him, "How did you bear all of this?"

He replied, "I was sure that my surgeons wouldn't let me die. They made me feel like I was a very special patient to them."

At that point, I realized that what we interpreted as torture, David interpreted as love and care from his doctors. With all the concern and attention they were giving him, he felt that they were going to great lengths to keep him alive and that he was in good hands. And just like when he was a 12-year-old transplant patient, David simply was not planning to die! Even transplant surgeons who operate on end-stage liver disease patients every day view David's survival as a miracle! When they consider the condition he was in both before and after transplant, they know that he truly beat the odds. David's optimism, hope, determination, and reasons to live are what kept him alive throughout his long wait on the waiting list and his battle with infections.

No surgeon can become a transplant surgeon without a positive attitude and a hopeful outlook. They can't walk into an operating room without the conviction that the hours they spend there will be well spent, that the surgery will have a good outcome, and that their patient will recover and return to a normal life.

As Dr. Starzl, a pioneer in liver transplantation, trained transplant surgeons to do liver transplants, he also taught them not to write off or give up on anyone. Dr. Starzl never wrote off or gave up on anyone and, as a result, his patients didn't give up either!

Above left: David's college graduation, 1993.

Above right: David and Sara's wedding, July 1994.

David with Rachael, December 1997.

David and Sara with Dr. Thomas E. Starzl in Japan at the International Congress of Transplantation Society, August 1994.

Rebecca and Dave Dahn's wedding, August 1998.
Standing, Ben, Laura, Dave, Rebecca, David, and Sara.
In front, Parichehr, Joshua, Jacob, and Joe.

Jacob, Rachael, and Josh,
with Ben, August 1998.

Rachael Yomtoob with
Edna Melamed, August 1998.

Above left: Rachael, Sara, and David , October 1998.

Above right: Sara, David, and Rachael, December 1998.

Below left: David with Rachael, January 1999.

Right: David, Sara, and Rachael, October 1999.

Below right: David, October 1999.

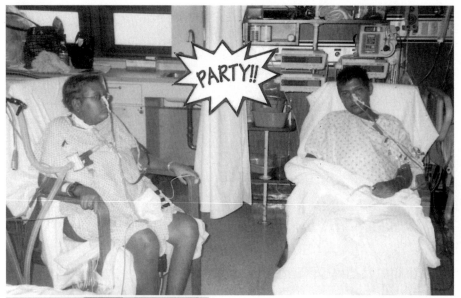

Above:
David with Kathryn Smith in the ICU,
January 2000.

Left:
David with Kathryn at the
"Thank You Party", May 2000.

Below:
Kathryn Smith, January 2002 Photos by
Good Housekeeping Magazine

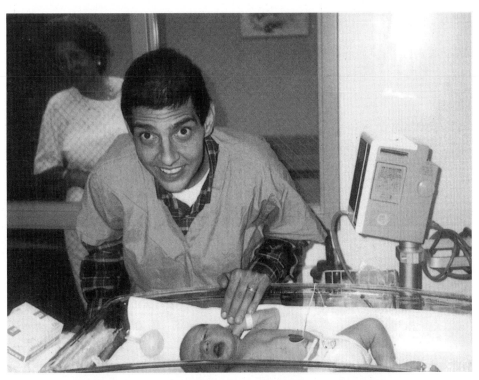

Above: David and Nathan with Parichehr (behind David), June 6, 2000.

Below left: David and Nathan, July 2000.

Below right: Rachael, David, Sara, and Nathan, August 2000.

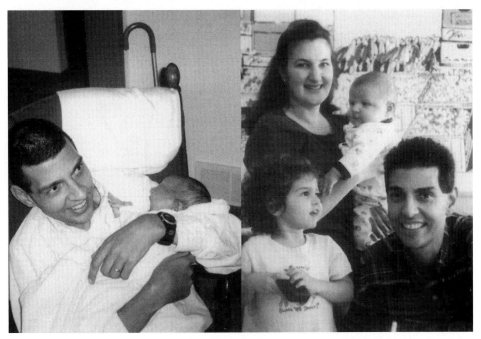

Above: At the XIX International Congress of Transplantation Society
in Miami, FL, August 2002.
(From left) Dr. David Levi., Dr. Michael Angelis, Dr. Antonio Pinna, David,
Dr. John J. Fung, and Dr. Andreas G. Tzakis.

Above: *(From Left)*
Dr. Roberto Verzaro, David,
Dr. Andreas G. Tzakis, Dr. Adrian Cotterel,
August 2002.

Dr. Akin Tekin

Rachael with Parichehr, June 2000.

Rachael and Nathan,
April 2004.

David, Sara,
Rachael, and Nathan.

Above: David with Debbie Weppler, January 2004.
Below Left: Todd McNeely, winter 2004.
Below right: Cory Lavigne with his daughter Kyra, December 2003

EPILOGUE

December 27, 2004 marked the five-year anniversary of David's third liver transplant at the University of Miami.

David's recovery progressed quickly once he arrived home. He started eating more and his body began absorbing the nutrients. His medication was gradually reduced to a minimum. Now, five years later, he has regained all of the weight he lost, plus a little more.

On August 25, 2002, David and I attended The XIX International Congress of the Transplantation Society hosted by the University of Miami. It was a great opportunity for David to visit with his surgeons outside the hospital setting, as a healthy individual, not as their patient. David's Miami surgeons, Dr. Tzakis and Dr. Levi, hosted the event. We also saw Dr. Starzl, Dr. Antonio Pinna, Dr. Roberto Verzaro, Dr. Michael Angelis, and Dr. Adrian Cottorreal. (Dr. Pinna and Dr. Verzaro are now running their own center in Italy.) The joy on all their faces when they saw David was unmistakable!

Of course, we also dropped in to visit with the SICU nurses and the 15th floor nurses. They were all happy to see David. Revisiting the 15th floor took me back to the hard days of David's illness and his desperate struggle for life. He had been a patient here for such a long time and I had pushed his wheelchair up and down these halls so many times. Now it was like a dream come true for me to return to these familiar haunts with David vibrant and healthy!

The best part for me was returning to the elevator after our visit. I remembered all those days and nights when I left David in the hospital and returned home alone with a heavy heart. Now David was leaving the SICU with me, taking the elevator down to the ground floor with me, and leaving the hospital with me. What a joy it was to no longer have to leave him there!

As of February 2005, David is living a normal life in Michigan with his wife Sara and three children, Rachael, Nathan, and Caleb. He owns a business called AirWave Computer Services, LLC which offers local high-speed wireless Internet service and onsite technology solutions for residential and small businesses. He is working on franchising this business concept.

David celebrated his thirty-sixth birthday in October. It is hard to believe that David has been living with the gift of life from strangers for the past 24 years, but it's true, and the heroic actions of Dr. Starzl and Dr. Tzakis made it all possible!

Rachael is now in second grade. She loves school and is adored by all her teachers. She still remembers riding the elevators with me during the days David was hospitalized, and when we talk about the period when she was not allowed to visit with David, it still brings tears to her eyes.

Nathan is an active four-year-old who enjoys playing with cars, trucks, and computer games (much like his father). He is doing very well in pre-school and is excited about going to kindergarten next year.

Caleb was born on February 14, 2005, weighing 8 lbs. 2 oz. and measuring 20 inches long.

We don't see David and his family as often as we did when David was ill, but as parents and grandparents, we are happy and proud of all of their accomplishments.

■   ■   ■

We have kept in touch with some of the patients we met while David was in the hospital. Like David, **Kathryn Smith** recovered completely. In December 2003, she graduated with highest honors from the Georgia Institute of Technology. In 2004, she was accepted into medical school at the Medical College of Georgia.

Laura Obregon is the mother of two children. She serves on Jackson Memorial Foundation's Board of Directors and is a co-founder and major benefactor of the Schiff Liver Institute. She is bringing one of Patrick's dreams to life by helping people with liver disease.

Allan Kolsky, Laura's co-founder of the Schiff Liver Institute, has his own successful transplant story. Allan, a shopping center developer, was diagnosed with cryptogenic cirrhosis at the age of 66. A quadruple bypass surgery eleven years earlier made him a high-risk candidate for liver transplantation. After receiving a liver transplant by Dr. Antonia Pinna at University of Miami in March, 2000, he is doing well and living a normal life. Allan also serves on Jackson Memorial Foundation's Board of Directors, and was elected president of The Transplant Foundation in 2004.

Of the patients we met in Pittsburgh during David's first transplant, **Todd McNeely** is in his mid-twenties and living a normal life. He is a tall man who is very much into working out and body building. **Corey Lavigne** is a body builder and the father of a little girl named Kyra. To see him today, it's hard to believe that he ever suffered from liver disease. **Kim Hudson**, whom we met at the reunion, is the longest living liver recipient. She has been married to Curtis Rasmussen, who is in the Air Force, since 1986. She is still doing well at 34 years posttransplant.

■　■　■

D avid is especially grateful to the wonderful men and women who created life at the times of their deaths by donating their organs. In his lifetime, David has received the gift of life from three of these angels. No matter where we go or what we do, the spirit of these wonderful people will be with us.

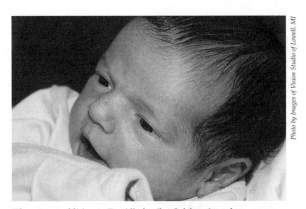

The newest addition to David's family, Caleb at 3 weeks.

Sarah, Rachael, Nathan and David, holding Caleb, March 2005

THE LATEST ON ORGAN TRANSPLANT ISSUES

Liver Support Systems

(Reprinted with permission from UNOS' patient Web site, www.transplantliving.org)

Although primarily experimental, artificial hepatic support systems are used when the liver can no longer perform its function of removing toxins from the body. These systems serve as a temporary liver support while allowing the liver to regenerate on its own or until a suitable organ becomes available for transplantation.

Methods of liver support used include:

- Extracorporeal whole organ perfusion (historical)
- Bioartifical livers
- Extracorporeal liver-assist devices, including charcoal column hemoperfusion and plasmapheresis
- Hepatocyte transplantation

GRAFT ACCEPTANCE AND IMMUNOSUPPRESSION

Dr. Thomas E. Starzl, M.D., pioneering liver transplant surgeon and author, chronicles the history of the field of liver transplantation in his autobiography, *The Puzzle People: Memoirs of a Transplant Surgeon*. His December, 1992 *Epilogue* and May, 2003 *Postscript* describe research and recent advances in the area of graft acceptance and immunosuppression.

The following excerpts, *Epilogue* and *Postscript*, are reprinted from *The Puzzle People: Memoirs of a Transplant Surgeon*, by Dr. Thomas E. Starzl, M.D., University of Pittsburgh Press, 1992, with permission from Dr. Thomas E. Starzl and the University of Pittsburgh Press.

EPILOGUE

From The Puzzle People: Memoirs of a Transplant Surgeon *by*
Dr. Thomas E. Starzl, M.D., University of Pittsburgh Press, 1992

With completion of each further page of *The Puzzle People*, I realized that I was describing deeds and events without understanding what they meant. The most humbling gap, because it was so fundamental, was the inability to comprehend or even to have a plausible theory about how a transplanted organ was able to weather rejection and later to merge half-forgotten into its unnatural new home. Yet, on the first page, I had written "It was not just the acquisition of a new part or parts; the rest of the body had to change in many ways before the gift could be accepted."

Had this been idle rhetoric or did the twenty-nine-word sentence subconsciously encapsulate a primary axiom that had eluded our inquiries and those of all others? Perhaps the secret lay within the puzzle people themselves—in those heroic patients who had lived through the terror of the unknown during the early days of transplantation. I decided to ask those who remained to complete their story by returning to the battlefield of their younger days. No one refused.

They came to Pittsburgh from all over North America in the spring and early summer of 1992, resembling the tattered remnants of a brigade revisiting a once hostile beachhead. Some were celebrities because they were the longest survivors in the world after kidney transplantation (twenty-nine and a half years) or after receiving a liver (twenty-three years). If they took pride from these distinctions, it was mixed with quiet sorrow, because to win meant that friends who had run the gauntlet before them had fallen. From each of these patients bearing someone else's kidney or liver, and also from more recent recipients of hearts, lungs, and intestines, tiny pieces (biopsies) were removed from the transplanted organ as well as from the patient's own skin, lymph glands, and other organs.

These bits of tissue were examined to identify the exact origin of cells that made them up—determining whether the individual cells were from the organ donor, the recipient, or both. This was done conclusively by means of two different corroborating procedures. One involved a special staining of the tissue for microscopic examination; the other used DNA fingerprinting, a technique now used widely in criminal laboratories to pinpoint the origin of blood, semen, and tissue found on murderers, rapists, and their victims.

As the results of the analyses poured in, a grand design could be pieced together that varied only in degree no matter what the engrafted organ. Within minutes after restoring the blood supply of the transplant, myriads of special white cells (leukocytes) that are part of the normal structure of all organs leave the graft and migrate throughout the body of the recipient. In the meanwhile, in successful cases, similar cells from the recipient's immune system rush into the transplant and replace the vacated donor leukocytes without disturbing the highly specialized cells that perform the unique functions of the organ in question. After the two-way traffic reaches a balance, the relocated and now intermingled leukocytes from both sides learn to live in harmony, provided they are given sufficient protection from each other during their nesting and exposure to each other.

The new drugs whose discovery was described in the pages of *The Puzzle People* could be viewed as "traffic directors"—allowing movement of the white cells in both directions but preventing the immune destruction that is their normal purpose. Apparently, it does not matter precisely how the immune reaction is disrupted, but only that this be achieved without killing all the altered cells that are progressively converted from harbingers of destruction to missionaries and peacemakers.

It is not known yet exactly how the two sets of white cells—a small population from the donated organ and a large one that is in essence the entire immune system of the patient—come to a stalemate so complete that in some cases that antirejection treatment can be stopped. Such a biologic "truce" can be reached more easily by the liver than by other transplanted organs because of the liver's higher content of the critical missionary leukocytes. While still incomplete, this much information may be a tool with which to carve a path into the future. Because these wandering cells can be obtained in extra supply from the bone narrow or certain other tissues of a donor, they can be purified and then used as an additive to improve the acceptability of various organs from that specific donor, including those taken from an animal for use in humans.

Now, it was time to tremble. We had come upon a cardinal principle whose very simplicity had cloaked its existence and delayed its discovery. Graft acceptance was a sleight of hand, made possible by man's misdirection of the normal defenses of a vigilant but ultimately distractible Nature. To have the fog lift, exposing this clarifying vision, was like being allowed a glimpse of eternity. The moment of tranquility that followed was a fair trade for the thirty-five years of work preceding it. And then it was gone, banished by the next set of questions.

December 5, 1992

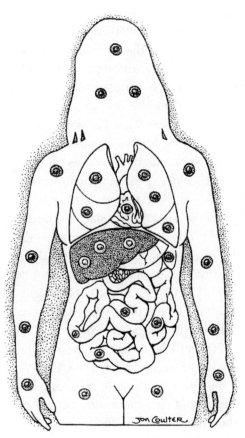

Illustration above: Exchange of white cells normally found in a transplanted organ (liver shown here) with similar cells from recipient. The resultant mixture in the transplant and throughout the recipient's body, discovered in 1992, has now helped explain how organ grafts are accepted.

POSTSCRIPT

From The Puzzle People: Memoirs of a Transplant Surgeon *by Dr. Thomas E. Starzl, M.D., University of Pittsburgh Press, 1992*

At the time the first epilogue was written in 1992, the patients who allowed their bodies to be searched for the presence of donor leukocytes already were the longest surviving "proof of principle" examples of what could he accomplished with organ transplantation. During the eleven years since, they have demonstrated more and more convincingly that organ transplantation can be followed by a full and normal lifetime. Eight of the kidney recipients from 1962-63, including a now eighty-year-old man, have reached or passed the forty-year post-transplant mark with function of their original allografts. Seven years behind them, the first liver recipients have crossed the third-of-a-century milestone.

However, the ripple effect of these remarkable puzzle people cannot be defined merely by the duration of their survival. Because of their generosity in submitting themselves to restudy, they became crucial instruments of discovery and reform. The demonstration in 1992 of donor leukocytes in their tissues and blood allowed an intellectual leap in collaboration with the Swiss physician-immunologist and 1996 Nobel laureate, Rolf Zinkernagel,[*][†] whereby the immunology of transplantation could be understood and placed on common ground with the immunology of infections, cancer, and self-nonself discrimination. This ultimately resulted in the development of better strategies of immunosuppression that promote organ transplant tolerance.[††]

It has been simple justice to have this happen in the lifetimes of those early organ recipients who began their desperate journeys with no other weapons than faith, hope, and fierce determination to live. But their delicious secret always will be the realization that they have left giant and permanent footprints in the sands of time.

May 21, 2003

---

[*] T.E. Starzl and R. Zinkernagel, "Antigen Localization and Migration in Immunity and Tolerance," *New England Journal of Medicine* 339 (1998):1905-13.

[†] T.E. Starzl and R. Zinkernagel, "Transplantation Tolerance from a Historical Perspective," *Nature Reviews Immunology* I (2001):223-39.

[††] T.E. Starzl, N. Murase, K. Abu-Elmagd, E. A. Gray, R. Shapiro, B. Eghtesad, R.J. Corry, M. L. Jordan, P. Fontes, T. Gayowski, C. Bond, V. B. Scantlebury, S. Potdar, P. Randlhawa, T. Wu, A. Zeevi, M. A. Nalesnik, J. Woodward, A. Marcos, M. Trucco, A. J. Demetris, and J.J. Fung, "Tolerogenic Immunosuppression for Organ Transplantation," *The Lancet 361* (2003):1502-10.

Striking the Delicate Balance: Managing Over- vs. Under-Immunosuppression

By Richard Kowalski, Ph.D., Nancy Hooper, MS, MT(ASCP) and Judith A. Britz, Ph.D.;
Reprinted with permission from Cylex

The immune system originally evolved to protect you against invasion from microorganisms. The white blood cells that circulate throughout your body act as a 24-hour surveillance system available to attack invaders. These same, white blood cells can recognize a donated organ as being foreign and spring into action to reject the foreign tissue. As a result, transplanted tissue becomes damaged and often nonfunctional. The principal targets for the immune system are foreign cell surface proteins present on the donated organ. To minimize the intensity of your natural immune response, tissue typing is performed to match the donor's organ as closely as possible to yours, the recipient. Unless you have an identical twin, seldom does a perfect match occur. In the last thirty years, the development of immunosuppressant drugs has allowed the functional existence of a foreign organ in a transplant recipient. However, the same white blood cells that protect against infection are also suppressed by these drugs, rendering the recipient susceptible to infection. In addition, many of these immunosuppressant drugs have unwanted side effects. Therefore, giving just enough drugs to inhibit rejection while maintaining enough immune function to fight infections and avoid side effects is a difficult balancing act. Most physicians feel that a combination of drugs can be used to achieve the best results. Because all transplant recipients are not the same, each treatment regimen needs to be tailored to each individual patient. This means that customizing the doses of these life-saving drugs becomes critical to maintaining your quality of life.

As a transplant patient, you undergo frequent blood testing in the first days, weeks, and months following surgery. Antibody tests, drug levels, and organ-specific chemistry tests are performed while drug doses are adjusted. Historically, assessing the effects of a patient's customized drug regimen on the immune system was not an easy task. Today, there is a new option available to you. In 2002, the Food and Drug Administration (FDA) approved a new diagnostic blood test (ImmuKnow™) that provides the doctor with additional information about how your immune system is responding to a particular combination of drugs. ImmuKnow™ is a simple blood test that is performed at the same time as your routine visit to the transplant center or your organ specialist. It requires less than a teaspoon of blood that is drawn into a standard blood collection tube. Once sent to the lab, results are available the next day.

Assessing the strength of a patient's immune system provides valuable information to the treating physician. Even before transplant, a baseline measurement provides an early indicator of whether the patient's immune system will be more difficult to suppress. Immediately following transplant, the immune system undergoes adjustments due to the effects of surgery, anesthesia, and blood transfusions. Before leaving the hospital, immuno-suppressants are administered orally instead of intravenously. Once the patient's condition has stabilized, the doctor's goal will be to gradually reduce the amount of therapy administered over time. By reducing the amount of drugs, potential side effects are minimized. When combined with your other routine tests, ImmuKnow™ is a valuable guide to assist your physician in adjusting the dose of your current drugs, substituting therapies with fewer side effects, or adding new drugs as appropriate (See Figure 1).

By understanding how your body responds to drug treatments administered over time, you can assume greater control of the options available to you to manage your health. Together with your transplant team, you can achieve a more ideal balance between lifesaving therapies and their potential side effects that affect your quality of life.

Cylex® ImmuKnow™ Assay
Alerts You to Changes in Your Immune System

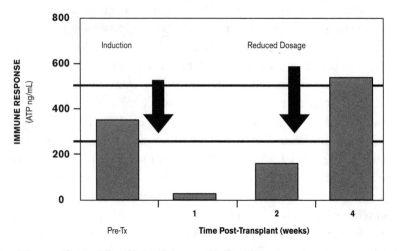

Figure Above: The Cylex® ImmuKnow™ Assay measures response to therapy changes. In this example, induction therapy dramatically reduces the number of lymphocytes and strongly suppresses the immune response as observed in the ImmuKnow™ test. For the next few weeks this patient was maintained on standard triple therapy. Because toxicity to one of the drugs developed, the dose was lowered. As a result of the reduced dosage, a rise in immune function occurred and exceeded pretransplant levels. At this point, the addition of another drug would be indicated. In this way, along with measuring therapeutic drug levels in the blood and considering other clinical signs, ImmuKnow™ can be used to guide the physician's recommended course of therapy.

To obtain more information on ImmuKnow™, you may access the Cylex website at www.cylex.net or ask your physician to call Cylex at 888-873-0871.

Dr. Kowalski is Head, Product Development, Ms. Hooper is Technical Support Associate, and Dr. Britz is Immunologist, Microbiologist and Chairman and CEO, Cylex Inc., 8980-I Old Annapolis Road, Columbia, Maryland 21045, U.S.A.; Tel.: 888-873-0871; Fax: 410-964-0367; e-mail:rkowalski@cylex.net

ABOUT THE AUTHORS

PARICHEHR YOMTOOB is a mother of three, grandmother of five, teacher, wife, volunteer, and an activist and educator for organ donation and transplantation. Her first book, *The Gift of Life*, was about her son David's Wilson's Disease and successful liver transplant. She coauthored the book with freelance writer Ted Schwarz. The book was published in 1986 in the U.S. and Japan and received rave reviews. Parichehr and her husband Joe reside in a suburb of Chicago.

LAURA YOMTOOB was born in 1965 and educated at the University of Michigan. She lives in the Chicago area with her husband and two sons, where she designs, makes, and sells lampwork glass beads. This is her first book.

DEBBIE WEPPLER is the Clinical Specialist/Senior Transplant Coordinator for the Liver and GI Transplant Team at Jackson Memorial Hospital, University of Miami Medical Center. As a Senior Transplant Coordinator, she is responsible for coordinating over 200 liver transplants and 30 intestinal transplants annually. She also follows approximately 600 pretransplant and 2,200 posttransplant patients, supervises seven posttransplant coordinators, five preoperative coordinators, three pediatric coordinators, and multiple ancillary personnel. In addition, she oversees multiple clinical research projects. She has been the author and coauthor of many medical articles and books. Among them:

Weppler, Debbie and J.M. Civetta

> **"Preventive care: Poorly appreciated and undervalued,"** *Critical Care*, J.M. Civetta, R.W. Taylor, and R.R. Kirby, editors. J.B. Lippincott, Philadelphia, PA, 1987.

Weppler, Debbie and J.M. Civetta

"Preventive care: Poorly appreciated and undervalued," *Critical Care,* 2nd edition, J.M. Civetta, R.W. Taylor, and R.R. Kirby, editors. J.B. Lippincott, Philadelphia, PA, 1992.

Weppler, Debbie and J.M. Civetta

"Preventive care: Poorly appreciated and undervalued." *Critical Care,* 3rd edition, J.M. Civetta, R.W. Taylor, and R.R. Kirby, editors. J.B. Lippincott, Philadelphia, PA, 1997.

Weppler, Debbie, R. Khan, G.P. Fragulidis, J.R. Nery, C. Ricordi, and A.G. Tzakis.

"Status of Liver/GI Transplantation," *Clinical Transplantation,* P. Teresaki and J.M. Cecka, editors. UCLA Tissue Typing Laboratory, Los Angeles, CA, 1997.

Fragulidis, G.P., D. Weppler, J.R. Nery, M.F. Khan, T. Kato, M. Webb, and A.G. Tzakis.

"Liver Transplantation," *Advanced Techniques of Liver Transplantation in Techniques in Liver Surgery,* A. Mazziotti and A. Vavallari, editors. Grenwich Medical Media, London, UK, 1997.

Fragulidis, G.P., D. Weppler, J.R. Nery, M.F. Khan, T. Kato, M. Webb, and A.G. Tzakis.

"Intestinal Multiorgan Transplantation." *Techniques in Liver Surgery,* G. Gozzetti, A. Mazziotti, and A. Cavallari, editors. Grenwich Medical Media, London UK, 1997.

Khan, F.A., J. Thompson , M.G. Webb, J.R. Nery, L. Olson, A. Viciana, J. Raskin, A. Rogers, C.R. Luque, D. Weppler, R. Khan , R. Koutouby, R. Romero, P. Ruiz, A. Gyamfi, J. Jacque, R. Reddy, P. Byers, C. Ricordi, and A.G.Tzakis.

"Intestinal and Multivisceral Transplantation," *Transplantation,* L.C. Ginns, M.D., A.B. Cosimi, M.D., and P.J. Morris, M.D., F.R.S., editors. Blackwell Science, Inc., Cambridge, MA, 1999.

INDEX

Questions for Discussion

1. The first book, *The Gift of Life*, published in 1986, described David's first transplant experience. Why did David's family feel they needed a book to guide them through the second transplant?

2. Why were David and his family shocked to learn that David needed another transplant?

3. David received his first transplant after his liver was damaged and destroyed by an accumulation of copper (Wilson's Disease). Why did this transplanted liver fail after 17 years? How come no one noticed and/or told David and his family that the second liver was dying until it was too late? Would it have been possible to prevent the failure of second liver if it had been noticed in time?

4. What is the role of the parent when an adult child develops a life-threatening illness?

5. Did David's family do the right thing by deciding to follow through on plans for his sister Rebecca's wedding while concealing the fact that David was on the waiting list for a liver? Or would it have been better to have a small ceremony immediately and postpone the celebration until after David's transplant?

6. Why did David and his family move to Omaha to be near the University of Nebraska Medical Center, instead of moving into their new house in Michigan? Why did they stay in Omaha for nine months? What made them finally decide to return to Michigan and wait at home?

7. Why was the transplant coordinator in Omaha unhappy with David and his family? What could David and his family have done to change her feelings?

8. David and his family met with a psychologist while they were in Omaha. If David had a physical illness not mental illness, was it really necessary to meet with a psychologist? Were the sessions helpful? Why did the family participate? What did they learn?

9. Why did David's brother Ben volunteer to become a living donor for David and why did the two brothers choose to hide it from their mother? When a patient is eligible for living donor transplant and several family members are a good match, whose responsibility is it to step forward and volunteer? Does a responsibility exist at all?

10. David's family learned that a direct or designated organ donation might give David the liver he needed. Why didn't this possible designated donor materialize? Should David's parents have traveled to California to meet with the family of the possible donor?

11. Where do the world's major religions stand on the issue of cadaver organ donation? Can anyone become an organ donor? Why don't more people sign their donor card?

12. David's mother was evaluated as a possible living donor at Northwestern University. What happened during her test to make the doctors feel she was ineligible? When she asked the doctor what they would do if the living donor surgery failed for her or David, what was she expecting to hear? Was it an unrealistic expectation?

13. Why did David's second liver transplant fail?

14. What was the key to David's survival? What role did David's daughter Rachael have in his recovery?

Praise for The Gift of Life 2

I can't tell you how much I admire the courage that David has exhibited, and the determination and faith of you and the family that never wavered.

Thomas E. Starzl, M.D., Ph.D.

Professor of Surgery, University of Pittsburgh School of Medicine
Pittsburgh, Pennsylvania

■   ■   ■

The Gift of Life 2 is a sequel, which the author surely wished she never had to write. Parichehr Yomtoob describes how her son David and her family had to go through another transplant more than 18 years after David's life was saved with a pioneering liver transplant in 1981. This time David was no longer a youngster. He was married, had a wife, a child, a second one on the way, and a good job. His life was in nearly perfect order. He flew close to the sun and his wings (indeed his liver) melted.

In 1999, over 18 years after the first one, liver transplantation was a ubiquitous operation. It was performed at many centers, by many well-qualified teams. The methods were a lot more sophisticated than in 1981. Interestingly, nothing seemed to be even at the slightest easier for everyone involved than the first time.

The plot takes the reader through the roller coaster of the second transplant. It is a thrilling but also terrifying testimony of the events. One can see the strength of family and faith and learn that miracles can happen even now. A series of nearly fatal events can still have a happy ending.

The book is also very informative. Debbie Weppler, one of the world's most experienced transplant nurses helps explain in lay terms liver transplantation, modern immunosuppression and almost all known complications. She also navigates a potential liver transplant candidate through the logistics and intricacies of the system as it is currently practiced in the Unites States.

Andreas G. Tzakis, M.D., Ph.D.

Professor of Surgery, University of Miami Leonard M. Miller School of Medicine
Miami, Florida

I found *The Gift of Life 2* both informative and inspiring. The book should be extremely valuable to families as it contains excellent new information — for example, about living related donations. Many books simply have "facts" but this book has both factual information as well as presenting the difficult story of transplantation and will inspire others to persevere when it seems that there is no hope.

J. Carlton Gartner Jr., M.D.
Pediatrician-in-Chief, A. I. DuPont Hospital for Children
Wilmington, Delaware
Professor of Pediatrics, Jefferson Medical College
Philadelphia, Pennsylvania

■　■　■

I found *The Gift of Life 2* to be very interesting. It reminded me of the time I spent taking care of David during his second and third liver transplant. Taking care of David was an exciting experience. We all learned a lot from him and his way of handling life. The co-authorship of Deborah Weppler, one of the most expert liver transplant nurses in the world, adds a lot to the medical aspects of this book.

As a doctor involved in the field of transplantation I have always found these books very fascinating. I think patients should share their stories to support each other. However David's story is a special one. It is *the story*. David's story keeps inspiring me in my daily job at the bedside of transplant patients. His daily fight has been a source of strength for everyone who's had a chance to meet him. I will recommend this book to my patients, students, residents, and to all the people involved in the field of transplantation: doctors, nurses, hospital personnel, patients and relatives. But I recommend this book to everyone involved with life itself, because David's story tells us something very important: life is a gift that is worth fighting for.

Roberto Verzaro, M.D.
IsMeTT (Institute of Transplantation of the Mediterranean)
Palermo, Italy
University of Pittsburgh Medical Center – European Division

■　■　■

The Yomtoobs capture the patient's plight in liver transplantation today. The daily struggles of being ill with the constant hope of a liver transplant in the near future are well-depicted. This is very helpful information for patients and families who are awaiting or who have had a liver transplant.

Tim McCashland, M.D.
University of Nebraska Medical Center
Omaha, Nebraska

As a transplant surgeon I was inspired in reading *The Gift of Life 2*. Not only does it document one man's battle with liver disease and liver transplantation, but we are able to get an insight into how liver transplantation has changed in the past 25 years through David's story of his first liver transplant as a child and subsequently his two other liver transplants as an adult. The book also gives up-to-date and informative and accurate information on liver disease and transplantation and will be an important source to patients and their families.

Michael Angelis, M.D.
Surgical Transplant Director, Florida Hospital
Orlando, Florida

■   ■   ■

As she narrates the story of her son David's second and third liver transplants, Parichehr Yomtoob powerfully transmits a vision of what can happen when family devotion, religious community and principles, medical skill, and the extraordinarily generous gift of organ donation converge to allow human beings to partner with God in sustaining the miracle of life.

The Gift of Life 2: Surviving the Waiting List and Liver Transplantation provides a wealth of information related to understanding and preventing liver disease and offers extensive resource material on where families can obtain medical and psychosocial support. A section of the book entitled "The Power of Prayers" offers traditional and modern adaptations of prayers and religious rituals gathered from Jewish tradition that will be profoundly strengthening to all of us — those of us who may one day benefit from organ donation, and the rest of us who bequeath the gift of continued life to others.

Rabbi Eric H. Yoffie
President, Union for Reform Judaism

■   ■   ■

David's story is presented in clear, straightforward style that synthesizes the scientific and the personal. *The Gift of Life 2* contains valuable sections that speak to the care, coping and financial concern incurred as a family deals with the challenge of organ transplantation. The book contains extremely valuable chapters that walk a family through the human and organizational resources that are available including lists of current centers that deal with organ transplant surgery and support.

The Yomtoobs trace the various religious positions on transplantation and teach the necessary lesson that organ and tissue transplantation is considered by the majority of contemporary American Judaism as a "modern mitzvah." The spiritual dimension of transplantation is presented with great care along with the personal, familial, medical and psychological concern presented by procedure.

The Gift of Life 2 is a welcome addition to the literature of family support and guidance in the area of organ transplantation.

Rabbi Richard F. Address, D.Min
Director, Department of Jewish Family Concerns
Union for Reform Judaism

■　■　■

Parichehr Yomtoob, and her co-authors Laura Yomtoob and Deborah Weppler, have made an inestimable contribution to society with their book, *The Gift of Life 2*. In telling the story of David's battle for life in partnership with family, friends, and medical professionals, the authors make the case for thinking about life-saving matters like organ donation before there ever is an emergency. Their book transcends theorizing, theologizing and debating, and places the issue in the simple context of the choice for life and for love. The reader will understand what it means to learn and find inspiration. How grateful we must be that this loving family has generously shared virtually every aspect of a journey that took them from Grand Rapids, Michigan to Pittsburgh to Omaha to Miami, and most importantly, to renewed hope and health. Read this book and learn about perseverance, heroism, courage, and faith... and devotion — of parents, children, grandchildren, physicians, nurses, patients, and families.

Rabbi Steven S. Mason, D.Min.
North Shore Congregation Israel
Glencoe, Illinois

■　■　■

To save a life is to save an entire world. To save a life is the greatest mitzvah our Jewish tradition teaches. To donate an organ is to save a life. David Yomtoob's life calls each of us to educate, to inspire, to save lives, each and every day.

Rabbi Lisa S. Greene
North Shore Congregation Israel
Glencoe, Illinois

■　■　■

The Gift of Life 2 captures the agony and pain, the joy and triumph of an ordeal that so many families experience. It is a courageous book that deserves our attention.

Rabbi Daniel B. Syme
Temple Beth-El
Bloomfield Hills, Michigan

I have often been with families as they made the decision to offer the gift of life. David's story reminds each one of us to speak with those whom we love and let them know that we desire to be organ donors. In our tradition, no mitzvah is more important than the saving of a life. With our death or the death of a loved one, we can take one or more names off of a long waiting list.

Rabbi Harold Loss
Temple Israel
West Bloomfield, Michigan

■   ■   ■

PASSION. DETERMINATION. TRIUMPH. Parichehr Yomtoob's saga of the battles with Wilson's Disease is sensitive and informative, chilling and warming, written with the fluid flowing from a mother's heart. Supported by the medical expertise of a most dedicated, competent nurse, and carefully and caringly edited by a friend who is married to her other son, this is a book for all who need an uplift (those in search of a transplant) or a download (those who can provide "the gift of life") or a good read.

Three times and more we are taken to the abyss with David. We are provided more information and detail than some of us might want. All is permeated with exquisite love and abiding hope.

Aside from the medical story is the narrative of a beautiful marriage, supportive family, caring friends and especially, a woman's crusade against pessimism and despair. Here the spiritual becomes real; the religious, secular. Faith translates to action.

Elliot D. Rosenstock, D.H.L.
Rabbi

■   ■   ■

Is there anything more meaningful than saving someone's life? The story of David's liver transplants should encourage others to consider organ donation. This great mitzvah may be the noblest holy deed.

Rabbi Morley T. Feinstein
University Synagogue
Los Angeles, California

The Gift of Life 2 is a rare and timely book that will both touch and save lives. Sensitively combining intense personal experiences with clear and accessible information on the medicine of organ transplantation, the authors will educate the ill-informed, inspire those offering the gift of life through donation, give hope to those awaiting donation, and provide courage and wise counsel to transplant recipients and their families. The reader is reminded that in addition to the lives saved through donation, countless others are blessed by the lives of loved ones and friends with whom they are enabled to share further years and productive lifetimes. Identifying organ donation as "a modern mitzvah", *The Gift of Life 2* will help guide twenty-first century souls of all persuasions in fulfilling the ancient scriptural command to intervene with life-saving action when the lives of fellow human beings are in danger and distress. By sharing their knowledge and experience with their readers, the authors have admirably responded to that divine mandate themselves.

Rabbi Joseph H. Prouser
Member of the (Conservative Movement) Rabbinical Assembly
Committee on Jewish Law and Standards, and author of its responsum,
"Hesed or Hiyuv: The Obligation to Preserve Life and the Question of
Post-mortem Organ Donation."

■ ■ ■

The Gift of Life 2 is an outstanding detailed account of what goes on behind the scenes involving a liver transplant. You included the various religious perspectives on transplant as well as many beautiful prayers. The details involving transplants that you included were as informative as those of a physician. An amazing amount of research and information was included in this book.

As a teacher of Responsa, I am most impressed with this publication and all the material that it contains. Thank you for giving me the privilege of reading and reviewing this outstanding and most informative work.

Linda K. Brodsky
Teacher of Responsa, Temple Israel
West Bloomfield, Michigan

The Gift of Life 2 by Parichehr Yomtoob, Laura Yomtoob, and Debbie Weppler is the gripping story of the experience of David Yomtoob, a young man who suffered from Wilson's Disease. David was not diagnosed in time to respond to medications and slipped into coma. A liver transplant saved David's life when he was twelve years old and David was free of Wilson's Disease. Seventeen years later the transplanted liver failed. All the tests indicated that Wilson's Disease was not the cause of David's liver failure for the second time.

The Gift of Life 2 is about David's multiple liver transplants and how this affected him and his very supportive family. It not only provides a first hand account of the organ transplant process, but is also chock-full of invaluable reference information on organ donation, transplantation and related topics. This book is a "must read" for anyone awaiting a donor liver or other organ, and his or her family and friends. It presents information in a very clear and accessible format, while telling the story of a remarkable young man, his extraordinary family, and the dedicated physicians and health professionals who saved his life not once, but three times. Of course we must also not forget about the importance of organ donors in the transplantation process, and the book gives us important perspective and information on organ donation.

I highly recommend this book for anyone with an interest in organ donation and transplantation, and I plan to give a copy to those I know who have had a transplant or are on the waiting list for an organ.

Carol A. Terry
Secretary, Co-Founder and past President, Wilson's Disease Association

■   ■   ■

Once again Mrs. Yomtoob has graphically depicted the anguish and suffering of her son and her family throughout the transplant process in *The Gift of Life 2*, sequel to *The Gift of Life*. Any reader, especially a parent, will feel as though they are living the anguish right along with the Yomtoob family as they struggle through David's second and third transplant experiences.

As a parent of two children with Wilson's Disease, I cannot even imagine having to endure what the Yomtoob family has. As an advocate for all Wilson's disease patients, it saddens me to know that any WD patient would have the need for a liver transplant given how easily treatable the disease is.

Also striking in the story is the empathy, compassion, and gratitude of the family for other transplant patients and their donor families, and the many caring physicians and staff who went above and beyond to make sure David would survive.

Mary L. Graper
President, Wilson's Disease Association

■　■　■

Jesus said: *"There is no greater love than to lay down one's life for one's friends."*

In my 21 years as a priest I have had no greater opportunity to follow Jesus' words and example than the opportunity that Miguel Zavala gave to me on April 17, 2002. One day this body will return to Mother Earth and we will receive a new resurrected body. After the resurrection, Jesus' disciples did not recognize him, partly because they were gazing upon the Risen Lord.

What better way to die to oneself in order to truly live than to participate in opportunities to donate parts of our earthly bodies so that others can live?

Father Gary Graf
Living liver donor
Pastor, Holy Family Church
Waukegan, Illinois

■　■　■

The writers of *The Gift of Life 2* have intertwined biographical, autobiographic and medical material in a way which will assist persons wrestling with the complex emotional and ethical concerns surrounding organ transplants. As a person who has served as a hospital chaplain and parish pastor, I found the book to be helpful and informative.

Reverend David L. Morton
Chapel Hill United Methodist Church
Battle Creek, Michigan

■　■　■

In my humble opinion, this book should be given as required reading to every liver patient who has had or may need a transplant, and their families.

Allan Kolsky
Liver recipient
President, Transplant Foundation, Inc.
Miami, Florida

ORDER FORM

THE GIFT OF LIFE 2

SURVIVING THE WAITING LIST AND LIVER TRANSPLANTATION

By Parichehr Yomtoob, Laura Yomtoob, and Deborah Weppler, RN, MSN

Send me ____ copies of **The Gift of Life 2** at $24.95 each, plus $4.95 shipping and handling per book. (Illinois residents please include 7% sales tax.)

NAME   TITLE

ADDRESS

CITY   STATE   ZIP CODE

EMAIL   DAYTIME PHONE   DATE

Make your check payable to Rainbow International Press and send to:

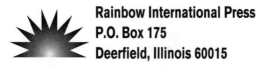

Rainbow International Press
P.O. Box 175
Deerfield, Illinois 60015

Thank you for your order. Please allow 2 weeks for delivery.

THE AUTHORITATIVE RESOURCE TOOL FOR ANYONE FACING LIVER DISEASE